MARY CADOGAN

—

FRANK RICHARDS

—

The Chap Behind the Chums

Swallowtail Books

Published by Swallowtail Books
3 Danesbrook, Claverley, Shropshire, WV5 7BB, England

First published by Viking Penguin 1988

This edition published by Swallowtail Books 2000
by arrangement with Penguin Books Ltd

Printed by Antony Rowe Ltd, Bumper's Farm, Chippenham, Wiltshire, SN14 6LH, England
Book cover and logo designs by Simon & Erica Minter Design Services
Cover line drawings by C H Chapman by courtesy of Collectors' Digest

To the memory of
my first literary love,
'Frank Richards',
and of my father,
Thomas Harold Summersby,
who introduced me to
the Magnet *and* Gem

CONTENTS

CONTENTS

Appendix Three
Charles Hamilton's Pen-names
237

Appendix Four
Editors and Illustrators of the *Gem* and *Magnet*
239

Appendix Five
Selected Papers and Books Containing Stories by
Charles Hamilton
241

Notes
243

Bibliography
251

Index
253

ACKNOWLEDGEMENTS
to the original edition

I am indebted to many people for help and encouragement during the preparation of this book, especially Una Hamilton Wright for generously sharing her memories of her uncle, providing photographs and giving me permission to use quotations from Frank Richards's autobiography and other works, and her own articles. My warm thanks are due to Howard Baker for permission to use text quotations and illustrations from his splendid *Magnet* and *Gem* facsimile publications. I would like to thank Mr John Wernham of the Museum Press and Charles Hamilton Museum, Maidstone, for his extremely ready assistance in providing photographs, letters and books for reference, and Roger M. Jenkins for lending me so many volumes from the library of the London Old Boys' Book Club and most kindly allowing me to quote from his articles on Frank Richards and from the author's letters to him. I extend deep thanks to Edith Hood and to Revd Philip Hobson; also to W. O. G. Lofts and Derek Adley, both for their unflagging researches and for their willingness to share the results. My gratitude is due to R. F. Acraman, for his helpfulness in making available the facilities of his Charles Hamilton Museum at Kingsgate Castle, and to Jack Adrian for the loan of books and research material and for general encouragement. I must also thank Eric Fayne, my predecessor as editor of the *Story Paper Collectors' Digest*, for all the help he has given me, both personally and through his many articles on the work of Frank Richards, and Patricia Alcock for passing on family memories of her grandfather, Richard Hamilton, and of Frank Richards.

In some cases I have been unable to trace the owners of photographs, letters and articles; to them I offer apologies, and gratitude.

I thank Tony Lacey, Tessa Strickland and Helen Jeffrey of Viking for their patience and help in what must sometimes have appeared to be a never-ending project!

Mary Cadogan
Beckenham, 1988

ACKNOWLEDGEMENTS
to this new edition

I would like to thank Una Hamilton Wright and Jeffrey Richards for their contributions to this new edition and also my publishers Andrew Pitt and Stephanie Perks of Swallowtail Books for their help.

Mary Cadogan
Beckenham, 2000

FURTHER ACKNOWLEDGEMENTS
to the original edition

Illustrations (pp. 3, 4, 8, 10, 13, 16, 19, 22, 25, 29, 36, 38, 43, 45, 51, 52, 57, 62, 65, 66, 70, 76, 80, 84, 86, 96, 99, 101, 103, 105, 107, 110, 114, 116, 121, 122, 124, 129, 134, 135, 137, 140, 143, 145, 149, 150, 159, 161, 164, 172, 174, 182, 189, 193, 196, 199, 201, 202, 213, 227) and extracts from the Howard Baker Press's facsimile editions of the *Magnet, Gem* and other Amalgamated Press papers are reprinted by kind permission of the publisher.

Extracts from the following are reprinted by permission of Una Hamilton Wright and the Frank Richards Estate: *Bessie Bunter of Cliff House School*, copyright Frank Richards, 1949; *The Autobiography of Frank Richards*, copyright Frank Richards, 1952; 'Charles Hamilton: A Background Note on His Early Days', copyright © Una Hamilton Wright, 1962; 'Christmas with Frank Richards', copyright © Una Hamilton Wright, 1962; 'Felix Kept On Walking', copyright © Una Hamilton Wright, 1976. *'Ultio Bunteri'* is reprinted by permission of *The Times Educational Supplement*.

The publishers are grateful to the following for permission to reproduce illustrations Charles Hamilton Museum Press, Maidstone (pp. xiv, 218, 224); *Collectors' Digest* (pp. 47, 219, 223); *Daily Telegraph* (p. 231); Express Newspapers (p. 229); IPC Publications (pp. 73, 75, 89, 139, 171, 178, 217).

LIST OF PLATES

Frank in his early thirties (courtesy Una Hamilton Wright)

Frank as he appeared in the thousandth *Magnet* (courtesy John Wernham, Charles Hamilton Museum Press, Maidstone)

Richard Hamilton and Emma Mary Cluley (courtesy Patricia Alcock)

Frank's birthplace at 15 Oak Street (copyright Trevor Adley)

The corner shop, Oak Street (copyright Trevor Adley)

Clyde Cottage at Hawkinge, Kent (copyright John Wernham, Charles Hamilton Museum Press)

A garden party at Mandeville (courtesy John Wernham, Charles Hamilton Museum Press)

Edith Hood, John Wernham and Roger M. Jenkins at Rose Lawn (copyright John Wernham, Charles Hamilton Museum Press)

Rose Lawn at Kingsgate, Kent (copyright John Wernham, Charles Hamilton Museum Press)

Una Harrison (courtesy Una Hamilton Wright)

Dolly in the garden at Mandeville (courtesy Una Hamilton Wright)

Frank and Dolly at Mandeville (courtesy Una Hamilton Wright)

Frank's study at Rose Lawn (copyright John Wernham, Charles Hamilton Museum Press)

The sitting-room at Rose Lawn (copyright John Wernham, Charles Hamilton Museum Press)

Frank in his early sixties (courtesy Una Hamilton Wright)

Frank enjoying a game of chess (copyright Keystone Press at Photosource)

Frank and R. J. Macdonald (copyright John Wernham, Charles Hamilton Museum Press)

C. H. Chapman (copyright John Wernham, Charles Hamilton Museum Press)

Frank and some of his young fans (courtesy John Wernham, Charles Hamilton Museum Press)

Frank reading a Greyfriars story (courtesy John Wernham, Charles Hamilton Museum Press)

FOREWORD
to this new edition

by Una Hamilton Wright

Welcome to this new paperback edition of Mary Cadogan's book, *Frank Richards: The Chap Behind the Chums*. Charles Hamilton ('Frank Richards') believed in paperback editions which made literature accessible to all readers. He always hoped that his hardcover Bunter Books would appear as paperbacks and would have given this new edition of Mary's book the warmest welcome.

Mary Cadogan successfully unravels all the complexities of Charles Hamilton's writing life. With at least twenty-eight pen-names and an output that was estimated to be the equivalent of a thousand full length novels – thus making Hamilton the most prolific author known – the clarifying of his writing life was a daunting task. Mary has fulfilled this brilliantly, giving a first-class exposition of what it was like to be involved with so many stories, serials, characters, settings, illustrators, editors and publishers.

Charles Hamilton's writing life started officially when he was seventeen and had his first short story published. (He had been making up stories for his younger brother and sister long before that.) Having started he never stopped. Success to him meant ever-increasing demand. He was so busy with his typewriter, which he bought in 1900, that he used to sign himself 'Click-Click' in his letters to my father (his brother-in-law).

He dreamed of making a fortune at the gaming tables on the Continent and then retiring so that he could write only when he had the urge, but his luck was out and he always left the Casinos with lightened pockets. Perhaps this was fortunate, for his work poured out continuously all through the twentieth century except for the duration of the Second World War when the paper shortage cut off his publisher's supplies.

Billy Bunter, his most famous character, was invented in 1900 but not published until the boys' weekly, the *Magnet*, was launched in 1908. Bunter had been shown to an editor in 1900 who turned the fat character down saying he "did not think the idea would catch on". Uncle loyally never divulged that editor's identity – and Bunter has never been out of print since 1908. His popularity helped to keep my Uncle at the top of his profession for the major part of the twentieth century and thus to establish him as a major influence on this country's youth.

He was ever conscious of the moral basis of life; to him, a sense of duty was essential. In the *Silverwings Stories*, a series of fairy tales he made up for me before I could read, featuring Silverwings the Fairy and her adventures down on earth, the good always triumphed and the wicked failed. I found this very reassuring. His parents were both very religious and his stories are imbued with the moral values which were taught to him and his siblings at home.

Charles Hamilton lived with my family from the time of my earliest memories. My mother was his youngest and favourite sister and my father his respected and admired friend. Uncle was always there from my earliest recollections, a caring, understanding presence, smoothing the way for his little niece. From the morning walk to the bedtime story he was in the picture and often taking charge. He never talked down to me like other grown-ups, he was more like an elder sibling. I could count on him for support and he never made me foolish or lost his temper. His patience seemed endless.

In his dealings with me he acted according to his own theories about childhood. Childhood should be a happy time, a child should not be crossed or teased but encouraged and respected as a person. Looking back I think my Uncle was delighted to be able to try out his theories of education on me, a live model. He believed in a wide general education with emphasis on the Arts, Languages and Philosophy. In the same way that his stories are peppered with quotations from famous writers, so was his conversation. I loved this, feeling that it admitted me to the interests of the grown-ups. Little bits of European languages were used as ordinary expressions and had the effect of making me long for more. He was very fond of Latin, both language and literature. This was our one educational stumbling block: my brain would not think the Latin way. I must emphasise that all these topics I regarded as fun and entertainment to be lapped up. Whether these experiments in educating a child taught him anything new about children I do not know – it always seemed to me that he was the perfect child's companion to start with. From when I was about seven Uncle used to read his *Magnet* typescripts through to mother and me before posting them off to the publisher. I loved the Greyfriars stories and thought they made wonderful bed-time stories.

Charles Hamilton's attitude to childhood inspired his school stories and helped to make them very popular, as is evidenced by Billy Bunter's continued popularity from 1908 until to-day, whether in the *Magnet,* or a Holiday Annual, or the hardcover Bunter Books, or reprints, or on television, audio-cassette readings or even in strip cartoon form.

Many people have asked me why this should be. I think the reason is because Charles Hamilton gave his readers exactly what they wanted – believable characters with whom they could identify falling into the sort of scrapes that normal people met with. As my mother pointed out to her brother when he was first asked to write a series set in a school, school life is really only a cameo of life in the world outside: problems with conscience, problems with authority and rule-keeping, problems with awkward characters who needed humouring, problems with bullying and problems with friendships and family. Out of this seething mass of bubbling humanity emerged the plots and themes that ensnared and then satisfied his readers. The underlying supportive message was always that by doing the right thing one could surmount one's troubles.

Lest the stories should be deadened by this serious message the author sweetened the pill with his ebullient sense of humour. Humour was more effective than condemnation in dissuading his young readers from drinking, smoking or overeating. Billy Bunter became the classic 'horrible example' who amused his readers but did not inspire emulation.

All the youthful vices were crammed into Billy Bunter: 'borrowing', fibbing, gorging, laziness, grubbiness, self-centredness and conceit. Thus any reader who allowed himself any of these weaknesses was immediately lining up with Billy Bunter – and *that* no one wanted to do. And yet people often wanted to forgive and protect him, notably Bob Cherry and Lord Mauleverer, as though he were a baby and did not know any better. So Bunter not only served to warn us from his many sins but also he stirred in us feelings of common humanity – obviously there *were* Bunters about but we had to learn to put up with them and perhaps even to take pity on them. Bunter it was who propelled his author to the forefront of twentieth-century thinking.

Charles himself was the very opposite of Billy Bunter: a fanatic on cleanliness, exercise and fresh air; abstemious in his diet; tidy in his appearance; conscientious about never letting people down; loyal, generous to a fault and utterly dependable. My Uncle's sense of humour – perhaps his strongest trait – was curiously omitted from

Bunter altogether.

Although morality was such a firm base to Charles Hamilton's writing, he never needed to preach: he laughed his readers out of their follies continuously throughout the twentieth century and with the reappearance of Mary Cadogan's excellent book he is already staking a claim to the twenty-first!

INTRODUCTION
to this new edition

by Professor Jeffrey Richards

In the summer of 1940 literary London was heartily amused by a vigorous exchange of views printed in the celebrated magazine *Horizon*. In the March issue George Orwell had published one of his pioneering and still indispensable articles on popular culture, a study of weekly boys' papers and their influence. In discussing the *Magnet* and the *Gem* he casually observed that the Greyfriars stories in the *Magnet* signed 'Frank Richards' and the St Jim's stories in the *Gem* signed 'Martin Clifford' could hardly be the work of the same persons as they had appeared every week for thirty years. Orwell was as staggered as everyone else when an article arrived at *Horizon* from Frank Richards, carefully rebutting Orwell's criticisms of the papers and pointing out that not only was there only one Frank Richards, who had indeed been writing the stories for thirty years but that he was also Martin Clifford. Orwell estimated that Frank Richards had written some forty-five million words to date. He would have been even more astonished if he had known the full story of Frank Richards' career. According to current estimates he wrote over seventy million words under twenty-five different pseudonyms between 1894, when his first stories were published, and Christmas Eve 1961 when he died. During this time he created not only Greyfriars and St Jim's, his most famous educational establishments, but over one hundred other fictional schools. Although the school story was his metier, he began by writing pirate yarns and over the years also gained a following for his westerns and his South Sea island stories.

This literary phenomenon is the subject of Mary Cadogan's book *Frank Richards: The Chap Behind the Chums*. First published in 1988, it was rightly hailed as definitive and it is a great joy to see it back in print in this new edition. For it is Mary Cadogan at her best, combining assiduous research, encyclopaedic knowledge, sympathetic understanding, perceptive insight and compulsive readability. The book combines a chronological account of the life of this most mysterious of writers with an analysis of his work, his characters, his attitudes and his values. No one who reads this book can be left in any doubt of the importance, literary, cultural and sociological of Frank Richards.

Although he came in time to think of himself exclusively as Frank Richards this was not in fact his real name. He was born Charles Harold St John Hamilton in Ealing in 1876, the son of a drunken consumptive journalist who died when Charles was only seven, leaving him to be brought up, along with seven brothers and sisters, by a widowed mother. The young Charles Hamilton was a shy boy with poor eyesight, slight in build, diffident and reserved. Like many boys of that type, he was a voracious reader, living his life vicariously through books and stories.

Charles soon began writing his own stories, sold some and at the age of seventeen embarked on a full-time writing career in boys' papers. From 1907 to 1939 on the *Gem* and from 1908 to 1940 on the *Magnet* he provided a weekly thirty thousand word story, as well as fulfilling many other commitments on other papers. This necessitated the use from time to time of substitute writers on *Gem* and *Magnet*, whose stories were published under Frank Richards' name, a practice he never forgave, angrily describing the substitutes as "impostors". Nevertheless Richards wrote two-thirds of all the St Jim's stories and 1,380 of the 1,683 stories about Greyfriars.

The excitement and drama that his life otherwise lacked were provided by extensive foreign travel both before and after World War One and an addiction to gambling, particularly roulette. Although he was briefly engaged once, he never actually married. When his eyesight worsened in the 1920s, he gave up foreign travel and settled down to a comfortable self-contained bachelor existence in Kent with his typewriter, his bicycle, his pipe, his cat and his garden, living as he always had a life of the imagination. It was an imagination dominated by the world of school. In an interview in 1961 he recalled: "When I'm sitting at a typewriter, I'm only 16 years old. Oh yes, I live at Greyfriars. I remember once in Italy when I came down to lunch, they told me there'd been an earthquake shock. I hadn't noticed it. I was at Greyfriars at the time. It's a curious thing that when I write I seem to see it all happening before my eyes as if I were looking at a picture. I had a sense of writing down actual happenings."

Of all the schools he created, Greyfriars was closest to his heart and has been the most popular with readers. Greyfriars featured 'The Famous Five', Harry Wharton, Frank Nugent, Johnny Bull, Bob Cherry and Hurree Jamset Ram Singh, embryonic officers and gentlemen all and stalwart upholders of the public school code. Their comic counterpart and antithesis was Billy Bunter, whom Orwell called "one of the best known figures in English fiction." He was the schoolboy Falstaff, a sacred monster, a larger than life embodiment of human failings: fat, sly, idle, prevaricating, cowardly, snobbish, racist, greedy and vainglorious. His regular chastisement by beating, booting, bouncing, detention, suspension and exclusion confirms the need to check these weaknesses, to mortify the flesh and purify the spirit. The fact that he survives to offend again testifies to the enduring strength of human weakness. Their form-master and one of the most celebrated pedagogues in fiction was the gimlet-eyed Mr Henry Samuel Quelch, "a beast but a just beast," as the boys put it.

When the *Magnet* closed in 1940, it looked as if the world had seen the last of Bunter and Co. But after the war Frank Richards revived them in hardback form and thirty-eight titles eventually appeared. Between 1952 and 1961 BBC TV ran five series of Greyfriars adaptations, popular with children and adults alike. Richards found himself in his seventies a national celebrity, with an entry in *Who's Who*, regular newspaper and wireless interviews and when he died, an obituary in *The Times*. Following his death Greyfriars became a cult, inspiring clubs and societies of passionate devotees, a school prospectus and an Old Boys' tie – I'm wearing mine now as I write these words.

What explains the enduring appeal of these school stories, set at St Jim's, Rookwood, Carcroft and pre-eminently Greyfriars? First, there is the atmosphere of timelessness, of comforting familiarity, of reassuring order, of innocence. "Greyfriars" said Frank Richards, "it is a life of innocence. It's as things should be." Alas there will never be such innocence again.

It is a world of unchanging patterns and eternal verities. The *Magnet* followed the course of the school year precisely, with the group assembling in September for the autumn term. The boys played football in the winter and cricket in the summer. There were Christmas vacation stories and adventures in the summer hols when the boys generally undertook an expedition to some exotic clime – Brazil, Egypt, India or the South Seas. The Christmas stories were particularly popular, frequently involving ghosts and secret passages, and always being set in snow-covered rural England, where the crisp air brings colour to the cheeks after a country walk or skating on frozen ponds, where there are roaring fires and tables loaded down with seasonal fare in venerable, holly-decked country houses. Richards succeeded in creating as warm and enduring a memory of Christmas as did his old favourite, Dickens. One thing remains constant. The boys always stay the same age and each autumn as term began and the cycle was initiated again, Harry Wharton and Co. were still to be found in the Remove. It was this as much as anything else which ensured that feeling of timelessness.

Second, there are the characters. Greyfriars features a whole range of rounded and convincing boy portraits. The idea that they are stereotypes, which some later commentators have advanced, is quite untenable. They are instead archetypes, something very different. A stereotype is a carbon copy of a well-established model; an archetype is the creation of a definitive idealization. There is irrefutable evidence in the attitude of boy readers. The characters served as role models. The historian Robert Roberts recalled that among his boyhood friends in Edwardian Salford one, "a natural athlete", modelled his conduct on that of Harry Wharton and another adopted a jerky gait "in his attempts to imitate Bob Cherry's springy, athletic stride." All his friends quite self-consciously incorporated Greyfriars slang into their own "oath-sprinkled banter - 'Yarooh', 'My sainted aunt', 'Leggo' and a dozen others."

G.R. Samways, the *Magnet* sub-editor, writes in his evocative autobiography *The Road to Greyfriars*: "To a great many readers these characters were not mere puppets of the author's creation but living, vital beings, leading a real existence in a real school." This is evidenced by the letter columns of the magazine, to which boys wrote seeking further information about the studies, habits, lives and backgrounds of the characters. The Amalgamated Press arranged with the G.P.O. to have the many letters addressed to Greyfriars School delivered to them. The editors of the *Magnet* set great store by readers' letters, regarding them as a valuable indicator of the popularity of themes and characters.

The prime favourite was Bob Cherry. According to Samways, "Bob had all the qualities which endeared him to youthful hearts – his sunny disposition, his gay courage, his sportsmanship, his irrepressible high spirits, and his ready championship of the underdog, all combined to make him not merely popular but universally beloved." After Bob Cherry the most popular characters were Mark Linley and Herbert Vernon-Smith. Linley, a Lancashire factory boy who won a scholarship and thus achieved the heart's desire of so many of the *Magnet*'s working class readers, instant translation to the sacred company, was the perfect role model for those readers, an exemplar of brains and hard work achieving success. Herbert Vernon-Smith, "the Bounder of the Remove", reckless and defiant but basically honourable, was the boy who kicked over the traces but always proved true-blue in the end. Bunter, however, was not a role model and was "an also-ran in the popularity stakes": "not many readers liked him," said Samways, "a good many positively loathed him; yet he was a never-failing source of mirth and merriment to all." Interestingly Harry Wharton, though he had his admirers, was not at the top of the popularity poll. Samways explained: "There was a touch of arrogance about him which caused him to be less well-liked than the characters already mentioned."

The third area of appeal lies in the depiction of friendship. Friendship is central to the lives of children. Who is the best friend of whom. Who is in whose gang. It is what sociologists call "peer group dynamics". The Famous Five are the ideal boy 'gang', a closely integrated group of friends, and if they fell out and the friendship was threatened, as it was periodically, usually by a misunderstanding, the story struck home.

Fourthly, there is the idealization of school life, schooldays as they should be – japes and scrapes, footer and cricket, study teas and practical jokes, and Dickensian Christmas hols. There were impots and whackings certainly but they were an accepted part of the system and life was fun. Writing of his childhood in Edwardian Battersea, Edward Ezard described his schooldays as "lacking the public school glamour which made us avidly read *Magnet* and *Gem* week by week and swap them over until they became tatty indeed."

Richards' success in writing for boys was partly due to the fact that like other great writers of the school story, Thomas Hughes, Talbot Baines Reed, P.G. Wodehouse for instance, he remained all his life a boy. He admitted in his autobiography to being "still a boy at heart." As such he said: "he liked school; he liked schoolboys; he even, amazing as it may seem, liked schoolmasters." However, what Richards was at some pains to conceal was that he himself had never been to public school, which is perhaps why he chose to begin his autobiography, one of the least revealing ever written, when he was seventeen and had already left school. As Mary Cadogan confirms, he attended a series of private day schools in Ealing and Chiswick. It is significant that the chief critics of the stories have been in the main former public schoolboys, who have denounced their lack of authenticity. But this is irrelevant. He was writing for boys who were not at and would never go to public school. The power of the stories is that they are in one sense unreal.

They are a distillation of elements of the public school story genre, transmuted into a dreamlike landscape, a mythic world, an alternative universe, whose surroundings and elements have a recognizable surface reality, but are subtly different, existing as it were out of time.

Richards lies in direct line of descent, almost an apostolic succession, from Thomas Hughes, F W Farrar and Talbot Baines Reed. Close textual analysis also reveals the imprint of H A Vachell's *The Hill*, Kipling's *Stalky and Co.* and the stories of Wodehouse and Desmond Coke, all of them – as Mary Cadogan reveals – to be found on Richards' bookshelves. All his life he immersed himself in school stories, revealing in 1961: "I like a school story best even at my present age. I can still read Talbot Baines Reed and I occasionally have a look into *Stalky and Co.* and even into *Tom Brown.*"

He believed you should never write down to a boy and he never did. But he saw himself as having a didactic mission, writing in his autobiography in the third person: "To entertain young people and in an unobtrusive way to guide and counsel them, seems to him a very worthwhile job." On a general level the stories enshrined the values and virtues of the public school code, endorsing those characteristics which the British believed sustained their empire and justified their role as the world's policeman: team spirit and fair play, duty and self-sacrifice, truth and justice. Richards believed firmly in discipline and the use of the cane and consistently denounced drinking, smoking and gambling. He defended himself against charges of hypocrisy by saying that his own gambling experiences put him in a good position to speak about its dangers. His attitude to women was one of chivalry. "Never try to be unpleasantly witty on the subject of women – a subject that should be sacred to every self-respecting man" was his advice to aspiring writers. He showed continual hostility to racism, snobbism and materialism. His inclusion of Hurree Jamset Ram Singh, the Nabob of Banipur, as one of the Co., was, he said, deliberate: "By making an Indian boy a comrade on equal terms with English schoolboys, Frank felt that he was contributing his mite towards the unity of the Commonwealth and helping to rid the youthful mind of colour prejudice." His boys are patriotic, royalist and conservative – with a small c – but then so was the bulk of the British people when Richards was writing.

Critics of Richards from Orwell on have claimed that his stories lack sex and violence, any reference to war, poverty or social change, and that his foreigners are cardboard characters. The last charge is certainly true. There is no sex or violence, and so much the better for that. World War One and the reality of poverty certainly do impinge on the stories very strongly. But then most of the critics of Richards have never read much of his work.

It was the boys of England for several generations who read his stories. Working-class and middle-class memoirs from the period of the *Magnet* frequently contain affectionate references to the paper. The actor Peter Cushing wrote of Frank Richards: "I owe him a great debt of gratitude, not only for the enormous pleasure I derived from his work, but also for his influence upon me as a person. Tom Merry was my hero, and I tried to mould my way of life according to his tenets." Cricket commentator John Arlott recalled: "Frank Richards! My word, how we lapped him up! When we were boys at a Hampshire elementary school, forty years ago... These were the things we would like to have done, magnified to something more than life size." Even Noël Coward admitted: "I took a fancy for the most tremendously hearty schoolboy literature. I read avidly *Chums*, *The Boy's Own Paper*, the *Magnet* and the *Gem*, and loved particularly these last two."

What was the influence of public school fiction on its middle-class and working-class boy readers? Popular fiction is one of the ways in which society instructs its members in its prevailing mores and ideas, its dominant role models and legitimate aspirations. It both reflects popular attitudes, ideas and preconceptions and it generates support for selected views and opinions. There is a two-way reciprocal process at work between producers and consumers. The consumers by what they buy tell the producers what they want. The producers, aiming to maximise profit, dramatize what they perceive to be the dominant ideas and headline topics of the day. Generic literature, like the school story, relying as it does on the regular reuse of the same elements, characters and situations, functions as ritual, cementing the ideas and beliefs of society, enforcing norms and exposing, labelling and isolating social deviants.

Popular fiction has been peculiarly potent because it feeds the imaginative life of the reader and this may have more immediate, more emotional and arguably longer-lasting impact than any number of school lessons, political speeches or church sermons. It provides a sediment in the mind, which it requires a conscious intellectual effort to erase. Since the majority of people are not intellectual, it follows that only a minority will for a variety of reasons make this effort.

Perhaps the best assessment of the influence of the public school story on the working class comes from Robert Roberts, one of the few historians to write from within that class: "In the final estimate," he said, "it may well be found that Frank Richards during the first quarter of the twentieth century had more influence on the mind and outlook of young working class England than any other single person." It is a bold claim but the more I study the history of the last century, it is one of whose truth I am increasingly convinced. The life of the remarkable man who touched so many lives and shaped so many dreams receives a full and fitting memorial in Mary Cadogan's splendid book.

FRANK RICHARDS

———

The Chap Behind the Chums

Frank Richards and his most famous creation portrayed by
Magnet illustrator C. H. Chapman.

AUTHOR'S PREFACE

———

THE IMPORTANCE OF BEING FRANK

Frank Richards: The Chap Behind the Chums is a celebration of the life and work of the most prolific published writer in the English language. Charles Harold St John Hamilton used more than twenty pen-names, created almost a hundred fictional schools and published well over 72 million words of fiction, or the equivalent of a thousand novels. He is better known as Frank Richards, the pseudonym he used when writing about Greyfriars School and its imperishable inmates. He created St Jim's as Martin Clifford and Rookwood School as Owen Conquest, but Frank Richards became more to him than just another pen-name – it was an *alter ego*. I have therefore referred to him as Frank rather than as Charles (or Martin or Owen, and so on) whenever this has seemed possible. In the early years of Charles's life, however, before Frank had come into being, I have called him by his real name.

Inevitably, this study of Frank's aspirations and achievements puts a great deal of emphasis on Greyfriars and the *Magnet*, as these stories embody much of his most stylish writing. I have, however, endeavoured to indicate the range and variety of his lesser-known stories in the fields of adventure, detection and the Western.

It is no exaggeration to say that Frank Richards set his stamp on a generation and that his influence is still felt today. Billy Bunter's name has become part of the language, a lurid synonym for comic and gluttonous obesity. In the late 1980s, over a quarter of a century after the death of Frank Richards, his stories of Greyfriars, St Jim's and Rookwood schools are still being regularly reprinted, and his fans range from nine-year-olds to nonagenarians, from school-children to surgeons. It is manly boys like Harry Wharton of Greyfriars and Tom Merry of St Jim's who are the true heroes of the saga, but the large cast of characters at Frank's most celebrated schools gives almost every type of reader someone with whom he or she may identify. Girls too appear in the stories, of course: rippers like Marjorie Hazeldene, who inspired undying (if unconsummated) passion in the rugged breast of Bob Cherry of the Greyfriars Remove. So real were Frank's characters in their heyday that the editor of the *Magnet* frequently received letters from readers requesting fixtures with the school's junior eleven or dates with the beauteous Marjorie. Readers were also inspired from time to time to send parcels of tuck for the famished Fat Owl, and at least one lady used to send packets of meat for the Greyfriars cat.

For hundreds of thousands of children during the 1920s and 1930s, Greyfriars had umpteen advantages over Eton, Harrow, Rugby and Charterhouse. One was that girl readers, as well as boys, could claim it as their Alma Mater, and another was that it cost only twopence a week (the price of the *Magnet*) to go there. Greyfriars represented both the real world in microcosm and the fantasy adventure, with boys taking responsibilities for their own destinies, looking to wonderfully broad horizons and also learning to function with *esprit de corps*. There is plenty to laugh at in the sagas, but they have always also had their serious effect upon readers. In his survey of Salford life in the early part of this century, for example, Professor Robert Roberts states that the stories

> set ideals and standards. This our own tutors, religious and secular, had signally failed to do. In the final estimate it may well be found that Frank Richards during the first quarter of the twentieth century had more influence on the mind and outlook of young working-class England than any other single person, not excluding Baden-Powell.[1]

Even readers who might have found the author's assumptions about adolescent honour and decency and cleanmindedness some-what inflated often responded to his irresistible enthusiasm, his comic use of the high-flown simile – 'Bunter paused, like Brutus of old, for a reply. Like Brutus, he paused in vain' – and to his charismatic characters. Of these, the most retarded has become the most resilient. Bunter is a law unto himself; he lives according to a much more elastic version of the strict 'no sneaking, no fibbing' Greyfriars ethic than the other fellows. He prefers frowsting over the study fire to healthy outdoor exercise; he spies on his schoolmates through the owl-like spectacles that adorn his wily gooseberry eyes; he tells lies and constantly snaffles 'comestibles' belonging to other Removites. Condign punishment is inflicted upon him in a variety of circumstances, but he never reforms. Yet he is more than just a clowning fatty. Ever since he rolled off his originator's Remington in 1908, he has symbolized the underdog who against all the powers of logic somehow manages to come out on top of the heap. 'Rolled' is the operative word where Frank Richards is concerned. Every one of his tales flowed out, according to Frank, 'of its own accord, with scarce an effort on the part of the writer',[2] which explains why his output leaves every other English-language writer so many miles behind in terms of word-count.

Asked once whether he would like to have written 'something better' than stories for boys' weeklies, Frank replied firmly that there *was* nothing better than writing for young people. He possessed the rare ability to convey without sentimentality the intensity of school-boy loyalties and chumminess. As Hurree Jamset Ram Singh, the Indian member of Harry Wharton's celebrated Co., expressed it, 'the ancient and ludicrous flame of friend-ship burns undimfully' throughout the thirty-two years of the *Magnet*'s life, in the post-war Bunter books and in the *Magnet* and *Gem* facsimiles published by the Howard Baker Press.

Despite the fame of his stories, the Greyfriars author has sometimes seemed a rather shadowy figure. *Frank Richards: The Chap Behind the Chums* will, I hope, provide insights into his rich and multi-faceted personality through an exploration of his works.

"Who is this Charles Hamilton?"
"I thought he was called Frank Richards."

The mission-hall was crowded ; in the glow from the swinging lamps dozens of couples glided merrily over the smooth floor—but Frank Richards slipped quietly away from the lights and gaiety, to the old typewriter in Mr. Smiley's study.

CHAPTER ONE

SCHOOLBOY RIDER OF THE EALING RANGE

Let youth be happy, or as happy as possible. Happiness is the best preparation for misery, if misery must come.[1]

Frank Richards's autobiography was published in 1952, and readers who had been devouring his stories for several decades received it with enthusiasm. There was, however, some disappointment that this selective and determinedly third-person narrative ('Frank Richards generally kept sensible hours') almost completely by-passed the first seventeen years of the author's life. All that could be gleaned about his childhood from his own writings is that 'as a very small boy' he 'secretly and surreptitiously' taught himself the Greek alphabet in the belief that this would unlock the mysteries of his father's library; that 'sprawling in a boat on summer days', he used to write 'reams and reams'; and that he saw himself in his imagination 'translating the *Iliad* ever so much more attractively than Pope or Chapman'![2] The omission of this significant period of his life from his autobiography was particularly confusing, because from 1917 to 1940 his own fictional accounts of his supposed schooldays in the Canadian backwoods had been published in several different boys' papers and annuals.

Charles Harold St John Hamilton was born on 8 August 1876 in Ealing, in the county of Middlesex, the sixth child of John and Mary Ann ('Marion') Hannah Hamilton. His birthplace, which was demolished as part of an extensive development scheme in the early 1960s, was 15 Oak Street. This small, flat-fronted terraced house must have been bulging at the seams, for Charles had four brothers and three sisters. The Hamiltons' eldest child, Maud Marion Margaret, was born in 1865 and the youngest, Una Isabel Gertrude, in 1881. In between, in addition to Charles, came Alexander Llewellyn Patrick (1867), Archibald Reginald Percy (1869), Edith Hilda May (1872), Richard Lionel Walter (1874) and Hugh Douglas Percy (1879).

It was a point of pride with his mother that she found good names for each of her offspring, and Charles came to share her sense of the rightness – or the inadequacies – of nomenclature. The choice of pen-names for his various writing roles and the naming of characters was always important to him:

> A rose by any other name may smell as sweet: but a scent appeals to the nose, not to the intelligence. Shakespeare . . . knew. He was not likely to name Falstaff Tommy Jones, or Aubrey de Vere . . . One has only to try to imagine Beethoven named Schmidt, or Shakespeare named Bert Wilkins, or Monsieur Arouet called Dupont instead of Voltaire – to realize how very much there is in a name.[3]

Because of the age disparity between the first and last, the Hamilton children divided naturally into two groups. Charles's strongest relationships were with Hugh ('Douglas') and, most resiliently, with Una ('Dolly'). The latter acquired her nickname when Douglas, taken to see his baby sister for the first time, was told that his mother had 'a dolly' for him; the name stuck. As children, both Douglas and Charles were fondly protective of Dolly, and Douglas's sadly premature death at the age of twenty-three forged an even closer bond between the two survivors of this trio. This was to continue throughout their lives and, as every relationship was grist to Charles's literary mill, to provide a feminine influence on many of his stories.

Charles's father, John Hamilton, appears to have had several skills, but was by profession a journalist; he managed to maintain a reasonably comfortable lifestyle for his large and demanding family, without providing a great deal of gilt for the gingerbread. He contributed to the *Freethinker* and other papers, but his real flair was for poetry. This seems to have been inherited by several of his children, including Charles, who, however, decided to concentrate on prose rather than verse as a result of his father's experiences. Years later, commenting on his boyhood in an article to mark the thousandth edition of the *Magnet* in 1927, he suggested that the remuneration his father received 'for his verses paid . . . for the ink he used, but not for the paper'.[4] The accuracy of this comment is open to question, because the then prolific Frank Richards, who was tossing off one and a half million words a year without apparent effort, might well have regarded John's (or indeed most other writers') output and earnings as puny. Besides, Frank had further reasons for wishing to feel dismissive of his father.

John Hamilton was a clever man who never managed fully to exploit his talents. He married Marion Trinder in 1864 at Ealing Congregational Church when she was only sixteen; moving to various houses before settling in Oak Street, they were quickly caught up in the responsibilities of family life. Economies had to be practised in the home, but at John's insistence these were sometimes carried beyond the bounds of necessity. His granddaughter, Una Hamilton Wright, provides a colourful vignette of life in the Hamilton household.[5] John, of Scottish extraction, was 'nae mean but carefu'', allowing nothing to be discarded that could possibly be mended, and 'Father will mend it with his glue-pot' became a family saying. He was a heavy, repressive 'Moulton Barrett type of father', forbidding his wife and daughters the frivolity of cutting their hair into fringes and generally inspiring awe rather than affection in his children.

He was, however, never abstemious in his intake of alcohol. Charles was shy, self-effacing, eager to please his parents and extremely sensitive to the difficulties imposed upon the family by John's drinking. As a small boy he was told that the father of one of his school friends had died, and he replied uncompromisingly, 'I wish mine had!'

What he may not have known then was that John suffered from tuberculosis during the last three years of his life. He died in February 1884 at the age of forty-five, when Charles was only seven and a half. The diffident small boy was able to find a new sense of security in his mother's warmth and vivacity, which flowered after John's death. His father's passing seemed to lift a burden from the whole family; 'the women went and had their fringes cut'; Marion could indulge her long-suppressed flair for entertaining, and the home became a happy one. Nevertheless, whatever relief Charles may have experienced at the time, it appears that his feelings for his father were not so clear-cut as he had imagined. There is evidence in many of his stories of his attempts to exorcize a sense of remorse and missed opportunity from father-and-son relationships. He wrote in

HARRY WHARTON & CO. are the FINEST CHUMS YOU COULD MEET!
(Make their acquaintance in the grand school yarn inside.)

his autobiography that 'almost everybody Frank ever met came, sooner or later, into his writing, in one form or another; and I do not think that there ever was a character in *Gem* or *Magnet* that was wholly imaginary'. He went on to say that, having passed through the crucible of his imagination, such real-life figures generally emerged in an improved or idealized shape.

By choosing to make boarding-schools the setting for most of his stories, Charles was able to tidy away unsatisfactory fathers (and, frequently, mothers as well). It is interesting that his two greatest hero-figures, Harry Wharton of Greyfriars and Tom Merry of St

Jim's, were orphans. Each was looked after in early life by a female relative or guardian who is presented sympathetically by the author, and masculine influences in their upbringing and character formation became prominent only when their boarding-school days began. Charles Hamilton created almost a hundred fictional schools, only a handful of which were day-schools, in spite of the fact that his own education took place in the latter. Significantly, the father in the stories who most resembles his own appears in the day-school series about Frank Richards's boyhood. This is set in an entirely fictitious framework of the backwoods of British Columbia. In real life Frank Richards never went further afield than Europe, but there were no limits to the world of his imagination, and from childhood he was attracted to the mythology of the Wild West and the Western. The nearest he got to intrepid cowboys and war-whooping Red Indians was a much relished trip to Buffalo Bill's celebrated show on one of its London visits. However, he frequently remarked in letters and articles that the exploits of Frank Richards & Co. at Cedar Creek School encompassed much of his own boyhood experience. (There seems to have been a possibility that the fictional setting for Frank's schooldays could have become reality. He wrote to W. H. Gander, the editor of the *Story Paper Collector*: 'I am disposed to wish sometimes that my father had carried out his intention of emigrating to Canada in the 1870s.')[6] It is a far cry from the confines of late-Victorian Ealing to the expansiveness of Canadian mountains, lakes and forests, but the Cedar Creek stories rang sufficiently true for many readers to believe for decades that their author must have grown up in British Columbia.

This long-running saga began in the weekly *Boys' Friend* in 1917, at a time when Frank Richards's stories in the *Magnet* had built up a tremendous following. The adolescent Frank is supposed to be living at his uncle's ranch and, with his boisterous cousin Bob Lawless, riding several miles on horseback each day to Cedar Creek School. Fresh from England, Frank starts out as the typical tenderfoot and is easily hoodwinked by his lively, teasing cousin; he turns up on his first day at school in the hilariously unsuitable garb of Etons and a topper. He soon becomes firm friends with Bob and another Cedar Creek pupil, Vere Beauclerc. The latter is the son of a work-shy, weak-willed and frequently alcoholic remittance-man who has been exiled to the wilds of Canada by his long-suffering aristocratic English family. Charles seems neatly to have transposed to Vere

THE BOYS' FRIEND 2^c

FRANK RICHARDS' CHRISTMAS

By Martin Clifford

A MAGNIFICENT STORY DEALING WITH THE FAMOUS AUTHOR'S SCHOOLDAYS

Beauclerc and his father elements of his own difficult and unresolved relationship with John Hamilton. Time and again Lascelles Beauclerc lets down his son by indulging in benders at the Red Dog saloon, and time and again he is saved from disaster by the boy's dogged devotion and belief in him. In 'The Parting of the Ways' Vere is reluctantly persuaded by his father to leave him – and Canada – for 'the old country', where Lascelles's brother, Lord St Austell, offers him the benefits of a vast estate and a public-school education.[7]

Embarking on his long journey from backwoods to baronial halls, Vere is suddenly beset by fears of hidden and horrific meaning in his father's words of farewell. The realization that he is being sent to 'a new home and protector' so that Lascelles can end his strange and shiftless life prompts Vere to rush back to his timber-shack home and, in the nick of time, to save the remittance-man from suicidal death by drowning. This episode and the dialogue that follows display an intensity that is unusual in the Charles Hamilton canon: ' "Oh, father, father, how could you . . . ?" "It was the only way," Lascelles muttered . . . "It was the first decent thing that ever came into my mind to do. Better to make an end of it, once and for all, than live to be a burden and disgrace to you!" ' There is a great deal more in this vein, but, after passionately declaring that he could bear 'anything else' but his father's death, Vere eventually extracts a promise that there will never again be a suicide attempt: 'His father was saved to him, and whatever wild ways Lascelles Beauclerc's feet might tread in future days, his promise was sacred, and the most dreaded blow of all would never fall upon the remittance-man's son.'

Almost undoubtedly there are for Charles aspects of wish-fulfilment in the new and close relationship that develops between the fictional father and son. In real life he was never to have the opportunity of knowing his own father at an age when there might have been some mutual understanding of problems and an appreciation of each other's talents. There was wish-fulfilment too in the adventurous excitement that the young Charles projected into his stories and imaginary worlds. He remained mild and reserved and was always anxious to patch up arguments between his brothers and sisters, thus earning the name 'Charlie the peacemaker'.

He was not only the family peacemaker, but the family story-spinner. He quickly learned the trick of providing what his audience wanted from his home-made Westerns and tales of adventure, creating an imaginary farm in Canada for Dolly, which contained every animal she requested, including camels and giraffes. His fascination with literature and language was evident from an early age; he read avidly, and his tastes ranged from the works of Sir Walter Scott, Charles Dickens, Lewis Carroll and Edward Lear to the stories of the colourful Chinese character Cheerful Ching Ching in the periodical *Boys' Standard*. When he was eleven, he memorized the whole of Scott's 'The Lay of the Last Minstrel' simply because he liked it, and this facility for learning long passages of poetry stood him in good stead throughout his life. (Writing in 1945 in an article entitled 'Boys' Writer', for example, he mentioned that when kept awake during the Second World War by guns, bombs and doodle-bugs, he had enjoyed running over in his mind a few scenes from Shakespeare, 'an ode of Horace and an ode of Keats, one or two of the livelier sections of Goethe's *Faust*, and a few hundred lines of Dante',[8] with Fitzgerald's *Rubáiyát of Omar Khayyám* and Byron's 'Apostrophe to the Ocean' by way of light relief.)

Because he created a fictional school, which was to become the Alma Mater of millions, and also because of his reticence in his autobiography about his schooldays, there has been a great deal of curiosity and speculation about Frank Richards's educational background. In fact, this seems straightforward enough, and it is surprising that he should have taken pains to conceal it. (Una Hamilton Wright, his niece, once suggested that his reluctance to talk about the schools he attended sprang from the fear of hurting the feelings of old friends, because 'many of his characters owed some of their traits to his classmates and masters'.[9]) He attended several different private day-schools in Ealing and Chiswick. After John Hamilton's death, Marion's fairly well-to-do Oxfordshire family augmented her income, and her brother, Stephen Trinder, a successful estate agent, made sure that there was always a comfortable house available for her and the children. This entailed several moves and changes of school for Charles and his brothers and sisters.

One school for young gentlemen attended by Charles and his elder brother Dick has been identified by W. O. G. Lofts and D. J. Adley as Thorn House School in Ealing. With its emphasis on the teaching of languages and offering as it did both Classical and Modern 'sides', this seems to have been cast in a similar mould to some of the fictional schools Charles was later to create.

Slighter than his brothers, Charles had the studious boy's admiration of his more sporty and boisterous schoolmates. He looked up

"WHO PUNCHED PROUT?" This week's breezy yarn of school life at Greyfriars.

No. 1,085. Vol. XXXIV. Week Ending December 1st, 1928.

The Magnet 2ᵈ

LIBRARY

EVERY SATURDAY

COKER—THE GREYFRIARS SAMSON!

(It took umpteen fellows to subdue Horace Coker—and they all had something to show for it! See the grand school story of the Chums of Greyfriars—inside.)

both physically and psychologically to Dick, aspects of whose robust, wholehearted nature were later to inspire one of Charles's most popular and humorous characterizations – the big, bossy and blundering Horace Coker of the fifth form at Greyfriars. According to Dick's granddaughter, Patricia Alcock, he was quite happy to have had this literary immortality thrust upon him: 'all the Hamiltons had the knack of "taking the mickey" out of each other and never hurting feelings, but ending up rolling on the floor with mirth!'[10] Charles was a natural and very able scholar, and, in spite of being two years younger than Dick, was in the same class. (Similarly, in the Greyfriars saga, Horace Coker's younger brother scholastically outstripped him.) From his early childhood Dick was an extremely lively boy and a favourite with his mother, though he sometimes drove her to distraction. His brothers and sisters used to chase behind him shouting, 'Richard Lionel Walter/He didn't do what he ought-ta'.

Dick included Charles in his schoolboy gang, and he was appreciated as a 'backer-upper' by its more adventurous members. He was willing, when requested, to offer opinions or to perform small tasks for these spirited characters. But he was often happier to slip away from them and bury himself in a book or to drift off into the worlds of his own invention. (A parallel may be found in the fictional Canadian boyhood experiences of Frank Richards, who would frequently separate himself from his gregarious chums when overtaken by literary inspiration.)

A dependable follower but never an instigator, Charles by his own admission accurately portrayed himself in Frank Nugent, the loyal chum, studymate and lieutenant of Harry Wharton, who was the charismatic leader of the Greyfriars Remove and that celebrated group known as the Famous Five. (This included, besides the heroic Harry and quiet Frank, warm-hearted, steamingly exuberant Bob Cherry; Johnny Bull, from Yorkshire, who was unfailingly phlegmatic and inclined to be a know-all; and Hurree Jamset Ram Singh, the 'lithe, inscrutable Hindu junior' who was a splendiferous nabob in his own country of Bhanipur, but graciously allowed himself when at Greyfriars to become the unpretentious 'Good Old Inky'.)

Although Frank Nugent was a self-portrait, the character did not share Charles's passion for learning or his predilection for Latin. Had he done so, he would have been categorized as that despised stereotype in schoolboy fiction, the swot, who was only a shade or two less contemptible than the most heinous of all – the sneak. At one of his schools Charles found out that the Latin master was just one chapter ahead of the class in the primer that he put into daily use with his pupils. Impishly and without difficulty, Charles decided to get two chapters ahead so that he could, on occasions, embarrass his teacher with unanswerably awkward queries. His childhood love for the classics increased with maturity and was maintained throughout his life. He enjoyed spattering his school stories with classical allusions and anecdotes; at the simplistic level, stupid fellows like Billy Bunter made comic howlers in their Latin translations under the 'gimlet eye' of Henry Samuel Quelch, the angular and impressive master of the Remove who was, according to his boys, 'a beast, but a just beast'. He also used classical imagery facetiously and to good effect: 'Bob Cherry roared in a voice that the ancient Stentor himself might have envied'; 'Mr Quelch's face bore a striking resemblance to that of a Gorgon as he went up the Remove passage.'

More subtly, Frank Richards regaled his young readers with episodes in which elderly academics gained strange satisfactions from the study of languages that were, to most boys and girls, not only dead, but terribly dreary:

Mr Quelch sat in an easy chair; the Head sat at ease in another. On a table lay a volume of that entrancing poet, Aeschylus.

To learned and scholastic minds like those of Henry Samuel Quelch and Dr Locke, Aeschylus was like unto a mine of gold.

But like all gold mines, this one had its dark and dim recesses, where it was not easy to find one's way.

On occasions, when a school holiday freed them from their multifarious duties, the two old gentlemen loved to explore those deep, dim and dark passages.

They made wonderful discoveries there – elucidating what Aeschylus really meant, admitting, of course, that he meant anything . . . The subject was an important one. For long centuries the world had gone on its way, while many an obscure passage in Aeschylus remained unelucidated. Probably the world would continue to roll on its appointed course, even if those passages continued unelucidated . . . But to a scholastic gentleman like Dr Locke the big world hardly existed. He lived in a little learned world of his own. After many years of patient investigation Dr Locke was practically certain that he had got at the true reading of the twelfth verse in the *Seven Against Thebes*!

This was thrilling.[11]

We are then told that Quelch and other authorities on Aeschylus do not concur with this 'epoch-making discovery'. Dr Locke, however, sticks to his guns:

> He was prepared to maintain his opinion against Mr Quelch, against Hermann, against Dindorf, against Madvig, against all the bald heads that had ever nodded over the *Epta epi Thebas*. And he was enjoying the discussion as keenly as Harry Wharton & Co. were enjoying cricket, almost as keenly as Billy Bunter had enjoyed the contents of the picnic basket.

Reciting '*Kai ton exebon chrono blastemon*' in a dreamy voice, the Head is dramatically interrupted by the sudden entrance of Loder, the unpopular sixth-form prefect, who, spluttering with soot, ashes, ink and fury, collides with a maidservant carrying a tray of tea for the

Bunter had laid the booby-trap for Harry Wharton & Co. But when he made the discovery that he had sooted, ashed, cindered, and inked Loder of the Sixth, the blood ran cold in his veins. With amazing promptness he circled round the staggering prefect, and dodged out of the study.

two ancient and enthusiastic scholars. Loder has been on the receiving end of a booby trap set by Bunter for someone else, and his wrathful clamour is increased by the crashing of crockery and the maid's frightful series of shrieks as 'in her terror and excitement she throws herself into the Head's arms, and clasps him hysterically'. All this cuts teachers and prefects firmly down to size for the youthful readers of the *Magnet* and illustrates Charles's capacity to send up his own (almost) sacred cows.

In many ways Charles Hamilton was self taught. Even as a small boy he understood that education meant far more than cramming for exams and qualifications. He believed that the purposes of school were to enlarge the child's powers of intellectual exploration and to put him in touch with the great thinkers and people of action and courage. When his schooldays ended, he was tutored privately for some time in Latin and Italian. For him the process of scholarship was to be lifelong. In an article entitled 'On Meeting Charles Hamilton', A. D. Newman writes that in 1951 he answered an advertisement in the *East Kent Times* for a tutor prepared 'to read Latin verse with a backward pupil'.[12] Summoned to the house in Kingsgate where Charles was then living, he was amazed to find that the 'backward pupil' was 'a venerable gentleman wearing a skull cap', the author of the Greyfriars stories. Apparently Charles considered that he had too long neglected Latin in favour of French, German, Italian and Spanish. Mr Newman visited him regularly from 1951 until 1960 (by which time Hamilton was eighty-five years old), and they read the whole of Horace, who was Charles's favourite author, 'most of Lucretius and much of Cicero'. The tutor was impressed by his pupil's 'phenomenal memory' (which seems to have been as sharp in old age as in childhood) and by his alteration of one of his favourite stanzas of Horace. This was the seventh in *Odes*, IV, 9, which Charles altered 'with one false quantity' to:

> *Vixere pingues ante Bunterium multi,*
> *Sed omnes illacrimabiles urgentur* [*sic*] –
> *Longa nocte, carent quia me Ricardo.*

In translation this reads:

> Many fat men have lived before Bunter
> But all have been unlamented, harried

And unknown, in the long night, because
They lack me, a Frank Richards.[13]

Charles understood that to a large extent a child will grow into the
type of adult projected by mental images built up during its early
years. Characteristically, in his 1940 reply to Orwell's criticism of
boys' weeklies he declared that childhood happiness was the best
preparation for any adult misery that might follow, and 'If there
is a Chekhov among my readers, I fervently hope that the effect
of the *Magnet* will be to turn him into a Bob Cherry.'[14] Even
when Hamilton had become the grand old man of boys' writers,
he retained a curiously Peter Pan-like quality. According to Una
Hamilton Wright, 'he never became middle-aged or pompous . . .
and would always reply to my childish question "Uncle, how old are
you?" – "No, my little dear, you should ask your Old Uncle how
young he is." '[15] Having experienced emotional insecurity in his own
boyhood, he hated even to hear a baby cry and was always sympathetic with children and any kind of underdog. (Billy Bunter is a
splendid example of the underdog who surprisingly, but satisfyingly,
manages to win the day.)

Despite his sensitive and retiring nature, the young Charles seems
to have coped remarkably well with the intimacies of family life in
somewhat crowded conditions. In order to dream up his stories, he
soon discovered the knack of making psychological space around
himself, and this technique was later to prove useful in a variety of
potentially disruptive situations. When he was writing, he was
always 'deaf and blind to all else'; on one occasion an earthquake
shock 'passed him unheeded while he sat at the typewriter'.[16] As he
wrote, 'the world of his imagination was much more real to him than
the humdrum world outside'. Whenever he did feel the need for
company or an audience for his tales, one or other of his siblings was
likely to be available.

Not surprisingly, boy-and-girl themes were frequently tackled in
his stories. One or two girls played significant parts almost from the
beginning of the Greyfriars and St Jim's sagas; it is interesting that
these sisters, cousins or chums often proved to be stronger characters
than the boys with whom they were particularly associated. At
Greyfriars, for example, Peter Hazeldene (nicknamed 'Vaseline') is
easily led astray by the cads and bounders and by his own impulses
to take the easy way out whenever possible. It is his sister, Marjorie,

who is the protective one of the pair. She frequently intervenes (with or without help from manly chums like Harry Wharton or Bob Cherry) to 'save him from himself'. She also manages on certain memorable occasions, by not much more than a disenchanted look or a determined compression of the lips, to shame some of the school's plentiful crop of 'smoky sweeps and shady rotters' into (temporary) abandonment of their less savoury activities.

Charles was a great believer in the power of young females to project this kind of reforming sweetness and light. Marjorie Hazeldene has masses of strength of the quiet, steady and unshowy variety. It is, however, rendered less effective by the fact that, at least in the early days of the *Magnet*, she spends most of her time on a pedestal, clambering off it only to make noble sacrifices for her wayward brother. (Later in the saga she is fleshed out into a robust and engaging character.)

Like Marjorie, Ethel Cleveland, who is the cousin of Arthur Augustus D'Arcy ('Gussy'), the swell of St Jim's in the *Gem*, is somewhat idealized. Both girls perform a double duty. They are real or surrogate sister-figures to the boys, and also the inspirers of romantic responses. Hearty decency rather than heavy passion is the keynote of such relationships ('"I say, I know I'm an ass, Harry, but – but what a ripping girl she is," muttered Bob Cherry'), which are rarely allowed to go far beyond the bounds of wholesome chumminess.

Frank Richards seems to have felt on surer ground with relations between brother and sister or boy and girl when he was able to indulge his taste for parody. Billy and Bessie Bunter could always be guaranteed to probe each other's weaknesses. Bessie first appeared on the scene in 'The Artful Dodger' (1919), in a rumbustious episode with Billy.[17] She not only shared his unappealing characteristics (conceit, untruthfulness, gluttonous obesity, and so on), but was more domineering, and was generally able to get the better of him by her nagging or head-smacking propensities:

Words failed Elizabeth Gertrude Bunter . . .
    No words, however expressive, could bring back her share of the toffee [which Billy, of course, has scoffed].
    Words being superfluous she went into action.
    Smack!
    The plumpest hand at Cliff House established sudden contact with the fattest head at Greyfriars.[18]

In 1944, when he had established a reputation as the doyen of boys' stories, Frank was approached by the journalist W. Bagley, who wished to produce an article on him for the *Writer*. He sent Frank a detailed questionnaire, and a lengthy correspondence followed. To the request to give advice to aspiring young writers, one of Frank's replies was that they should 'Never try to be unpleasantly witty on the subject of women – a subject that should be sacred to every self-respecting man.' His strongly chivalrous impulses, however, fail to encompass the belligerent Bessie.

'Tom Redwing's Quest' provides a glimpse of Billy and Bessie, together with their younger brother Sammy, bored to the back teeth with each other when forced to spend part of their holidays together at their family home.[19] (Normally they are notoriously successful at gatecrashing holiday house parties arranged by their various school-mates.) The Bunters are always bragging about the imposing façade and vast acres of Bunter Court, which, it transpires, is actually a small, suburban villa:

> The poet has told us that 'tis distance lends enchantment to the view. Certainly that was the case with Bunter Court. Generally a building seems small in the distance, and grows larger the nearer one approaches to it. In the case of Bunter Court this well-known natural law was reversed.
>
> Bunter Court loomed as a large and imposing mansion from the distance of Greyfriars. Close at hand, it diminished remarkably into the moderate dimensions of a villa in Surrey. Five or six Rolls-Royce cars woke the echoes of the wide domain of the Bunters when Billy was at Greyfriars. When he was at home, a single Ford spread its scent of petrol over the whole place, and did not have to spread it very far.

But domestic bliss can flower, of course, in meaner abodes than the Bunter home. Sadly, Bessie, Billy and Sammy achieve in their family relationship something far short of bliss, or even tranquil coexistence. Billy's psyche – hardly ultra-sensitive – is suffering constant erosion from his sister's nagging:

> He owed Bessie five shillings. Five shillings was not a large sum: but if it had been five hundred thousand pounds, Bessie Bunter could scarcely have dwelt upon the subject with more

eloquence. In season and out of season, Elizabeth Bunter dwelt
on that topic timelessly. Bessie was, in Billy's opinion, a cat.
Bessie's opinion of Billy could not be expressed so laconically.
Her vocabulary on the subject was very extensive indeed.

Billy eventually masterminds a plan of travelling to Southampton to
stow away on a yacht that is to take some of his fellow Removites on
an exciting holiday trip. As he leaves the house, he hears his sister
calling him animatedly:

Bunter smiled. At the moment of parting Elizabeth Bunter
seemed to realize what a nice brother he was, and wanted to say
good-bye – perhaps to hand him a cake or a packet of toffee for
the train. Bunter's fat face was quite genial as Bessie rolled up.

"Billy! I say, Billy! Stop!" Billy Bunter stopped, and looked round. Bessie Bunter was coming after him at a run,
red with haste and excitement. "You're going away?" asked Bessie. "Yes." "Well, then, what about that five
shillings——" "Wha-a-at?" "That five shillings you owe me!" gasped Bessie Bunter.

'You're going away?' gasped Bessie.
'Yes.'
'Not coming back?'
'No – n – no!'
'Well, then, that five shillings!'

Billy's geniality vanishes when he realizes that Bessie is raising 'once more, that old, distasteful question' of the loan. And with a parting exchange of 'Beast!' and 'Cat!', brother and sister go their separate ways. Ten years later, in the *Magnet*'s Cliff House Feud series,[20] Bessie is *still* hounding Billy for the repayment of a five-shilling loan. If this is indeed the same debt as that mentioned in 'Tom Redwing's Quest' perhaps Bessie might after all be forgiven for deciding that head-smacking was a more effective weapon than nagging against a brother whose behaviour constantly falls short of her expectations.

During the *Magnet*'s 32-year run, the Bunters' relationship fluctuated between parody and knockabout farce, and was a far cry from the affectionate one that Frank enjoyed with his sisters. However, physically on the small side and self-effacing by nature, he seems always to have enjoyed creating such larger-than-life characters and relationships.

CHAPTER TWO

MANY TRADES, BUT
MASTER OF ONE

I wanted to be an author: also I wanted to be a great
scholar . . . I saw myself as a 'ship's boy on the high and
giddy mast': I saw myself knocking up centuries at Lord's
and bringing off miraculous catches in the field . . . If I
couldn't do them all, I could at least write about them.[1]

At seventeen, Charles had still not decided which career he would
take up. There is no doubt that he was attracted to classical
scholarship and to the study of modern languages, and that he had
the mental equipment to succeed at either – or, indeed, at both. He
earned some money from pen-and-ink drawings and from songs that
he wrote in co-operation with Dolly (who was to become a professional musician) and her husband-to-be, Percy Harrison. In addition, Charles cherished genuine ambitions to go to sea.

From early childhood, however, writing had been his consuming
occupation. He covered hundreds of pages of foolscap with small,
neat handwriting, fictionalizing all his strong interests, but never
with the consciousness of 'making up a story'. Characters and plots
flowed from his pen (and later his typewriter) with virtually no effort
on his part: 'It was a curious thing that when I wrote I seemed to see
it all happening before my eyes, as if I were looking at a picture. I had
a sense of writing down actual happenings.'[2] Time and again in
letters and articles Frank Richards comments on the absence of
technique in his steady output of fifty words a minute. It would be no
mean feat for a professional typist to produce this number of words
consistently, over a stretch of several hours on an electric or elec-
tronic typewriter. Frank Richards bought his first Remington in
1900 and, never teaching himself to type by touch, had to resort to
the slower process of search and peck. His machine was, of course, a

manual one, which required a good deal of physical thumping. (I know, because it has been preserved, with his second typewriter, which is also a Remington, and I have had the opportunity of using it. Both machines have done such yeoman service that they are well worn; on one, not only has the black enamel covering of the space-bar been worn away, but the wood itself has been sculpted into a deep hollow by the constant pressure of the author's thumb.) And as well as banging out the words, of course, Frank Richards had to create the stories at the same time. With regard to his production, it is no exaggeration to say he was a literary phenomenon; had he been

a less firmly down-to-earth figure, it might also have suggested that he was the instrument of truly automatic writing.

Although he began to write when he was seven, Frank comments wryly in his autobiography that his earliest works are

Through the mist Wharton saw the shape of a vessel. Clinging to the binnacle, he shouted for help. "Help ! Ship ahoy !" But there came no answer from the other vessel.

fortunately lost to humanity. In his eighteenth year a relative put him in touch with a 'publisher and printer' whom he describes mysteriously as 'Mr M'. This was Dowling Maitland, who seems to have been an agent, buying stories from writers and then finding markets for them. He might also have edited one of the short-lived, late-Victorian boys' papers. Frank was obviously his greatest find, but the boy counted himself lucky to have his first story so quickly accepted by Maitland and to receive a cheque for five guineas in payment. (At a time when working men might well be supporting large families on two pounds a week, this was not a niggardly fee.) To Frank 'This was Golconda! This was the mines of Mexico and Peru! This was the treasure of Ali Baba!'[3] The cheque was pinned over his bed for several days before he could bear to cash it, because he was less interested in its purchasing power than its symbolic value. Holding that cheque and a note from Maitland requesting more manuscripts in his hand, Frank was moved to make the decision that he would definitely earn his living as a writer. He decided too to concentrate on fiction.

In fact, that famous five-guinea fee was not his first literary remuneration. He had previously earned twelve shillings and six-pence for some small published work, the nature of which has not been recorded. It is likely, however, that this was a newspaper article. When they were young, Charles and his brother Dick, according to Patricia Alcock, had tried their luck 'on a Fleet Street newspaper'. For Charles, at least, this experiment seems to have been of short duration and, from what he said later in life about newspapers and journalists, hardly fulfilling:

The Institute of Journalists would be well-advised to counsel young journalists to study the Bible. In the first place, they might learn the English language, which is quite useful when writing for English readers – so much better, if they only knew it, than the strange lingo in which newspapers are written . . . And then, if their unfortunate minds have not been too utterly dried up in the arid deserts of Darwin and Huxley, they might even get a spot of religion, which would do them worlds of good . . . The modern journalist, as a rule, will never 'go on his way' if he can 'proceed on his journey'; some awful Fate seems to drive him to words of foreign derivation. He will always say 'prior to' instead of before, and 'commence' instead of begin. Yet to be readable, prose must be written in words derived from the Saxon, even those from the Norman-French being used as sparingly as possible: and an author's chief aim should be to exclude Latinity as much as ever he can. Or, as a journalist would say in his jargon, to the total extent of his ability![4]

In the abundance of boys' fiction published in weeklies of the mid-1890s it has been impossible to trace Charles's first story for Dowling Maitland, but, from comments made by the author at various times, this is thought to have been some epic of the frozen West, involving wild flights from wolves across slippery Canadian wastes. Charles responded wholeheartedly and with versatility to his agent-cum-editor's request for more material; he plied him with boys' stories covering a broad range of themes, from cowpunching to pirate sea sagas. High adventure was the mainspring, because Charles, although experimenting with it, had not as yet discovered that his forte was the school story.

Dowling Maitland was based mainly in the north. A few months after accepting Frank's first story, he came to London, and, curious about his new author, arranged a meeting in Bouverie Street at an office he sometimes used. Despite his natural diffidence, it was in buoyant mood that Charles presented himself to 'the great man' who was publishing his stories and paying him five guineas a time. Maitland was less cheerful when they came face to face:

> For a long, long moment he gazed, or rather goggled at Frank, and then ejaculated: 'You're very young, aren't you?'
> It could not be denied. Frank, undoubtedly, was very young. He could not help it: but there it was! It was a fault that time would cure . . . but there, for the moment, it was! Frank has never forgotten his first editor's first remarks. Editors – alas – never say that to him now![5]

(Frank Richards was in his seventies when he described this encounter.)

Once Maitland had satisfied himself that this 'blushing boy' really was his new literary find and not a schoolboy leg-puller, their discussion became pleasant and fruitful. Frank was asked to step up his production and readily agreed. He left in a happy frame of mind, feeling as he turned into Fleet Street that it was 'paved with gold'.

His glowing mood, however, was soon to become tarnished; he received a letter from Dowling Maitland informing him that 'owing to [undefined] circumstances', a new rate of payment would apply for Frank's future contributions; he would receive four pounds for each story instead of five guineas. In Frank's words, 'such was Mr M's graceful tribute to his youth and innocence'.[6]

At this stage in his life, and, indeed, later on, Frank was prepared to take the line of least resistance and allow his publisher to dictate all the terms of business. Wrestling with figures had always reduced him to boredom and bafflement, and his schoolboy irritation with numbers was, many years afterwards, to be transmuted into fierce resentment of the machinations of the Inland Revenue. As soon as he could afford it, he wasted no time in employing an accountant to clear up the recurring mysteries of his income- and super-tax demands. But in the 1890s such affluence was a long way off. Charles's association with Maitland lasted for about two years, after which, in full literary flood, the young author had no difficulty in placing his stories without assistance. In later life he was always surprised when he was questioned about his 'early struggles', as he never felt that he had experienced any. His only difficulty was the fact that, because his writing took off so quickly, he could not find sufficient time for his other interests.

One of these was drawing. He produced an illustration of Arthur Augustus D'Arcy, the St Jim's glass of fashion and mould of form, which was published in the *Gem* (no. 176, 1911) and for which he received the fee of seven shillings and sixpence. (This seems a curious contribution for the paper's sub-editors to have approved, as the *Gem*'s regular artist at that time – R. J. Macdonald – had his own distinctive and attractive style.) Frank obviously had a talent for pen-and-ink drawing, as several of his nursery-tale illustrations were published elsewhere.

Although writing kept Charles busy from the middle of the 1890s, his rate of story production had reached nothing like the peak of the years during and after the First World War when he was writing every week for the *Gem, Magnet* and *Boys' Friend* and occasionally placing stories in other papers. He had time to enjoy outings with his brothers, particularly visits with Alex and Dick to Gilbert and Sullivan operas, which were favourites with them all. Several of the young Hamiltons were musical; Charles had a pleasant bass voice, which was later trained by Dolly, who became a teacher of singing.

Music is featured both farcically and seriously in his stories. In the *Gem* Gussy fancies himself as a tenor, though his threatened performances usually have the effect of rapidly clearing the rooms in which these are to take place. His repertoire is restricted to 'O Star of Eve' from Wagner's *Tannhäuser* and the 'Prize Song' from *Die Meistersinger*. However, on at least one occasion he proposed to sing 'the famous Territorial Song "What's the Matter with England?"' The fame of

" Look here, you cheeky fags ! " shouted Hoskins. " Oh, my hat ! Mind my music ! Oh, crumbs ! " Five pairs of hands jerked the musical genius of the Shell off the music-stool. He sprawled on the floor in a gasping heap.

this might well have failed to penetrate the minds of Charles's readers. He was actually giving a plug to the sheet music of one of the songs for which he had written the words. (In this case the music was composed by 'Dennis Carey' – a pseudonym for Percy Harrison. Charles was to write several lyrics for songs composed by both Dolly and Percy and he managed to introduce the songs into various St Jim's episodes.) The words are intriguing because of their high-flown patriotic mood, which, though the song was published in 1909, presages the jingoism of the First World War.

Charles also allowed his fictional heroes, at least in part, to endorse his passion for the opera. In his young days he was 'enchanted' by the voices of Melba and Tetrazzini and had 'haunted Covent Garden', even though this temporarily cut back his writing energies. In 'Darrell's Secret' Tom Merry & Co. attend an operatic performance and share the whole audience's silent ecstasy during the *Miserere* scene from *Il Trovatore*:

> 'Bai – bai Jove!' gasped Arthur Augustus D'Arcy, when the scene was over. 'I – I feel wathah queer about the thwoat, deah boys.'
>   Even Lowther, the mocker, was silent and touched.
>   If the whole thing was melodramatic the boys did not notice it. They were thrilled through and through by the sweetness of the music and the wonderful power of the singing in that splendid duet.[7]

The musical mood is less inflated when Frank Richards focuses on Claude Hoskins, the would-be composing genius of the Greyfriars Shell. Hoskins, who is nothing if not arrogant about his creative powers, is always inflicting his wild and way-out compositions upon his schoolmates. Frank revels in providing descriptions of the comic and startling fruits of Hoskins's labours and the composing techniques by which these are brought about.

The pattern of frequent house moves, dictated by what was provided by Marion's brother, was maintained for those Hamiltons who were still at home. When Charles celebrated his twenty-first birthday, they were living at Mill Hill Park, near Acton. They moved from this attractive residential area at his urging after his younger brother Douglas died in 1902, and they settled briefly in Chiswick. Douglas's death heralded the change in the pattern: in 1903 Marion remarried, but was widowed again during the following year. She then moved into a small flat, as most of her offspring had by now flown the family nest. Charles and Dolly, however, were somewhat stranded for a period. Dolly's accommodation problem was solved when she secured a place at an Upper Baker Street boarding-house for students at the Royal Academy of Music, which she was then attending. Charles remained rootless, moving into various temporary homes and lodgings. He stayed sometimes with his mother and sometimes with Dick, who had married in 1900 and moved to Coventry, where he built up a very successful signwriting business.

Charles quite liked this frequency of moves, because from childhood he had always enjoyed change, wandering and exploration. It must, however, have been difficult at times for him to churn out his copy when he lacked a settled base. Una Hamilton Wright has suggested that the family's regular upheavals forced him to sort out his priorities early in life; he never bothered as much about 'sticks' (furniture and domestic trappings) as people, and the things of the mind were far more important to him than property.

As a boy he would wander by the hour through the open fields around Gunnersbury. When he had grown up, the restlessness of his nature – in surprising contrast to his scholarly, sedentary writing life – was never quite appeased. He looked to more distant horizons, and would have loved to have gone to sea:

> Frank had always wanted to sail the South Seas, amid reef and palm . . . if he could not scour the Pacific on the deck of a schooner, he could at least do so imaginatively on a Remington. He had to see the islands of the south through other eyes [those of his characters]: but he saw them very clearly.[8]

Among the most cherished books from his childhood were Charles Kingsley's *Westward Ho!* and *Perilous Seas: A Naval Romance* by S. Whitchurch Sadler. Once established as an author, Charles seized the opportunity to play God with intrepid heroes who, in frail craft or mighty steamships, had to grapple with savage seas (and even more savage mutineering crews). He indulged to the full his youthful taste for thrills and chills, producing maritime adventures in the tradition of the Victorian bloods, even though he later wrote of his dissatisfaction with and disgust for the 'trash' that the publishers of these papers then 'purveyed for boys to read'.

Charles's early sea adventures were a rung or two higher on the literary ladder than such works, but in plot, character, inventiveness and style they fell far short of his subsequent school stories. They were over-the-top tales of upright young Englishmen gamely battling against 'dago' buccaneers and bullies, as may be seen in 'Captain Nemo' in the *Union Jack* (1897):

> 'Halt!' shouted Harold, springing ashore, and raising his pistol. Neither of the fugitives heeded him, and without delay he fired . . .
>
> 'Turn, murderer!' cried the young Englishman – 'turn, and defend yourself!'
>
> With a fierce oath, the Black Pirate faced him and, raising a pistol, fired at his heart. But the water of the bay had wetted the powder, and no report followed the falling of the hammer. Just as the pirate pulled the trigger, Harold lunged at his breast, and his blade pierced the body of the outlaw, stretching him on the sand. 'Mother! thou art avenged!' Harold cried exultantly.[9]

Even in such melodramatic pieces as this one, the influence of Charles's family relationships was occasionally evident: the pretty and plucky young leading lady is, like his sister, named Una. (Rather surprisingly, Charles flew in the face of deeply held superstitions that the presence of a woman on board any ship would bring about its destruction. The sailors' wives and their nubile daughters who appeared in his stories became temporary victims of the baddies and inspired the goodies to even greater feats of heroism.) 'Bold British Boys' opens with young Lancelot Coningham going to sea to get away from his cruel and conniving guardian. On his first voyage he is befriended by John Gascoyne, a 'stalwart seaman' who is strangely drawn to the new cabin-boy:

> 'Coningham, I am interested in you . . . Will you tell me your history as far back as you can remember?'
>
> 'Certainly, if it would give you any pleasure to hear it,' Lance answered cheerily. 'But there is very little to tell. My father was John Coningham, the chief mate of an Atlantic liner . . . When I was seven years old my father disappeared and I never saw him again.'[10]

A GRAND SEA-STORY BY CHAS. HAMILTON.

THE UNION JACK

16 PAGES ILLUSTRATED

1d 2

A COMPLETE
BOOK
EVERY
FRIDAY.

LIBRARY OF HIGH CLASS FICTION

Bold British Boys!

There stood the would-be murderer, knife in hand.
He was caught. No lie could save him now.

No. 274

Charles too, when he was only seven, had lost his father, who had the same Christian name as the hero's long-departed parent. Fiction being so often more satisfactory than fact, Lance's father (who, as readers suspect from the beginning, is John Gascoyne) is eventually restored to him – but Charles's loss could never be made good.

Charles's ambition to go to sea was not unusual in a boy growing up at the end of the nineteenth century in a country whose security and prosperity had long been dependent upon its naval strength. He would naturally have been responsive to national pride in the achievements of sea-faring forebears and contemporaneous sailors. The ubiquitously reproduced 'Boyhood of Raleigh' by John Everett Millais, showing the old salt inspiring youth with tales of derring-do on and beyond the seas, conjured a potent image for several generations of Britons – including, perhaps, the would-be mariner Charles. (Even today many of us who positively dislike messing about in boats still find it hard to shake off deep-rooted mental pictures of ourselves actually wanting to 'go down to the sea in ships'.)

The popularity of sea stories towards the end of Victoria's reign is indicated by the fact that many issues of the halfpenny *Union Jack* (1894–1903) devoted most of their space to these. The editor's weekly chats appeared beneath the illustration of a ship and were entitled 'From the Quarter-deck'. They provided plenty of useful tips for readers with ambitions to sail, emigrate or 'fight for the Empire's rights'. Towards the end of 1903 publication of the *Union Jack* ceased. Relaunched in the same year, it soon became purely a detective paper, with Sexton Blake as its regular star.

Sea stories remained in Charles's repertoire. It was no accident that he sited Greyfriars School on the Kentish coast, thus enabling Harry Wharton & Co. easy access to shipboard adventures. The holidays too would bear them off into far-flung foreign parts over waters both peaceful and tempestuous:

Dawn on the Pacific.
Harry Wharton came up the companion-ladder of the *Aloha* as the round, golden sun rose over the sea.
Scarcely moving on the calm waters of the lagoon, the schooner lay at anchor, her cable dropping straight as a string to the coral bottom.
In the clear, pellucid waters . . . the anchor could be seen

hooked in the coral, with fishes swimming round it, and crabs crawling over the rusty iron.

Ashore, the beach of white sand and coral was beginning to gleam and shine in the sun. Beyond rose graceful, nodding palms, and, farther still, the line of hills that ran like a backbone across the island of Caca from north to south.[11]

Let no one be taken in by this serene moment from 'The Rival Treasure Seekers' (1927); excitement and challenge are only a coral strand away from the juniors.

On their second visit to the South Seas eleven years later, disaster really strikes hard when the Famous Five, Bunter and their lazy, blue-blooded form-mate Lord Mauleverer find themselves adrift on a raft on the Pacific, with their food and water almost exhausted: 'Silence – dead silence – reigned on the raft as the Sea Cat grew smaller in the distance. The juniors watched the sails fading away . . . It was hard to believe that they were abandoned – that a white man had left them to perish.'[12] Hard indeed, especially for Bunter who, as 'the terrible day wears on – with dazzling sunshine and burning heat', grows faint and delirious from lack of food. The perpetual joke about the Fat Owl's gargantuan appetite is turned on its head, and Bunter is transmogrified from a figure of farce to one of pathos. That he makes this switch believable is a measure of Frank Richards's story-telling skill. When Bunter, lacking the physical strength and psychological guts of the others, is on his last knockings, Mauleverer takes something from his pocket and gives it to him:

> The Famous Five watched him in silence. It was twenty-four hours since a fragment of food had passed their lips. They knew now that it was forty-eight hours since a fragment had passed Mauly's, as they saw him take the greasy chunk of canned beef, and put it into Bunter's mouth.
> Bunter gobbled.
> 'Oh, Mauly, old man!' murmured Bob. 'Mauly, you old ass!'
> Mauleverer grinned faintly.
> 'I can stand it better than Bunter!' he said.

Frank Richards was often at his best when he brought together his two long-standing loves – Greyfriars and the sea. In 1913 'Chums

Afloat' appeared in the *Magnet*,[13] and it was reprinted in the *Greyfriars Holiday Annual 1938* under the more appropriate title of 'Mutiny on the Spindrift'. This is a dramatic story of Harry Wharton and Bob Cherry being cast adrift at night on the North Sea (after being goaded into acceptance of a dare by the 'Bounder' of the Remove, Herbert Vernon-Smith). Rescued by a passing ship, they become involved in a life-or-death struggle with its crew of murderous

" Harry, old man, what do you think has happened on this ship ? " asked Bob Cherry, pausing in the scrubbing. " Mutiny ! " said Wharton briefly.

mutineers. The author handles this rather far-fetched plot with his customary aplomb, helped by his knowledge of seafaring and his consistency of characterization. It is a heroic fantasy rather than a schoolboy story, but Wharton's and Cherry's response to grim and gory challenges is entirely in keeping with what readers would have expected from them. Their pluck is dogged and conveyed uninflatedly:

'If the skipper's there wounded – why have they let him live? They must have killed the others,' said Bob.

Wharton shook his head. 'I don't know the reason. But I'm going to find out.'

Bob Cherry gave his chum a startled look. 'What are you going to do, Harry?'

'If there's an honest man left on board this ship, we're going to help him, Bob!' said Harry, in low, determined tones. 'We're not going to make ourselves party to a crime!'

'They'd pitch us overboard as soon as look at us if they had trouble with us, Harry!'

'I know they would.'

But nevertheless the two chums of the Remove make up their minds to defy the mutineers and to save the badly wounded captain. This is stirring stuff, but Frank's watery fiction was often more mellow in mood. Small boats, as well as big ships, featured in both his life and his stories. He and his brother Dick loved being on lakes and rivers, and when for a period they lived at Teddington, they had a boat of their own.

We know that in his boyhood Frank loved to be in a boat, where he would write for hours on end. In adult life he would often take to the river when he had some knotty problem to work out. His autobiography records the fact that when he had agreed to produce a weekly 20,000-word story for the *Magnet* (in addition to the one of the same length that he was writing regularly for the *Gem*), he tackled the challenge of inventing a fresh set of characters for the new paper 'as usual', by thinking things out while 'drifting in a boat'.

Frank's prodigious output in his heyday of one and a half million words a year must have been achieved at the expense of personal experience. He liked sometimes to write outdoors, which mitigated the tyranny of the typewriter. Patricia Alcock comments: 'Charles used to like to write in the garden during the summer months, and at one time used to chain "old Remington" to a tree stump and rig up a milk-drip so that he wouldn't have to stop for meals!'[14]

To leap into a boat was his real escape. When he was staying at an inn on Lake Maggiore, and pounding the typewriter for the necessary three, four or five hours a day, he could not always resist the call of 'the shining lake, the boats passing to and fro, and the lazy boatmen loafing on the old wooden quay ... he would abandon Remington even without completing his quota, and push out his boat, or jump on the steamer going down to the Isola Bella'.[15]

" Bend over that boat, Bunter ! " cried Mr. Quelch angrily. " I—I——I say, sir——" " Bend over ! "   " Oh crikey! " Billy Bunter bent over.   Three fellows coming down to the boathouse, stared and grinned.   Bunter did not grin, he roared. " Yow-ow-ow-ow-wow ! "

Not surprisingly, many of the happiest incidents in the *Magnet* and *Gem* have river backgrounds; these also provide dramas, both comic ('Bend over that boat, Bunter!') with Mr Quelch inflicting well-deserved punishment on his most backward pupil, and serious, with almost every boy in the Remove at one time or another either saving someone from drowning or getting pulled out himself. (A *Magnet* sub-editor, Hedley O'Mant, once commented that 'if all the Richards characters fished out of an imminent watery grave were laid end to end they would dampen the entire length of the Great North Road!')

Charles was almost entering his seventies when in 1945 he wrote about himself and his work in the article 'Boys' Writer' for *The Saturday Book*. Without any suggestion of tongue in cheek (and still favouring the autobiographical third-person narration that readers often found irritating), he wrote that 'water fresh or salt, always had a deep attraction for Frank: even now he would like to be a sailor, if some discerning sea-captain wanted a recruit of a really ripe vintage'. And in 1957 a note from him to the editor of *Collectors' Digest* (no. 123) mentioned that the Bunter book to be published that year was 'a boating story of a holiday on the Thames, a subject that makes me feel a teenager when I write of it, bringing back to mind lovely old days when the water rippled under the willows – as no doubt it still does!' Frank – then in his eighty-first year – adds rather wistfully: 'Who wouldn't like to be sixteen again, just for a day in a boat!' (Frank Richards's first full-length Bunter book was published in 1947 by Charles Skilton; the series ran to thirty-eight titles.)

As well as the sea story, the Western genre always intrigued him, providing inspiration for many of his early stories. Much later the pupils of his most popular schools were to be packed off for long holiday trips to the American or Canadian West and, as mentioned earlier, he was to create Cedar Creek School for the *Boys' Friend*, chronicling his supposed British Columbian schooldays. Another of his Wild West schools was the rumbustious Packsaddle in the *Gem*, whose headmaster was drawn in sharp contrast to the gowned, mortar-boarded dignitaries on the Greyfriars staff: Bill Sampson, 'long-limbed and loose-jointed, in leather crackers and a red shirt', had switched careers from cowpunching to running a school; his methods, as might have been expected, were often unorthodox: 'Under Bill's left arm was a quirt. He never used a cane. He had found a quirt OK with refractory steers when he rode with the Kicking Mule bunch. He found it OK with the boys of Packsaddle.'[16]

The most memorable of his Western sagas, however, was that which starred the Rio Kid, a teenaged loner who, framed for a crime he never committed, was constantly hitting new trails and coping with fresh challenges. His exploits ran for two years in the *Popular* at the end of the 1920s, and for some time during the 1930s in the *Modern Boy*.

Around the turn of the century, Charles, who was always endeavouring to put his literary eggs into as many different baskets as possible, dreamed up a detective named Sedley Sharpe for the Trapps Holmes paper *Funny Cuts*. This promising character was a forerunner of the more rounded-out schoolboy sleuths, such as Len Lex and Jack Drake, who came into being only after Charles had established himself as a school-story writer. As we shall see later, he was also producing fictional adult detectives early in his career, both serious (Ferrers Locke) and spoof (Herlock Sholmes).

It is surprising that one of the characters with whom he was experimenting in 1899 did not immediately become fleshed out. This was Billy Bunter, though at this embryonic stage in his development, he almost certainly had no name. Charles offered the idea of this juvenile Falstaff to an editor who 'didn't see much in him', and, diffident as always, the author put his fatty into cold storage for almost a decade, until the advent of the *Magnet*: 'It is quite curious that best-sellers are generally turned down by publishers: a circumstance that ought to be very encouraging to young writers.'[17]

When Charles started to write for the boys' papers in the 1890s, there were plenty of different ones on the market. The fact that few of them survived for longer than a year or two, however, is an indication of their limitation and lack of appeal. Durable quality magazines like the Religious Tract Society's spiritually uplifting *Boy's Own Paper* (which began in 1879 and lasted for almost ninety years) were often bought for children by their eager parents. Even so, some of these had short runs. One of the very first boys' papers ever printed, somewhat dauntingly called 'The Young Gentleman's Magazine, or Monthly Repository of Science, Moral and Entertainment Matter' (1777), ran for only seven months. By the 1890s, when a mass readership had been considerably increased as a result of the Education Acts of the 1870s, boys from different strata of society were able to spend their own halfpennies or pennies on magazines or the cheaper pulps, and if one paper did not prove sufficiently addictive, they would quickly change to one of its competitors.

Charles Hamilton's stories lacked the didacticism of the papers packing a religious message; they offered a wide variety of thrills and chills, but were far less bloody and thunderous than the general run of tales in the papers that sprang from the surprisingly long-running first Penny Dreadfuls, such as *Boys of England* (1866–1906). Charles realized that sensational adventure, though temporarily addictive, had a restricted appeal, and that the essential ingredients of a good story were pace, believable characterization and conflict between the characters at a deeper level than the conventional heroes-versus-villains clashes of the established bloods.

Many of Charles's writings between 1894, when his first pirate stories appeared, and 1906, when the St Jim's tales began, are lost to us, because he used so many pseudonyms. In an article called 'The *Vanguard*' (1952), Tom Hopperton suggested that Frank Richards might have written a few dozen stories for the publishers Trapps Holmes.[18] This stirred Frank into the indignant reply that he had written 'not less than one thousand stories for their *Smiles*, *Funny Cuts*,

World's Own Picture Fun, Vanguard and *Coloured Comic*.[19] Those inde-fatigable literary sleuths, Lofts and Adley, in company with others on the long, winding Charles Hamilton trail, after years of meticu-lous research have unearthed several thousand stories from his pen in these papers and comics.

Of course, many of his early sea, Western or sleuthing stories seem undeveloped and rough-hewn when compared with the sharpness and subtleties of his later work. However, one type of fiction did emerge almost fully fledged from his first attempts at it: the school story. The earliest of these to have been discovered in print was in Arthur Pearson's boys' paper *Best Budget*, dated 3 May 1902. Whether or not Charles knew straight away that he had now found his literary niche is uncertain, but the demand for his school stories grew quickly, with an insistence that left his future in no doubt. He would never become (like the character about whom he wrote three novels in the 1950s) a jack of all trades, but was to be swept along on the tide of his own talent, and the voracious appetite of publishers and readers who recognized a good thing as soon as they saw it.

CHAPTER THREE

THE 'SAINTS' (AND 'FRIARS') COME MARCHING IN

I know that I can write a good school story: on that point,
as our old friend Gilbert remarked, there is no possible
probable shadow of doubt, no shadow of doubt whatever.
But I wrote my first school story in fear and trembling.[1]

Although Charles seems to have coped remarkably well with his
peripatetic life and words continued to roll unabated off his Remington, he was happy to have the opportunity of sharing a flat with Dolly
at 7 Dorset Square, near Upper Baker Street, from the spring of
1907. They rented this until the autumn of 1908, when they moved to
56 Antrim Mansions in Belsize Park, which remained their base
until Dolly married Percy Harrison in 1911. However, Charles still
felt the need to be on the move, so he embarked upon his travels on
the Continent, which were to add spice to both his life and his work.
(Una Hamilton Wright has likened him during this period to the
celebrated cartoon character Felix the Cat, who was also always on
the move.)

In the 1890s Charles had undertaken extremely strenuous cycling
tours in Britain, exploring Wales and the West Country. When he
stayed with his brother Dick in Coventry, they would cycle together
around Warwickshire or take trips much further afield. (Had Scotland been nearer they would almost certainly have gone there.
Charles was proud of his Scottish ancestry on his father's side of the
family. When replying to letters from his readers north of the border,
he would describe himself as 'the auld carle' and sign off 'with best
wishes frae an auld Scot'. It seems possible that his family could

claim tenuous links with the dukes of Hamilton.) There were also less energetic holidays, taken with Dolly at south-coast resorts. As always, he was drawn to the sea. His brother Alex had settled on Canvey Island, which also appealed to Charles, who in 1908 bought Hazlewood there, his first house. He became very attached to Alex's children, and especially to Rosie, the eldest. It is interesting that, although Charles was to achieve celebrity as a writer for boys, he always had a soft spot for small girls and seems to have felt an empathy with them. First, of course, came his sister Dolly; then Rosie, whom apparently he would have liked to adopt; and, later, Dolly's daughter Una. He was never to have children of his own and, like Lewis Carroll, whose Alice books he much admired, he was eventually to bring his 'dream child' – or ideal daughter – into being through his stories. Ethel Cleveland in the *Gem* and Marjorie Hazeldene in the *Magnet* could compete for this title; equally, however, they could have been fictional embodiments of his ideal woman.

STRAIGHT
FROM
THE
SHOULDER!

Cardew leaped back and avoided the slash of the heavy stick, and at the same moment Ernest Levison sprang at the ruffian and struck. His clenched fist landed on the side of the Rat's head, and the man went staggering.

Charles's first travels across the seas were unambitious. Dolly, who had been there before, persuaded him to accompany her on a trip to the Isle of Man. The beauty of 'Ellan Vannin with its green hills by the sea' must have appealed to him. There is hardly a high spot on the whole island from which one cannot see the waters that surround it; the snag is that, because the island is situated in the middle of the Irish Sea, reaching it often entails rough crossings. To his chagrin the ocean-loving Charles discovered that he was not, after all, a good sailor, and it took all Dolly's powers of persuasion to make him agree to take his first trip across the Channel to France with her in 1909. Once he had done so, the pattern was set for his spending a good deal of every year on the Continent, until the outbreak of the First World War changed everything.

Another pattern was established around this time. Although he continued to write various tales of adventure, Charles began to give his main energies to the school story and, in particular, to the exploits of the juniors of St Jim's and Greyfriars. From 1894 he had been writing sea stories for Harmsworth papers such as the *Union Jack*; his first school story for this publishing firm, which came to be known as the Amalgamated Press, appeared in the *Marvel* in 1903.[2] The boys' school concerned was called Cliff House, a name that Charles eventually pressed into use again for the most famous of his girls' schools, which was to include Bessie Bunter as its most uproarious inmate. He produced school, football and cricket stories for Harmsworth's *Boys' Friend*, *Boys' Realm* and *Boys' Herald*, edited by Hamilton Edwards. In 1906 Harold J. Garrish, the editor of *Pluck* for the same publishers, asked Charles to write a series about a set of schoolboys for his paper. St Jim's was created for this purpose, the early characters being Blake, Herries and Digby of the School House, and Figgins & Co. of the New House. They were soon joined by the Honourable Arthur Augustus D'Arcy, one of Hamilton's most charismatic characters, who seemed, at least initially, to owe something to editorial influence. It was Garrish who suggested adding an elegant and fastidious junior to the already established cast, and Charles moulded Gussy on Charles Maurice Down, whom he described as 'a very elegant and beautifully mannered young gentleman who was a sub-editor'.[3] (Down later became editor of the *Gem* and *Magnet* in 1921 and remained in charge until the papers folded in 1939 and 1940 respectively. Charles always spoke warmly

Tom Merry and Knox stood staring at Arthur Augustus D'Arcy on the top of the wall. "Come down from that!" roared Knox. "Wats!" answered D'Arcy. "Knox, you may inform the Housemastah that I am wetirin' fwom the school, where I have not weceived justice or pwopah considewation. I am goin' home!" "Oh gad!" gasped Knox.

of their association; it was generally harmonious, in marked contrast to his relationships with some of the other Amalgamated Press editors.)

The monocled Gussy, resplendent in sleekest Etons and topper, wearing impeccable fancy waistcoats and lisping aristocratically, was a curious character to star in a penny paper bought by many boys from working-class homes. Nevertheless, suspended somewhere in psychological space and time between Burlington Bertie and Lord Snooty, Arthur Augustus captured the imagination and sympathies of readers from the beginning. Far more than just a tailor's dummy figure of fun, Gussy is a complex creation. There is no serious snobbery about him, though there are occasional unconscious touches of arrogance – 'those wottahs have tweated me in a spiwit of wibaldwy' – but, after all, he *is* the son of a full-blown lord. He also sometimes prattles about his 'supewiah' tact and judgement, to the unfailing amusement of his chums, who know that these supposed qualities rarely work when he graciously applies them to a situation. But he is sensitive and courteous to everyone, full of pluck and imbued with a sense of honour; he is also rather simple. He thinks of himself as the natural leader of the chummery to which he belongs, but actually Jack Blake & Co., his studymates and closest friends, have always to protect him.

The stories in which Gussy is the protagonist generally make sparkling reading. Excellent character though he is, at St Jim's he was always *primus inter pares* rather than the one star burning much more brightly than the others. Gussy had to share the honours not only with Blake & Co., but with another group of juniors who were imported into St Jim's when Charles was transferred from writing regularly for *Pluck* to writing for a new paper, the *Gem*, which started on 16 March 1907.

An ambitious editor named Percy Griffith – dubbed at their first meeting and referred to ever afterwards by Charles as 'the pushful Percy' – was looking for a writer of gripping school stories for the *Gem*, of which he was to be in charge. He might have settled on Henry St John or David Goodwin, who had been producing very successful school stories for Edwards's *Boys' Friend*, *Boys' Realm* and *Boys' Herald* for some time. Instead he selected Charles, who, as well as his commitments for *Pluck*, was now supposed to produce a story about a school called Clavering for the *Gem* every other week.

Charles was happy to take this on; he invented a new hero – Tom Merry – for Clavering and, at Griffith's insistence, a new pen-name for himself. He was writing the St Jim's stories in *Pluck* under his real name; for his new series he assumed the identity of Martin Clifford, taking the Christian name from Ballantyne's *Martin Rattler* and the surname from Bulwer-Lytton's *Paul Clifford*. Martin Clifford, like Frank Richards, proved to be a long-standing pseudonym, which he used not only for the *Gem*, but also for the *Boys' Friend* Cedar Creek stories later on. (In the Amalgamated Press weekly papers and associated annuals, Martin and Frank were to become characters as well as authors, each bringing the other into a story from time to time. Charles must sometimes have felt like a puppeteer as he manipulated his fictional characters and his own different identities. This process worked well, but could very easily have got out of hand when, for instance, Charles (as Martin) was writing about himself (as Frank) and his entirely imaginary schooldays in Canada.)

Tom Merry was a well-balanced, sunny-natured hero, and he struck the right note with readers from the beginning. Griffith, though sensing the potential of the new series, felt that something was lacking, and decided it was St Jim's. First of all he arranged that Charles should write the main story for the *Gem* each week instead of every other week. Then, during one of the 'editorial solos', which he called 'discussing the stories', Griffith announced that he had decided to amalgamate the St Jim's series from *Pluck* with the Tom Merry tales in the *Gem*. Clavering would be dropped and St Jim's would be switched from *Pluck* to the *Gem*; Tom Merry and his chums Manners and Lowther would join Jack Blake & Co.

The normally mild Charles was furious at this intervention in the structures he had so carefully built up; also, in effect, Griffith was filching him from *Pluck* and from Garrish, an editor with whom he had enjoyed working. 'He fancied that Garrish might intervene, and save him from being wholly devoured by the insatiable Percy. But his former editor made no sign: and the pocket-Dictator had his way, as he always did.'[4] Commenting further on this, Charles suggests that, although Griffith was 'an extremely clever man . . . what he did not know about writing a story would have filled huge volumes'. However, as an editorial decision, the amalgamation of Blake, D'Arcy, Figgins and Tom Merry into the already well-established school was sound. St Jim's, with its School House and New House rivalries, provided its author with plenty of scope for the chums-and-rivals themes he was beginning to exploit with a very individual skill. St Jim's and the *Gem* went from strength to strength.

TOM MERRY

A ROLLICKING STORY OF SCHOOLBOY LIFE.

No. 36.   64 PAGES.

The DIAMOND LIBRARY   1D

The Bully of St. John's.

By CLIFFORD OWEN.

Griffith tried to put pressure on Charles to stop writing for other papers, but for a time he asserted his independence and wrote serials for Edwards, a comical series about Cliveden School for the *Boys' Herald* and 'huge chunks of copy' for the Amalgamated Press's competitor, Trapps Holmes. His stories were also appearing regularly, under the name of Clifford Owen, in the Aldine Company's

Diamond Library, though these novella-length tales of St John's and Cranmere schools might have been written earlier and stockpiled by the publishers. The astute Griffith then niftily produced the trump card that he was holding up his sleeve. He told Charles that he was planning to bring out a new paper, on similar lines to the *Gem*, which would be called the *Magnet*. As readers were lapping up the St Jim's stories, Charles was to be commissioned to create yet another school and a fresh set of characters for the new paper. Even the steam-rollering Griffith harboured slight doubts about his author's ability to produce two 20,000-word stories for him week after week, but these were quickly scotched when Charles expressed his willingness to oblige. Doubtless he was flattered to have not one but two papers virtually created for his talents: also, of course, his fees from the Amalgamated Press would considerably increase. His average payment for a single *Gem* or *Magnet* story during the early years of the papers was eighteen guineas. Five pounds a week was then a very good wage, so Charles, at the beginning of his thirties, was a big earner. (He was also a big spender, with a taste for betting and gambling that remained unabated throughout his long and, later, semi-reclusive life.)

Hamilton and Griffith were like chalk and cheese, but Charles soon found a way of dealing with 'this vehement and volatile young man' who, though 'not of great stature', seemed overwhelmingly large, indeed 'to fill the room, and to breathe most of the air in it'.[5] The author's defensive technique was to let the dominating Percy talk without interruption and to switch off from the torrent of words by running over in his mind some master-games of chess he had memorized or lines from his favourite poets. So long as Charles fixed his face into an expression of earnest attention, Griffith seemed happy; and as Charles had little intention of taking seriously his editor's suggestions concerning future *Gem* and *Magnet* stories, it did not matter that Griffith (as Charles might have expressed it) was wasting his sweetness on the desert air: 'Sometimes, in a conversation-piece of this kind, Frank would play the Immortal Game through from start to finish, and have time for a spot of Dante or Keats to follow . . . [then] editor and author would part with a cordial handshake, both satisfied.'[6] Griffith wanted the *Magnet* stories to be produced under a different pen-name from Martin Clifford. As Charles always attached so much importance to names, he gave very serious consideration to this, eventually coming

up with 'Frank Richards', the appellation that was to provide him
with not just a disguised identity, but an *alter ego*. 'Frank' came from
Scott's Frank Osbaldistone and 'Richards' from the pluralization of
his brother Dick's name.

Frank explains in his autobiography that, once having settled his
name, he was able to build up the atmosphere and images of his new
fictional school, Greyfriars, and the characters of its pupils. As Frank
Richards he would write quite differently from Martin Clifford (and
he seemed to feel that the pen-names themselves somehow governed
this). Certainly the Greyfriars juniors seem slightly more rugged
than their St Jim's counterparts, perhaps because, as Eric Fayne
remarked, 'the St Jim's tales were mainly stories of school life, the
Greyfriars yarns were stories of schoolboy adventure'.[7] There *are*
distinct differences in the flavour of the tales of each school, and even
in old age Frank (and Martin) never confused one with the other.
Similarly, having created an enormous cast of characters for Greyfriars, St Jim's and (in 1915) Rookwood, the author never muddled
them up or made them act in a way that was inconsistent with the
traits he had bestowed upon them so many years earlier.

In letters and articles Frank describes how some of the most
popular Greyfriars characters came into being. Often they were
derived from someone he had met in real life, but transposed from
the boredom (to Frank) of fact and reality to the 'pure gold of fiction'.
'Harry Wharton was mine own familiar friend. He is still sixteen in
my mind's eye [this is slightly older than in the stories] for owing
to circumstances which it would be interesting not to relate, I never
saw him after that age.'[8] (Maddeningly, this enigmatic statement is
never elucidated for us.) Bob Cherry is simply a certain type of
extroverted boy whom 'everybody must have known'. Johnny Bull is
a back-to-adolescence projection of a man whom Frank met only
when he was in his forties, while Hurree Jamset Ram Singh is
inspired by 'a dark gentleman' encountered for only five minutes
during the 1890s, who greeted the author with the memorable phrase
'the top of a beautiful morning'. Though this is more Irish than
Indian, it was to trigger off the creation of this amiable but sharp-
witted 'dusky' nabob of Bhanipur, whose mind-spinning mixed
metaphors and word-play ('the fairplayfulness is terrific!') were to
weave a joyous thread through the *Magnet* from the early days until
its demise. (Hurree did not arrive at Greyfriars until the sixth story
in the saga. He had come via the *Marvel*, in which he had first

appeared almost a year earlier in Hamilton's stories of Netherby School; then he attended Beechwood Academy, which, like Grey-friars, was established in Kent. Frank must have realized that this intriguing character was too good to waste in the more ephemeral of his scholastic establishments, and he lost no time in slotting him into Greyfriars.) In the answers to Bagley's questionnaire we are told that 'Frank Nugent is, or was, no other than Frank Richards himself, as far as one could draw one's own portrait: quite a nice boy, I am persuaded, but booked always to go in with the tail.'

Frank also claims that 'Tom Merry is just an average healthy schoolboy such as one may see every day'. As an assessment of the leader of the Shell and the Lower School at St Jim's, this de-scription seems watered down, to say the least. Tom Merry was hardly ordinary. Good-natured, straightforward, even-tempered, approachable – yes – but with that extra spark of magnetism and integrity when it counts that lifts an all-rounder into a leader. Tom had a great deal to overcome, too. Orphaned, from early childhood he has been brought up by his devoted and besotted nurse, Miss Priscilla Fawcett, a fusty old sketch who in 1907 still sports a

"Good-bye, dearest Tommy!" said Miss Priscilla. "Mind and not forget the hot-water bottle on cold nights."

Victorian bonnet and shawl, a crinoline *manqué* and, one suspects, elastic-sided boots and horribly heavy undergarments. The perpetual joke of her relationship with her young charge is that she treats him like a delicate plant on whom the winds of heaven must never dare to breathe, while his sturdy physical and psychological make-up give the lie to her morbid misgivings. Her exaggerated concern for his health finds expression in hot poultices, flannel vests, cod-liver oil, chest-protectors and the constant administration of alliteratively named remedies: 'Have you taken all the purple pills I sent you?' asked Miss Priscilla. 'And the Terra-Cotta Tablets for Pining People?' Here Frank is guying the once celebrated Dr Williams's Pink Pills for Pale People.

It says a great deal for Tom's inner strength that he not only survives this spoliation, but manages to develop his natural robustness without trampling all over Miss P's terribly tender feelings.

When – reluctantly – she sends him off to boarding-school (Clavering), he is ridiculously garbed in a lace-collared velvet Fauntleroy suit, in which no self-respecting fifteen-year-old boy would have been seen dead, let alone alive. Tom overcomes this horrible handicap – and a long-winded, high-falutin manner of speech, which is another anachronism inflicted upon him by Miss Priscilla – to become quickly accepted by his studymates, Harry Manners and Monty Lowther, and to prove that he is a great man at boxing and cricket. Life is tough for Tom, however. Because of Griffith's editorial edict that Clavering should be scrapped and St Jim's substituted for it in the *Gem*, our hero has to start all over again as a new boy (once more forced by the tearfully persuasive Miss Priscilla into the Fauntleroy gear). At St Jim's, of course, he soon establishes that, far from being an effeminate freak, he is a natural leader. (Frank Richards's moral here seems to be that a woman without a man is unable to cope with the training of boys; in other words, it takes a real man to make a right-minded manly boy.)

Going back to Greyfriars, Frank Richards's fat boy had, as we know, been waiting in the wings ever since he had been turned down by an editor at the end of the 1890s. Frank unilaterally decided to make the neglected William George Bunter a member of the Greyfriars Remove. From the first story he was in evidence, but he was plump rather than obese and almost apologetic when compared with the grandiose character into which he was soon to be inflated. When asked if there was a real-life model for Billy, Frank Richards would reply that the original Bunter was divided, like ancient Gaul, into three parts, derived from 'at least three different persons. His extensive circumference came from an editorial gentleman who . . . seemed to overflow the editorial chair and almost the editorial office.'[9] Apparently his large spectacles were borrowed from a relative of Frank's who would peer like an owl over them, and the eternally expected, but unforthcoming, postal order was the fictional representation of a cheque that someone of his acquaintance constantly anticipated, on the strength of which he was anxious to borrow a pound or two. Frank never named those concerned when he wrote about Bunter's origins in his autobiography, but Lofts and Adley have attempted to put names to the relevant people. They suggest that the overflowing editor was Lewis Ross Higgins, 'editor of the comic paper *Chuckles* 1914 to 1919, and on the staff of many comic papers prior to this'.[10] Chestertonian in appearance, he was a clever cartoonist who drew the pictures supposedly by Frank Nugent in the *Greyfriars Herald* and the illustrations for the Herlock Sholmes parodies by Frank Richards, which carried the byline 'Peter Todd', the name of a Greyfriars junior. But Bunter was alive, if not actually kicking, in the mind of his creator as long ago as 1899, when Higgins – who died in 1919 at the age of thirty-four – could have been only fourteen. It seems hardly likely that so inexperienced a member of staff would even sit in an editorial chair, let alone overflow it. Possibly speculation on this matter has run riot; Lofts and Adley say that Bunter's spectacles might have been inspired by those worn by Dolly, whose eyesight had been rather poor since childhood. In fact, glasses belonging to Frank's Aunt Annie were the model for Billy's. They are probably correct in stating that Frank's brother Alex – who had tried to break into journalism, as had Frank and Dick – was, like Bunter, always waiting for something to turn up in the post. Whoever might or might not have been the inspiration, the characterization of Billy quickly developed from the impetus of its own inner logic and consistency. This was a natural creative development; Frank planted the seed of the character, and it grew and flourished. He once said that he never controlled – nor even really invented – his creations; like Topsy, they 'just growed'. 'If a character doesn't live already, how can anyone breathe into its nostrils the breath of life?'

Frank's flair for choosing names to suit characters is nowhere more felicitously demonstrated than with Billy Bunter. The name not only seems entirely apt, but also has a familiar ring, even when we first come across it. Yet it is not common. (Of the four Bunters in the Central London telephone directory, for example, three appear to refer not to individuals but to restaurants named after the Greyfriars character, and in some years the directory has contained no mention of this illustrious name.) However, when the Greyfriars stories began, more than one Bunter loomed large on Frank's horizon, even if he was registering a couple of them only half consciously. He would surely have been familiar with Bunter's Nervine Tonic, a cure-all that had been around since 1885. And he had previously used the name for the boozy, bleary-eyed, crib-cracking tramp Bill Bunter, whom he introduced into the *Gem* to skirmish with Herbert Skimpole, the proselytizing, pseudo-progressive freak of St Jim's.[11] (Charles may have realized that the tramp's name could be slightly adapted for the Greyfriars fatty who was soon to be launched; the first *Magnet* (15 February 1908) came only a few weeks in the wake of the Bill Bunter *Gem*.) Charles had introduced the name into another series in the autumn of 1907. The school porter and his wife, the tuck-shop keeper, in the humorous Cliveden School tales in the *Boys' Herald* were also of the Bunter tribe.

The character who embodies a minor literary mystery is the Billy Bunter of a school called Blackminster (only a shade away from Greyfriars), who appeared in several pre-*Magnet* stories in the *Vanguard* during 1907. These were attributed to H. Philpott Wright (actually an author named J. Weedon Birch), and it seems that there is no conscious connection at all between the *Vanguard*'s Billy Bunter and the character who was to become the anti-hero of the *Magnet*. In his article in *Old Boys' Book Collector* in 1952 Tom Hopperton suggested that Charles Hamilton might have glanced at some of Philpott Wright's Blackminster stories in the *Vanguard* and peripherally registered the Bunter name.[12] Frank's reply was swift and uncompromising:

> For the love of Mike, not so many of your wild surmises! . . . I never even knew Philpott Wright's name, let alone his works. I cannot remember ever looking even once at a *Vanguard* number not my own – why should I? I was asked to write all I could for the paper, and did so – and did not care a single solitary boiled bean how the remaining numbers were filled . . . My dear boy, your exploits remind me not of Sherlock Holmes, but of Herlock Sholmes [the last named was Hamilton's spoof detective] . . . you say that I might have looked at the *Vanguard* to make sure that I was not traversing the same ground as other writers! Can you possibly suppose that a busy author could find time to do anything of the sort? For all I know, similarities may have cropped up: I did not know and certainly do not care. I had quite enough to do minding my own business: and when I had time for reading I read Horace, Keats, Dante, Shakespeare and Milton: most assuredly not the *Vanguard*![13]

Frank Richards was a truthful man, with a long and accurate memory, so his rather Olympian disclaimer has to be accepted. The matter of the two Billy Bunters, however, remains a curious coincidence. (It is worth noting that the Blackminster variant was not a fat boy.)

Greyfriars was addictive from its inception, though Frank Richards's stories did not reach their peak of style and presentation until the early 1930s. By then the author had perfected his use of the form that best suited him, the eight-part serial, which allowed plenty of scope for development of plot and characterization. What it was that made the *Magnet* so different from other boys' papers of the time is not easy to assess. Other authors produced good stories, but they lacked the sparkle of Frank's dialogue and the conviction that lifts so many of his characters off the page. The early *Magnet* steered a middle course between the Victorian moral tale and the lurid blood. Frank's purpose was primarily to entertain. He was emphatically on the side of the boy, and he always retained tremendous empathy with children. He put across an ethical code, but he avoided didacticism by the simple device of equating morals with common sense. His plots can be criticized for implausibility, yet they remain immensely readable; his characters are often overdrawn, yet for generations of young readers they were more real than their own friends and schoolmates. And what was savoured uncritically by the child reader could later be applauded by the adult for its technical accomplishment and flexibility of mood and style, which ranged from drama through irony to music-hall rumbustiousness.

Frank was the equal of P. G. Wodehouse in giving a high-flown or hackneyed simile a comic flavour: 'as he blinked to and fro through his big spectacles, Bunter could see no pursuers. Like Moses of old, he looked this way and that way, and there was no man.' (He is scoffing purloined tuck in the shelter of the old ruins at the time.) Affinities between Wodehouse and Frank were noted in the *Economist* in a 1961 review of Richard Usborne's book *Wodehouse at Work*, which commented: 'that other octogenarian, Mr Frank Richards, hardly gets enough credit here for his part in the Wodehouse story. When we are ancient history, some smart pundit may well prove that Wodehouse wrote Richards as well, or even vice versa.' The idea of Richards and Wodehouse in the roles of Shakespeare and Bacon is an intriguing one that both authors might have relished. (A nice point here is that when Frank Richards died at the end of 1961, P. G. Wodehouse became his successor as president of the northern section of the Old Boys' Book Club; Hubert Gregg followed Wodehouse, and was later joined by Mary Cadogan.)

In the *Magnet* Frank's enthusiasm is irresistible to readers who accept his basic assumptions about the nature of schoolboys and the value of concepts like honour and decency and *esprit de corps*. However, Harry Wharton, the leader and linchpin of the Greyfriars Lower

HE TORE HIMSELF FREE AND GLARED AROUND!

School, is far from being a cardboard hero or the stereotype of the un-thinking, unquestioning, upright young Englishman that prevailed in so many boys' and adult books in the period between the wars. It is true that during the thirty-two years of the *Magnet* he never told a lie, but his character is flawed (or made sympathetic, according to one's point of view) by an overdose of pride, which brings him into Titan conflicts with chums, rivals and masters – and, of course, himself.

From the first sentence of the first *Magnet* – 'Send Master Harry to me!' – we are made aware of Wharton's arresting and complex nature and of the author's deftness in describing this. Harry, an orphan, starts off as a sulky boy who, like Tom Merry of St Jim's, has been coddled by an elderly female and needs some rugged masculine attention. Colonel Wharton, his uncle and guardian, comes back from India to provide this by sending the spiky but interesting Harry to Greyfriars, his own Alma Mater. Harry is described as a 'well-built lad, finely-formed, strong and active. Handsome indeed was the face, with its well-marked features and large dark eyes. But there was a cloud upon it . . . and in the dark eyes was a glint of suspicion and defiance. The whole manner of the boy was one of suppressed hostility.'[14] Frank Richards was creating in Harry Wharton a very different hero from the equable Tom Merry. Wharton goes reluctantly to Greyfriars, where he is (literally) knocked into shape by his peers after he has contemptuously spurned their overtures of friendship. His emergence as leader is both authentic and significant; Wharton was to become the focus of the Greyfriars ethic – the leader who would set standards for his schoolmates (and the *Magnet*'s readers) to follow – and Frank Richards cast him in the only mould that could retain long-term credibility. He had to be a boy with whom readers could identify, even if they lacked the qualities of leadership he embodied. His quick temper and Achilles' heel of pride cut him down to the size of the ordinary boy sufficiently often for him to become the most popular character of the Charles Hamilton canon. Teenagers are notoriously difficult to write for and to write about. It is a measure of Frank Richards's skill that he managed to fix Harry at the genuine cross-over point from childhood to manhood: he is not too old for his fifteen years and he is not irresponsibly juvenile. He is neither infallible nor gauche, and is never afraid to make decisions or to instigate action.

Although Harry Wharton is the central character of most of the *Magnet* stories, it is Billy Bunter, who began on the periphery, whose name is now most vividly associated in many people's minds with the Greyfriars saga. By sheer weight and loudness of manner, Bunter imposed himself upon his form-mates, upon the *Magnet* itself, which by 1938 carried the subtitle 'Billy Bunter's Own Paper', and upon his creator, who was forced more and more to make the Remove's most retarded pupil the pivot of his plots. (Significantly, all the hardback books about Greyfriars that Frank produced after the

Second World War carried the name Bunter – and not Wharton or Greyfriars – in their titles.)

Apart from Wharton and Bunter, Frank's most impressive Greyfriars characters were the bounders, 'knuts' or would-be sophisticates, boys such as the showy, but resolute, Herbert Vernon-Smith ('Smithy'), the *nouveau riche* millionaire stockbroker's son, who was not only attracted to smoking and gambling, but arrived the worse for liquor on his first day at Greyfriars.

The Greyfriars microcosm was built up organically without a detailed overall plan, true to the nature of schools featured in boys' papers that were likely to be ephemeral. It developed its own atmosphere, its own style and its own language. Throughout its 32-year run, boys and masters roared and raved, howled and hooted, snorted, sneered and sniffed, gurgled and gasped, bawled and burbled, chuckled and chortled, exclaimed and ejaculated and, in the case of Bunter, squeaked and cachinnated. With its japes, booby traps and barrings-out, its cosy study teas after cricket and its confabs beneath the ancient elms, Greyfriars seemed to George Orwell a sham and unreal world.[15] For fans like James C. Iraldi, it is a

> Scholastic Shangri-La . . . a world sometimes more real than that sorry affair in which we struggle . . . a world that exists somewhere between Yesterday and Tomorrow, yet not quite in Today. It exists in a plane all its own, a sort of Fourth Dimension of the Mind, a warm and friendly world, where deceit and chicanery are frowned upon, where violence is unknown, and where everything is secure and healthy and wholesome.[16]

To this Iraldi adds, 'Well, almost', for, of course, there *was* violence at Greyfriars in beatings, bashings and boxing, and there were also plenty of hiccups in the social set-up, which undermined all that security and wholesomeness. Even if everyone knows his place, he does not always stick to it. For example, William Gosling, the crusty old porter who has been looking after the gates since the year dot, suddenly develops illusions of grandeur when he thinks he has 'a rich widder what keeps a prosperous public-'ouse' in the matrimonial bag. The hoped-for marriage falls through, but not before Gosling has truculently asserted his independence, squared up for a fight with Mr Prout and been insulting to the Head. Geoffrey Wilde extends Iraldi's image of Greyfriars as an ideal world. Writing in *Collectors' Digest* he comments:

> To judge Hamilton's work in terms of social realism is to misjudge it. Like any art it is doubtless, in Matthew Arnold's phrase, a criticism of life, but it does not portray 'real' life, nor was it ever seriously meant to. Greyfriars is a true literary creation, and stands in the line of a long literary tradition, with Malory's Arthurian romances, the Arcadian novels of Elizabethans like Lodge and Lyly, and the whole convention of pastoral poetry from Virgil onwards. It is the creation of a stylist . . . whose individual employment of language evolves new regions of the imagination. These regions are timeless and idealized: they transcend reality, and if life isn't really like that, then so much the worse for life.[17]

Greyfriars may also be seen as the projection of a perfect world at a more down-to-earth level. Frank's disposition was an extremely retiring one, yet he was obviously greatly drawn to young people, as well as to scholarship. He could bring all this together in his fiction, playing God with his characters and living out any personal fantasies he might have had about achieving recognition in the scholastic system – as a classics master, perhaps, or a classics scholar. With Greyfriars, he could create not only his own perfect school, but a complete world of his own.

Arguments about the necessity (or otherwise) of children's literature being rooted in reality wax unabated in the society of the 1980s. Concepts of acceptable themes and settings move from comprehensive-school stories to fantasy game books, from classics to kitchen-sink confrontations – and back again. In 'Boys' Weeklies', his review of boys' papers, George Orwell condemned what he called the unreal atmosphere of Frank Richards's public schools and the gulf between this and the quality of life known to working-class boys who read the *Magnet* and *Gem*.[18] If his criticism were accepted, one could equally indict the writers of fairy stories, thrillers and science fiction for creating worlds removed from the reality of the lives of readers from underprivileged homes. Frank pointed out in his reply to Orwell's essay that the critic's description of reality would destroy rather than edify the typical working-class reader about whom Orwell showed so much concern: 'Mr Orwell would have told him

that he is a shabby little blighter, his father an ill-used serf, his world
a dirty, muddled, rotten sort of show.'[19] Frank was convinced that
his own approach of injecting hope and humour into the lives of poor
readers was the correct one. He might have echoed Goethe's words
(quoted by James Iraldi) that 'Nothing is illusion if it brings
happiness.'

At Greyfriars, however, it was never really a case of 'roses, roses,
all the way'. Whenever a lone boy or master ambled innocently along
the footpath by the River Sark, he took his life in his hands, for, as
Orwell noted, the woods around the school were infested with petty
criminals of a typically British variety who, with coshes at the ready,
would try to strip any passer-by of his portable assets: ' 'And over yer
watch, you old bladder o'lard!' And even within the school precincts,
no one was entirely safe from physical assault. A master taking his
constitutional in the quad on a really murky evening might suddenly
receive a punch in the eye from an unrecognized assailant; indoors he
might find himself smothered in soot and glue as a booby trap did its
work. Boys had to suffer a variety of 'whoppings' from masters and
prefects, and the intensity of these was alarming. On more than one
occasion even Quelch, the 'just beast', seems to get carried away:

'I shall give you twenty strokes for your iniquitous conduct this
afternoon. I shall give you ten strokes in addition for having
played a further prank and attempted to deceive me.'
    'Oh, lor!!'
'Bend over that chair, Bunter.' . . .
Whack, whack, whack!
'Yoooo-ooo-ooooop!'
Whack, whack!
'Yarooh! Help!' . . .
The cane was still whacking rhythmically. Billy Bunter's
yells rang far and wide. Towards the end of the infliction the
strokes fell a little more lightly. Perhaps Mr Quelch thought
that Bunter had had enough. If so, for once Bunter was in full
agreement with his Form-master. He had had enough and to
spare.
    'There, Bunter!' gasped Mr Quelch at last. Vigorous gentle-
man as he was, he was a little tired, though not so tired as Bunter.
    'Yow-ow-ow-ow!'
    'You may go!'[20]

This scene is a typical one, and, although Bunter resents being on the receiving end of Quelch's cane, the other juniors remain remarkably stoical when up for 'six of the best'. Occasionally some recalcitrant bright spark, like Herbert Vernon-Smith, the Bounder, will rag the study of a master or prefect who has caned him, but this is likely to happen only if he feels his punishment has been undeserved or of unreasonable severity. Coker of the fifth frequently advances the theory that walloping is good for fags (juniors) and bemoans the current liberalism at Greyfriars, where 'lickings' are less frequent than they were in the past: 'They used to get it hot and strong, and serve 'em jolly well right! It's a good training for 'em!' (Coker's pro-caning stance may be influenced by the fact that fifth- and sixth-formers are rarely beaten by either masters or prefects.) At both Greyfriars and St Jim's corporal punishment of the worst and most humiliating kind comes when a bullying prefect beats one of the boys. It seems amazing that the august, majestic and fearfully brainy Heads of the schools, Dr Locke and Dr Holmes, do not show a little more intelligence and common sense when selecting their prefects. Loder of Greyfriars and Monteith of St Jim's, for example, seem to have sadistic streaks, as well as a fancy for smoking and gambling, and should be the last fellows in the school to be given powers over others.

Even young, sporting and much admired masters are dab hands at inflicting punishment. Larry Lascelles, a one-time professional boxer turned maths master, gives Captain Punter, a confidence trickster, a

The delinquents were ranged in a row before Mr. Dalton's desk, and then one after another the unhappy culprits went through it!

decisive lashing with a stout cane, and Harry Wharton & Co. watch with evident appreciation: ' "My hat!" murmured Bob Cherry. "I didn't even know that Larry was such an athlete. What a carpet-beater he would make!" ' Meanwhile, the writhing shrieking captain is begging for mercy and the beating continues.

Another popular master, Mr Richard ('Dicky') Dalton of Rook-wood, on at least one occasion whops the whole of the fourth form, and the fact that his manner remains as genial as ever while he does so is probably no compensation to the unfortunates who have had to bend over.[21]

Caning, of course, was a universal leveller. Aristocrats and schol-arship boys, snobs and knuts, sneaks, toadies and slackers, bullies, bounders and manly boys alike all, on occasion, had punishment of this nature inflicted upon them. Whatever the rights and wrongs of corporal punishment as a means of cutting boys down to size, it played a part in the plot structure of many of the stories. Bunter, while wildly fleeing from the swishing ash-plant of a wrathful prefect, is likely to shut himself up in some strange bolt-hole, where he will stumble upon the clue to whatever weird mystery is at that moment baffling the Remove or, indeed, the whole of Greyfriars.

However, there is another way in which we may regard the plethora of corporal punishment that is inflicted over the decades at the Hamilton schools. It is in the same bracket as the biffs, bangs and wallops meted out to Donald Duck, Tom and Jerry and other stalwarts of the animated cartoon. In both cases pain is symbolic rather than actual, and the victims spring back to normality with indiarubber-like resilience. It is bizarre that the tender-hearted Charles Hamilton, who hated even to hear a baby cry in discomfort, should approach the subject so zanily. He did occasionally mix profound authenticity with caricature and, although this degrades a story for adult readers, it might well have got laughs from his schoolboy audience, which, after all, was what he was primarily writing for.

Greyfriars may fall short of Shangri-La, but it remains a vivid and satisfying world of its own and has put its stamp on several genera-tions of children and young people. Fashions in manners and mores may have altered radically since Frank Richards first created Harry Wharton, but there is a hardy perennial quality about the 'loyalty to chums' and 'sneaks never prosper' Greyfriars ethics, to which many readers from nine to ninety still respond.

CHAPTER FOUR

THE FAT OWL, FOREIGNERS AND THOSE FEARFUL OUTSIDERS!

'We were bound to see the esteemed Bunter soonfully or latefully, but the laterfully the betterfully,' remarked Hurree Jamset Ram Singh sadly.[1]

It was with William George Bunter that Frank Richards most completely indulged his talent to amuse. It seems likely that he was originally intended to be little more than a peripheral character, but from his early days as a sneaky and insignificant schoolboy he was quickly inflated to the level of farcical anti-hero, to become one of the *Magnet*'s main attractions. By the 1930s he had become so popular with readers that parcels of tuck would arrive at the offices of the Amalgamated Press for the ever hungry fat junior.

He appeared in the very first *Magnet* story, though there is little there to suggest the importance he was later to assume.[2] Harry Wharton, all sulks and resentment at being sent to school, has just been skirmishing with Bulstrode, the toughy of the Remove, who has unceremoniously given him a sharp left-hander to the chin, which has floored him. For a moment or two, Harry is too dazed with shock to rise from the carpet:

As he sat there, another junior belonging to the Lower Fourth came hurriedly into the study, and ran right into him. The newcomer was a somewhat stout junior, with a broad, pleasant face and an enormous pair of spectacles.

'Ker-woosh!' ejaculated the junior, as he sprawled on the floor over Harry Wharton's legs. 'What's that in the way? What do you mean by having a dog in the study, you silly bounders, for a short-sighted fellow to fall over?'

'Ha, ha, ha!' roared Bulstrode.

Billy Bunter looked round as he rose, and peered at Harry through his big glasses. It was pretty clear that, big as his spectacles were, they did not assist his vision very much, for he had to put his head within a foot of Harry's to make him out.

'My word, it's the new kid! Well, what does he mean by sprawling on the floor? I say, you new fellow –'

What Billy Bunter was going to say remained a mystery, for the new boy shoved him violently away and sprang to his feet. Bunter collapsed into a chair.

As the years went by, the broad face became smug rather than pleasant, the famous cry 'Yarooh!' superseded 'Ker-woosh!' and, of course, 'I say, you new fellow' broadened to encompass groups rather than an individual, and, as 'I say, you fellows!', became Bunter's catch-phrase.

— BILLY BUNTER —

Bunter's name is known even to those who have never read a Greyfriars story; it quickly entered the English language as a synonym for anyone gluttonous and obese, and by the 1940s was even insinuating itself into other tongues in such phrases as '*Gros comme le Buntair*'. Nevertheless,

despite his larger-than-life quality, the image of Bunter projected in the stories is far from consistent. At first he was merely stupid; later he became unscrupulous and cunning, then irritatingly arrogant and snobbish. In whatever role he was cast, however, he had his moments of Falstaffian buffoonery, which ensured that his popularity would keep rolling along to the end of the saga. In fact, he is the only Greyfriars character who has been continuously in print ever since 1908. Even when the *Magnet* ended in 1940 and the post-war Bunter books had not yet begun, he was kept afloat as a comic-strip character in *Knockout*; when the Bunter books finished in 1965, the strip appeared in *Valiant*. By 1968 the Howard Baker series of *Magnet* facsimiles had started, and in the late 1980s they have continued to come off the press. (Bunter has also been in print in other formats.)

Frank often said that when Bunter first rolled off his Remington, he had no idea how resilient he would be. Certainly, although even Orwell was to concede that Bunter was a first-rate character, few readers in 1908 could have guessed the importance of Billy's future role. Frequently, of course, he is the comic relief that high drama demands, like the grave-digger in *Hamlet* or the porter in *Macbeth*. But he is much more than that. Fatuous, lying, conceited and infuriating, he somehow brings out the best in his fellow Removites, who generally recognize his weaknesses, refuse to let him be bullied and are surprisingly protective, despite the epithets they bestow upon him: 'You blithering, burbling bandersnatch!'; 'You piffling, potty, pilfering porker!' In essence he is the underdog who hilariously manages to come out on top. He collects many kicks on the way, but these are well deserved. No one ever rolls up his sleeves and fights Bunter, because his stupidity would then rub off on his attacker, and, as Harry Wharton remarks, 'he's a born fool and simply doesn't understand the seriousness of what he's been doing'.

The quintessential point about Bunter is that many plots would falter to a standstill without him. The upright and manly boys must always remain true to the Greyfriars ethic and their own lights; if one of them is suspected unjustly of wrongdoing, he cannot speak up to defend himself if this involves sneaking to a beak, a prefect or sometimes even to his peer group. And under no circumstances – not even to save himself and his chums from crooks or kidnappers – will he tell a lie. Bunter, however, has no regard for truth. His propensity, through obtuseness, for letting the cat out of the bag, even when he has no intention of sneaking, frequently opens the way to justice being done or to some otherwise insoluble mystery being resolved. And, of course, his lack of schoolboy honour, coupled with a nose for news and gossip, pushes him into the role of the fool puffing in where decent boys will not deign to tread. Bunter has no conscience-wrestling to do when he eavesdrops behind screens or curtains or armchairs in boys' or masters' studies; or when he pries through keyholes or windows; or when he listens to the many nefarious plots against Greyfriars heroes, which are hatched in railway carriages in which the podgy and panting Fat Owl has had to hide himself under a seat, being temporarily unable to afford the fare.

We may like Bunter; we may merely tolerate him; we may even dislike him – certainly, for much of the saga, he was given far too much prominence by Frank Richards – but there is no doubt that his place in the stories is a key one. Without him, many of the great series could never have been produced. It is his presence that gives Greyfriars the edge over Frank's other fictional schools and over those of many other writers.

A large number of dramatic tales are spiced with vignettes of
Bunter telling 'crammers' determinedly but ineptly, in hopes of
avoiding retribution:

> Like the celebrated witness in Dickens who was prepared to
> swear 'in a general way, anythink!' Bunter was not particular
> what he said, so long as it staved off punishment. That was the
> important point . . .
> 'I say, you fellows –' he gasped.
> 'What have you been up to, you fat villain?' asked Harry
> Wharton . . .
> 'Nothing,' answered Bunter promptly. 'You fellows know
> whether I'm the sort of chap to bag a fellow's cake.'
> 'Oh, my hat!' ejaculated the three together.
> 'Of course, I never went into Smithy's study at all,' explained
> Bunter. 'I never saw him bringing the cake from the tuckshop,
> never saw him take it into his study, and never waited behind
> the door in Study No. 7 till he went out again. The fact is that I
> was talking to Toddy, in the gym, at the time.'
> 'Oh, crumbs!'
> 'Being in the library at the time – I mean the gym! – naturally
> I never knew anything about Smithy's cake,' explained Bunter
> with dignity. 'Knowing nothing whatever about it, how could I
> have snaffled it? I ask you!'[3]

Of course, Bunter's stupidity had the effect of making even the
least intellectual of schoolboy readers feel superior, in a genial way.
So too did his philistinism, as may be seen in the same story:

> There was no escape for Bunter. He was booked for a whole
> hour of English literature: a subject in which the Owl of the
> Remove took no interest whatever. 'Gray's Elegy' was the order
> of the day . . . really it was an excellent poem: and there were
> fellows, even in the Lower Fourth, who could appreciate its
> beauties. But William George Bunter was not one of those
> fellows. Bunter would have given the Complete Poetical Works
> of Thomas Gray for a cake, and thrown in those of William
> Shakespeare as a makeweight and considered that he had got
> the best of the bargain.

Bunter's arrogance knows no bounds. A typical instance occurs in 'Bunter Comes to Stay' when, having landed himself uninvited at Wharton Lodge, where Harry and Inky are preparing for the Christmas festivities, he presumes to dictate to his tolerant, good-natured host, who lets him stay only on sufferance:

'The fact is, Bunter, the fellows are coming tomorrow,' said the captain of the Remove.

'Oh, I don't mind,' said Bunter generously. 'Ask whom you jolly well like, Wharton. After all, it's your place.'

'Oh!' gasped Wharton. 'Thanks!'

'Not at all, old fellow! Don't mind me. Of course, Bob Cherry is a noisy beast –'

'Eh?'

'Johnny Bull is a good bit of a hooligan –'

'What?'

'And Nugent's rather a namby-pamby.'

'You cheeky porpoise –'

'But have 'em if you want 'em,' said Bunter. 'After all, I never expect you to be considerate to a fellow, Wharton. You always were selfish.'

'My only hat! . . .'

And Bunter rolled away in search of a second breakfast.

Harry Wharton gave his dusky chum an eloquent look. 'Shall we take him out on the ice, and drown him?' he asked.

The nabob chuckled.

'The drownfulness is the only way,' he remarked.[4]

Billy is at his most Bunter-ish in this Christmas series – full of cussedness, condescension and cunning. He even tries to borrow money from the butler and yawns aloud when Colonel Wharton is telling the juniors a ghost story. The rest of the Famous Five join Harry and Inky at Wharton Lodge, and Bunter hits on a 'brilliant' scheme for feathering his own nest. Trading on the generosity of the chums, he announces on Christmas Eve that he intends to give each of them a 'really decent Christmas present' – a gold watch for Nugent, a fur-lined overcoat for Hurree Singh, a gramophone for Johnny Bull, a new bike for Bob and skates for Harry. (Bunter, of course, always lacks the proverbial penny to bless himself with.) He mentions that there is one little snag – the money he will have to request from his pater for these purchases cannot arrive in time for Christmas, so his pals will have to wait a little for their wonderful presents. Bunter hopes to receive glorious gifts from Wharton & Co., who, he feels sure, will be moved to tremendous generosity by his lavish – but empty – promises. It seems that his ruse has worked when Bob, silencing Bull's cynical comments, remarks that the least they can do is to 'play up and treat Bunter with the same generosity' that he is showing them.

Billy Bunter unrolled the paper and revealed—a cake of soap bearing the inscription : PRICE THREEPENCE. " Beasts ! " he roared angrily.

Bunter spends the rest of Christmas Eve in happy anticipation: the next morning his beauty sleep is broken by the Co.'s hammering on his door. They present him with a very large parcel, which contains, they assure him, something he really wants, something he has wanted for a very long time, something he has needed badly – in fact, in Inky's words, they 'thinkfully opine' that there is nothing he needs 'more preposterously'. Touched, Bunter asks if the present is very expensive. Bob explains that all the fellows have gladly clubbed together for it; they are determined to give him something of the same value as the presents he will be giving them. However, they have actually spent a little more than this – to be precise, exactly threepence more! Intrigued, excited, envisaging tuck and all manner of delights, Bunter struggles with string, several layers of paper, cardboard and straw packing. At last – at long last – still watched happily by the Famous Five, he unearths the final, very small package. 'Bunter's thoughts ran on gold watches, diamond pins, and such things.' But his present is not such a glittering prize; it is, as the heroes of the Remove have explained, worth exactly threepence more than the presents that Bunter will give to them; it is a small, simple threepenny cake of soap. Much needed, certainly, even if not much wanted. Bunter, as happens so often, has been hoist with his own petard.

Bunter is not entirely without scruples. Anyone's tuck is fair game, and he has no compunction about 'borrowing' money (which he will never repay) on the strength of his apocryphal, long-awaited and rarely delivered postal order; he would, however, express lofty disdain if categorized as a thief, and would never deliberately snaffle another fellow's cash. He sees himself as a cut above most Greyfriars juniors and boasts constantly about his (non-existent) titled relations. When not engaged in scoffing his form-mates' grub or cadging loans, he enjoys assuming uppity attitudes towards them all, with the exception of Lord Mauleverer, whose social credentials can hardly be sneered at, even by Bunter at his most arrogant. There is a particular nastiness about his attitudes towards the scholarship boys of the Remove, such as Mark Linley, whom he will address, despite receiving kicks from Bob Cherry for so doing, as 'you scholarship bounder' or 'you beastly factory rotter'. As well as identifying with the upper classes, he can be British in a particularly jingoistic manner and contemptuously dismissive of the various foreign students at Greyfriars.

According to Orwell, in this he is imitating his creator. In 'Boys' Weeklies' Orwell complains that Frank Richards makes fun of foreigners: 'In the *Gem* of 1939 Frenchmen are still Froggies and Italians are still Dagoes. Mossoo, the French master at Greyfriars, is the usual comic-paper Frog, with pointed beard, pegtop trousers, etc. Inky, the Indian boy, though a rajah and therefore possessing snob appeal, is also the comic babu of the *Punch* tradition.'[5] Replying to this, Frank wrote disarmingly: 'I must shock Mr Orwell by telling him that foreigners are funny. They lack the sense of humour which is the special gift of our own chosen nation: and people without a sense of humour are always unconsciously funny.'[6] As an example of this he cites Hitler and his pretentious symbols – swastika, 'good German sword', fortifications named after Wagnerian characters, his military coat that he has sworn never to take off until he marches home victorious – and the fact that the Germans 'lap this up like milk', whereas in England 'the play-acting ass would be laughed out of existence'.

In the stories, although Frank engineered several comic situations during the First World War period by sending up Huns and Prussians, many of the boys from overseas are treated sympathetically. Nevertheless he was a Victorian, and nineteenth-century humour about minority groups (as well as women, the working classes and animals) could be ruthless. Frank moved on a great deal from this, questioning the established social and political structures of society and making at least some juniors from abroad as memorable as the stars among the home-grown group. He gave those from the Commonwealth and Empire a decided preference, while, on the whole, Americans came off badly. He seems never to have quite forgiven them for the Boston Tea Party: 'In American history there have been many great disaters, such as the earthquake at San Francisco, the Great Fire of Chicago, and the Declaration of Independence.'[7] There is nothing in his autobiography to suggest that at the personal level he had any unpleasant encounters with Americans: in fact, the reverse is true, for he struck up a warm relationship with a 'Miss New York' during his continental travels before the First World War. On several occasions he denied having any anti-American prejudices and his letters to readers often show great admiration of transatlantic enterprise and progressiveness. The *Gem* and *Magnet* stories rarely reflect this, but in the 1920s and 1930s Frank did produce a truly sympathetic American hero, the Rio Kid, in the *Popular* and the *Modern Boy*.

As early as in 1909 Tom Merry & Co. take a lengthy trip to and across America at the invitation of Tom's uncle, who is a very successful rancher in Arizona. On their way they visit the Chicago stockyards and make the acquaintance of Hiram K. Potts, 'the Chicago meat-king', and his daughter Constantia, with whom D'Arcy becomes instantly infatuated:

he was considering whether to lay his fortune – consisting just then of seven or eight trunks of clothes [Gussy could never travel

"My particular friend, Mr. D'Arcy, the son of Lord Eastwood, pop!" said Miss Potts. Mr. Potts' face was growing purple, but at the mention of "Lord Eastwood," a gentle calm seemed to fall upon him.

light] and about two hundred dollars in cash – and his heart at the feet of Miss Potts, to say nothing of the title of honourable, which would probably weigh more in Hiram K. Potts's estimation than either the heart or the fortune.[8]

Most Hamiltonian Americans tend to be overwhelmed by British aristocratic handles. Constantia is charming, but her father embodies the worst aspects of the callous capitalist exploiter. In 1906 revelations of the harsh conditions of employment in the killing and packing departments of the Chicago meat-packing industry had, through media coverage, shocked the world, and, apparently, made an indelible impression upon Frank. The St Jim's juniors are horrified by the desperation of the unemployed men, who crowd the gates of the stockyards each day, hoping for work at what would be pretty pitiful wages. D'Arcy feels obliged to take up the matter with Mr Potts:

> 'I wegard it as wathah wuff on them.'
> 'Oh, they don't count!' said Mr Potts. 'Nothing succeeds like success . . . Imagine every man employed . . . We could only get extra labour by paying high wages . . . Why, if every man were certain of employment, the employers would be at their mercy. Look at it in that light . . . I should never dare to fire a man from my works if there weren't plenty of unemployed . . . anxious to take his place.'
> D'Arcy looked very thoughtful. 'Is that American business?' he asked.
> 'It's business the world over, only everybody isn't as frank as I am,' smiled Mr Potts. 'I'm giving you straight goods, Honourable. If I were speaking on a public platform, of course, I should deplore unemployment, and suggest remedies, as they all do. Only I should take pesky good care not to suggest a real remedy, for if the remedy ever came along, I might as well close my factory.'
> 'Bai Jove!'

Frank does not have much respect for what he calls republican ideas of democracy. Pompey, a small black pageboy at their hotel, is treated so badly by other members of the staff that Tom Merry and his chums intervene. Pompey becomes attached to Tom and insists on travelling to Arizona with him, turning up at the station when the juniors leave Chicago and getting into their train. Again an aspect of American society is shown in a bad light: 'The conductor came along the car . . . "Guess that nig goes," he said. "He can travel in the nigger car, not here among white people."' There is an ugly insistence on this, and Tom is appalled, especially by the prejudiced attitude of the friendly and helpful Colonel Stalker, who is looking after the St Jim's boys on their journey across America: 'Tom Merry was silent, but he wondered. It was forty years and more since the

"I say, do let him off!" said Tom Merry, putting a dollar into the angry chambermaid's hand.

great Civil War had abolished slavery in the United States, but the line of cleavage between black and white was as strongly marked as ever.'

English schoolboys in the sagas also sometimes show racist tendencies, but, at Greyfriars, it is once more an American boy who is the extremist:

Fisher T. Fish was a member of the greatest democracy that had ever existed; the biggest and freest country on the 'face of the yearth,' as he often told the Greyfriars fellows . . . Fishy might have been expected to extend the right hand of friendship to the black man from Africa.

But Fishy didn't. The rights of man . . . were embodied in the American 'Constitootion'. But the rights of man, it appeared, were limited to the smaller section of mankind whose skins were white. The majority of the human race, being coloured, were altogether excluded . . . according to the democratic beliefs of Fisher T. Fish.[9]

Fisher T. Fish arrived on the Greyfriars scene in 1910 in 'The Yankee Schoolboy'.[10] From the beginning he was brash, boastful and determined always to make a quick buck. Much of the humour in the stories about him is derived from the farcical manner in which his money-making schemes misfire. Fish inherits his would-be business acumen from his hustler, 'Noo Yark' based 'popper', Hiram K. (originally Vanderbilt) Fish, and, generally speaking, the Removites take his wheeling and dealing in good part. However, during the early years of the First World War, when America remained neutral and Fish (who, amazingly, stayed in England, despite food rationing and the threat of Zeppelin attacks) made plenty of tactless remarks about the war, he became something of a *bête noire*. Frank accentuated his money-grabbing characteristics, and the 'schoolboy Shylock' became, for a period, distinctly unpleasant. Episodes in which he was featured at that time were charged with a rather sick and sour

"I'll mention that skating is jest where I live," said Fisher T. Fish.   "I'll be sure pleased to show you guys a thing or two."   "Go it !" said Bob Cherry.   Fisher T. Fish went it.   He slid, he slipped, he gyrated on one leg, and he yelled : "Aw !   Give a guy a hand—wake snakes !   Yaroooh ! "

humour. Fish, as a character, lay fallow for much of the decade following the war, but by the beginning of the 1930s he was rehabilitated. At this time, of course, many of the boys and girls who read the *Magnet* were ardent film fans, responsive to Hollywood versions of the American way of life; they would have been more inclined to view the American at Greyfriars with affection than children during the First World War would have been.

Play was always made of the differences between American and British cultures:

Dr Locke gazed at a slip of paper on his writing-table, passed his hand over his brow, and gazed again. There was an expression of the deepest perplexity on the scholastic features of the Head of Greyfriars. It was a cablegram that lay before him . . . It was just like the hustling Mr Fish to send him a cable from New York. And it was just like him to word it in language that was totally incomprehensible to Dr Locke. The learned headmaster knew many languages; Latin and Greek were merely pie to him. It was said that he could read the *Rubáiyát of Omar Khayyám* in the original. Had that cable been couched in French or German, Spanish or Italian or Portuguese, Latin or Greek, or even Persian, Dr Locke could have dealt with it easily. But as it stood, it beat him to a frazzle, as Mr Fish himself might have expressed it.

'Bless my soul!' said the Head . . . 'Really – really –' He read it again. Fisher T. Fish, had he been present, could have translated it easily enough. But it beat the Head hollow. It ran: 'Dr Locke, Greyfriars School, England. Keep tabs on Fisher. Tough bunch aiming to cinch him. – FISH' . . .

'Bless my soul!' said the Head, again. He touched the bell, and when Trotter [the page] appeared, directed that youth to request Mr Quelch to step to the study . . . For the matter was important. It must be important, or Hiram K. Fish would never have spent money on a cable. Mr Quelch entered the study . . . with a pleasant smile on his face . . . he supposed that the Head had come on some specially knotty knot in the classics, and desired to compare notes with him.

'Pray be seated, Mr Quelch,' said the Head . . . 'I am somewhat puzzled to understand some very curious, indeed, mysterious expressions which are quite new to me . . .'

'I am entirely at your service, sir,' said Mr Quelch. 'And if you are referring to the *Epta epi Thebas* –'

'No, no!' . . . said the Head hastily. 'It is not a point in the classics, Quelch – but – please look at this cablegram.'

'Oh!' said Mr Quelch . . . he was not so interested in modern languages as in ancient ones. And the language he had now to deal with was the most modern of all languages . . . Mr Quelch looked rather puzzled . . .

'Probably some of these expressions are a kind of slang,' he remarked. 'Such colloquialisms are, I think, in common use on the other side of the Atlantic.'[11]

Quelch elucidates that 'keeping tabs' on a person is an Americanism, implying watch, and that 'bunch' implies a 'number of persons in association, such as a gang'. 'Is it possible?' said the Head, with interest . . . 'What a very extraordinary expression! But a tough bunch, Mr Quelch – how could a number of persons in association be described as "tough"? A bunch of asparagus might be tough –'

Quelch patiently explains that 'tough' is an American expression, to a certain extent equivalent to the English word 'rough' or 'lawless'. There still remains the baffling phrase 'aiming to cinch'; the two learned gents work out that 'cinch' is derived from the word for some sort of buckle in connection with the harness of horses, and that it probably means to get hold of – or, in the context of the cable, to kidnap.

'The word "aim" is evidently used in the sense of to "intend" . . .' said Mr Quelch . . .

Dr Locke looked at the cable again.

His face was very serious now . . . the meaning was clear, and it was rather alarming.

Rendered into English, the message implied: 'Keep watch on Fisher, lawless gang intending to kidnap him!'

Wharton never quite gives up trying to make a decent chap of Fish, by discouraging his business enterprises, such as lending money to the other fellows at high interest rates, 'cornering' the market in certain kinds of tuck and selling this to his schoolmates at inflated prices:

'You rotten rascal!' said the Captain of the Remove, with a frown at the wriggling Fish. 'You've been flogged for that sneaking game, and you ought to be jolly well bunked.'

'Aw, can it!' growled Fisher T. Fish. 'I guess you jays in this pesky old mouldy country don't know the first thing about business. I'll say I never struck such an all-fired bunch of boobs.'[12]

Fishy's inability to get to grips with the Greyfriars ethic probably encouraged readers to feel superior to the embryonic American manipulator of money, whose falling foul of the good guys of the Remove – 'Aw, carry me home to die!' 'Wake snakes!' 'Well, search me!' – was generally a lively process.

At another extreme Greyfriars had its two Chinese juniors, Wun Lung of the Remove and his younger brother Hop Hi. For a long time they adorned the scene, clad in flowing silk and complete with pigtails and pidgin English. Over the years the oriental garb was dropped; so too were the pigtails, but after several decades at Greyfriars there was no noticeable improvement in the little Celestials' expertise in the English language.

Boys came to Greyfriars and St Jim's from the furthermost corners of the Commonwealth and the Empire, doubtless owing their creation to the papers' campaigns for ever more vast circulations. Generally speaking, the Commonwealth juniors were sporty, frank, likeable and suggestive of clean, healthy, open-air tastes; one wonders whether readers living, say, in Australia, really identified themselves with Sampson Quincy Iffley Field ('Squiff'), the fifteen-year-old cricketing genius from New South Wales, or whether, like so many other readers, they felt a special empathy for Harry Wharton or Bob Cherry.

Each school had Irish boys 'begorrah-ing', and Welsh juniors 'indeed to goodness-ing', and Scottish boys who managed without catch-phrases, but were generally described as being astute (thus reflecting Frank's pride in his ancestry). Frank also introduced Jewish boys into both his main schools. Monty Newland arrived at Greyfriars in 1912 and Dick Julian entered St Jim's in 1915. Each had to deal with a certain amount of prejudice, though in both cases the majority of their form-mates accepted the newcomers without any fuss. Dick finds himself up against not only the nastiness of

"We're rather gone on Jews, you know," said Crooke. Lowther kicked his ankle. "Gone on Jews!" repeated Julian, in wonder. "What do you mean?" "You're a Jew, ain't you?" "Yes." "We like 'em at St. Jim's," explained Crooke, "that's why we've come to meet you."

baddies like Crooke and Mellish – for whom any new boy is a sucker to be bled dry – but also the normally decent member of Tom Merry's chummery, Monty Lowther. Frank niftily mutes the embarrassment inherent in this gentile versus Jew situation by making Julian very straightforward and natural, and his detractors – by contrast – pretty shoddy.

Monty Lowther is the joker of St Jim's; this time his wheeze is hurtful rather than hilarious. His idea is that Julian, being a Jew, will have a deep-seated reluctance to spend his money. He suggests that a party of juniors meet the new boy at the station and inveigle him into paying his share of a slap-up tea, a visit to the cinema, a taxi ride, etc. There are no takers among Monty's chums for participation in the joke; Arthur Augustus D'Arcy, in particular, makes clear his dis-approval:

> 'I wegard your ideah as bein' in bad taste. I shall make it a point to be vewy fwiendly with the new kid, to show him that we are not all sillay duffahs heah. I wegard wace pwejudice as a widiculous thing. Of course, a decent fellah must be a bit standoffish with lowah waces like the Germans. [The First World War is in progress, it should be remembered.] But a Jew is not a German. When you weflect, Lowthah, that there are many Jews now at the fwont fightin' for their countwy, I wondah that you are not ashamed of yourself.'[13]

Dick Julian turns out to be a sterling character, who can give as good as he gets, but is prepared to take a joke against himself in good part. It is Lowther who shows up as petty-minded – and, of course, prejudiced. He insults Julian, who challenges him to a fight and licks him, after which Lowther refuses to shake hands, so that the St Jim's code of honour is dented by the whole business. The story is rather tasteless, and seems almost to have got out of hand; but Frank brings in his old standby – water. Julian plunges into the river to save Lowther from being swept by the current into the weir. The damping brings him to his senses, and all ends well:

> 'You jolly nearly went under with me,' said Lowther. 'If you'd had any sense, you'd have let me go ... A silly, fatheaded, unreasonable idiot might as well be drowned as not. Still, as you've fished me out, would you mind kicking me?'
>
> 'No, I won't kick you,' said Julian, laughing. 'I'll shake hands with you if you like.'
>
> 'After the caddish way I've treated you?' said Lowther.
>
> 'Oh, let bygones be bygones! If you don't like Jews you can't help it,' said Julian. 'It's a bit unreasonable, but nothing to worry about.' [Surely a strange statement, which carries toler-ance too far?]
>
> 'It isn't that,' said Lowther. 'I'm not such an ass as that. It was just sheer cussedness ... because I had made up my mind that you were an outsider, and you weren't. I called you a funk, and then you came in for me. You can call me anything you like.'

'I'd like to call you my friend,' said Julian.
'Done!' said Lowther instantly.
And he held out his hand.

Julian has the makings of an interesting character, but once
established on the St Jim's scene he spends most of his time in the
background. It rather seems as if Frank wrote the story to satisfy
editorial policy, as this issue of the *Gem* carries a displayed announcement addressed to 'Every Jewish Reader', asking anyone 'who
admires the hero of this story . . . kindly to hand his copy of this
week's Gem Library to a non-reading Jew chum' (non-reading in the
sense of not already reading the *Gem*, presumably).

So it seems that the presence of various nationals and members of
ethnic groups did affect the circulation of the papers. The boy from
overseas who proved most successful as a popularizer was almost
certainly Hurree Jamset Ram Singh, who arrived at Greyfriars in
'Aliens at Greyfriars'[14] and remained fairly prominent in the stories
until the end. Despite his mixed metaphors and flowery speech –
'The proof of the pudding is the pitcher that goes longest to the well'
– he is far from being merely 'the comic babu of the *Punch* tradition',
as suggested by Orwell. Frank said, 'I liked the idea of making a
coloured boy a friend on equal terms with the other boys, and a
valued member of the Co. I thought it would have a good effect.'
Certainly Hurree Singh's arrival is described in a manner that leaves
no doubts about Hamilton's sympathy with the character of the
young nabob of Bhanipur. Assigned to Study No. 1 (already somewhat overcrowded by Wharton, Nugent, Bulstrode and Bunter),
the handsome, lithe and inscrutable Hindu junior is insulted by
Bulstrode:

The dark eyes of Hurree Jamset Ram Singh had a flash in them
now. 'Did you call me a nigger?' he asked quietly . . . 'I have a
great respect for negroes, as much esteemfulness as I have for
other persons . . . But if the intention is to insult –'
   'Oh, rats!'
   'It is impossible for a nabob of Bhanipur to allow anyone to
treat him with the great disrespectfulness,' said Hurree Singh.
'The apologize is necessary.'
   'Ha, ha, ha!'

'If you will express your regretfulness –'

'Catch me!'

'Otherwise I shall become angry with you –'

'That will be really terrible,' sneered Bulstrode.

'And eject you roughfully from the apartment.'

He does, too, though at first Wharton fears he is not up to Bulstrode's weight, and offers to fight the bully of the Remove on Hurree Singh's behalf. After Hurree has flung Bulstrode headlong through the door, he graciously apologizes to the other juniors for 'creating the disturbfulness' in the study; he is immediately drawn to Wharton and Nugent, as they are to him, and from that moment, in Hurree's words, 'the ancient and ludicrous flame of friendship burns undimfully' between them. Even when he first arrives, he is inclined, not surprisingly, being a nabob, to be superior and to see himself as a potential leader of the Co.:

> Dr Locke raised his hand for silence . . . 'I suppose one of you is leader. Let him speak.'
>
> 'With great pleasurefulness, sir. Although I am not yet the leader of the worthy youths who belong to my study, yet I have the anticipatefulness that in a shortful time I shall become so, from the superabundance of my superiority in the various abilities,' said the nabob. 'Therefore –'
>
> 'Therefore shut up,' growled Bob Cherry, 'and let Wharton speak!'

Inky's amiability is often mentioned: 'his good nature was as boundless as the floweriness of his language', but he is always firm about his knowledge of the English tongue, claiming to have studied this under the 'toppingest' native master in Bengal: 'the causefulness of the differentiation is that the English tongue has degenerated, and the English I speak is in the old, original, ripping good English'.

Hurree Singh's pride and shrewdness, as well as his deep regard for Wharton, are illustrated in the Da Costa series.[15] Arthur Da Costa is a Eurasian from a very different Indian background than Hurree's. The nabob's response to him is largely the cautious one of the Hindu caste conditioning, though he is also influenced by the Greyfriars philosophy of 'he's all right, so long as he plays the game'.

"You are in my hands at last, Hurree Singh," said Baji Rao. "Your life is at my mercy. You will never leave these vaults alive unless it is to leave me in possession of the throne of Bhanipur." Hurree Singh smiled contemptuously. "Never!" he answered. "I am Nabob of Bhanipur, and I will live or die nabob!"

Mr Quelch expresses the earnest hope that, as the only boys at Greyfriars from India, Hurree Singh and Arthur Da Costa will become friends. 'Hurree Singh marvelled at the abysmal depths of ignorance that were possible in a very learned gentleman. But his polite, dusky face revealed nothing.'[16] Inky soon realizes that Da Costa is up to no good. In fact, he has been sent to Greyfriars for the purpose of discrediting Harry Wharton and engineering his expulsion. The nabob monitors his every move, and, when he realizes the full extent of Da Costa's treachery against his chum, he confronts the Eurasian with the controlled intensity of a tiger, waiting to pounce on his prey. He makes it clear to Da Costa that he – Hurree – will not permit the scheme for disgracing Wharton to succeed and that he will go to extreme lengths to protect his chum. The Eurasian is suitably intimidated. 'Da Costa felt a chill of ice at his heart. Always he had feared the nabob.'

Hurree Jamset Ram Singh's wholehearted friendship for Wharton is a joyous thread running through many stories. Early in the saga the nabob leaves Greyfriars to return to Beechwood Academy,[17] but finds that he cannot accept separation from Wharton and his other chums of the Remove, and so he returns, almost immediately. 'My heart had the hungerfulness for the respected school where I was happy in the attachfulness of my chums,' he explains when he is reunited with his friends.

In 1926 Harry Wharton & Co. (and the readers of the *Magnet*) had the chance of seeing the nabob in native splendour at Bhanipur. For the Famous Five and Bunter (who, as usual, has gatecrashed the holiday party), even the journey there is fraught with thrills. (The series has such authenticity of atmosphere that it is difficult to realize that Frank Richards never set foot in the subcontinent, or, indeed, anywhere outside Europe.) On the approach to Bhanipur they are received by a glittering cavalcade of troopers, officers and dignitaries. Hurree Singh is regarded with awe, and his officer-subjects kneel to touch his feet with their foreheads. He is suddenly every inch a monarch, and Bob Cherry has misgivings about how to treat him: 'Is this the same old Inky we've always known? Blessed if I shall thump him on the back, or buzz a boot at him while we're in Bhanipur. I should expect one of these johnnies to slice off my napper!'[18] Harry finds himself addressing Hurree Singh as 'old bean' and suggests that he'd better learn instead to say 'Your Highness' to his chum:

'Fathead!' said the nabob of Bhanipur. 'In my kingdom and at esteemed Greyfriars the samefulness is the proper caper. To my subjects I am Huzoor, which is to say, Highness; but to my esteemed and ridiculous friends the old-beanfulness is still terrific.'

'Good old Inky!' chuckled Bob.

Hurree Singh is an example of someone who came to Greyfriars from half a world away, but found his niche there. The real outsiders were generally not foreigners, but home-grown boys. There were smoky sweeps and shady rotters, sneaks and slackers, bullies and bounders. On the whole, the chums and decent boys managed to

contain the nefarious doings of the others, but occasionally a baddy
became top dog and had a surprisingly long period of ascendancy.
Herbert Tudor Vernon-Smith, who has a *nouveau riche* background, is
a case in point; from the day of his arrival (in a 'bosky' state from
having drunk champagne) in 'The Bounder of Greyfriars' (1910),[19]
he was a thorn in Wharton's side, always with an eye for the
captaincy, the ability to lead weaker schoolmates astray into betting,
pub-haunting and smoking, but, despite all his scheming, remaining
a charismatic personality. He had rather too much of his own way for
his first two or three years at Greyfriars, even managing at one time
to manoeuvre the (temporary) expulsions of every member of the
Famous Five:

'I'm going to be top dog in the Remove, and I'm going to down
No. 1 Study . . . you'll have to resign the Captaincy . . . stop

Harry Wharton walked across to the Bounder, and every occupation in the Rag was suspended at once. " Vernon-Smith ! "
Wharton's tone was quite calm. " You've been gassing about cutting the cricket to-morrow ! " " Not at all," said the
Bounder, with an insolent smile. " Statin' a fact ! " " You'll turn up on Little Side at three ! " went on Wharton. " Rats ! "
retorted the Bounder.

interfering with me and my friends when we go out at night, and leave the Cliff House girls alone – Marjorie Hazeldene is going to be my chum, not yours . . . If you agree, it's peace between us . . . if not, I'll drive you and all your pals out of the school.'

Smithy had developed into a semi-reformed and more complex character by the early 1920s – showy, sardonic and knowing beyond his years, but capable of friendship – as shown in his relationship with Tom Redwing, the scholarship boy and fisherman's son. With Wharton & Co. he still vacillates between friendship and rivalry, but the original, no-holds-barred animosity has gone, in favour of mutual respect and the agreement to differ.

The Bounder was too intriguing a character not to be duplicated – or, rather, triplicated – by Frank Richards. There were appropriate variations on the theme, but in essence Ralph Reckness Cardew at St Jim's and Valentine Mornington at Rookwood derived from Vernon-Smith. Unlike him, however, they were aristocratic by birth and background; this gave them a distinction of their own, but they lacked the absolute cutting edge of the Bounder's ruthless go-getting and his rugged, hard-hitting persona. Many schoolboy readers, brought up to believe in team spirit and always playing the game, must have found the determined individualism of Smithy, Cardew and Mornington attractive by its contrast. The tentacles of the Bounder's influence stretched also to girls' fiction; the Cliff House authors who followed Frank Richards on the *School Friend* (launched in 1919) created teenage firecracker show-offs like Augusta Anstruther Browne in the 1920s and Diana Royston-Clarke ('I'll only play if I'm Captain!') in the 1930s.

Frank Richards's 'bad hats' come in almost infinite variety, and to Harold Skinner goes the honour, or otherwise, of being the cad of the Remove. A weedy, slacking, smoky rotter, he is nevertheless a leader in his own small way, his Co. consisting of Snoop and Stott, whose names exactly suit their dingy personalities. All three have been at Greyfriars since the early days of the *Magnet*, and Skinner was mentioned in the very first issue. There is little to commend him, except the occasional flash of caustic humour; he thrives on making trouble for others, is a coward, a snob and a frightful sneak. The favourite target of his mordant wit is Harry Wharton; being everything that Skinner is not, Wharton is much resented by his caddish form-mate. Whenever Skinner really wants to get Harry's goat, he

addresses him as 'Mr Magnificent Wharton', or 'Your Magni-
ficence'. Wharton is often at a disadvantage in dealing with Skinner,
who, rather like Bunter, is sometimes protected from having to
answer for his malicious tricks in a straightforward bout of fisticuffs,
on account of his flabby condition. So he can often put in the needle
with impunity.

To discuss Frank Richards's full cast of outsiders would occupy at
least a whole book. In passing, however, some mention should be
made of the cranky, freakish characters who enlived many *Gem* and
Magnet episodes. The prize duffer of St Jim's is Herbert Skimpole of
the Shell, who espouses a variety of weird and wonderful causes and
is forever quoting by the yard his mentor, Professor Balmycrumpet.
Skimpole's pet crusade is socialism, in the early days of the *Gem*,
though later in the saga a socio-political doctrine called determinism
is substituted for this. (In some of his letters to readers in the 1940s
Frank explained that his editors felt socialism had eventually to be
dropped, because once it had become a popular movement it could
no longer be used as a subject of farce in his stories. He questioned
this editorial attitude, remarking that in his view socialists would
have sufficient sense of humour to accept and even to enjoy Skimpole's diatribes.)

There is no doubt that at first socialism is considered to be a
radical doctrine:

'Come to the common-room and see. Skimpole's got a new idea
in his head –' Gore broke off, to yell with laughter . . . 'He's
turned a Socialist!'
'A-a-a-a-a what?'
'A Socialist, a real, giddy, red-hot Socialist. I wondered what
he meant by wearing a red necktie the last week or two. It makes
his greeny-yellow complexion look horrid. But a red necktie is
the badge of the revolution, according to Skimpole.'[20]

Gussy is amazed, on entering the common-room, to find himself
under attack from the skinny and slightly scruffy, but usually
mild-mannered Skimpole:

'Ha!' he exclaimed. 'Here comes the bloated aristocrat. Here
comes the oppressor – the roller in wealth – the downtrodder of
the toiling millions.' . . . The right hand of the orator rose, and a

A COMPLETE STORY FOR EVERYONE, AND EVERY STORY A GEM!

SKIMPOLE'S LITTLE SCHEME.

A Splendid Long,
Complete Tale of
TOM MERRY'S SCHOOLDAYS.
By
MARTIN CLIFFORD.
❖❖❖❖❖❖❖

bony finger pointed at D'Arcy. 'Look at him! Look at the bloated –'

D'Arcy screwed the monocle tighter into his eye, and took an extremely disdainful survey of the orator on the table.

'Are you wefewwin' to me?' he asked languidly . . . 'I pwotest against such a term . . . I have usually been considahed slim. But can I weally and twuly be descwibed as bloated. I ask you –'

Skimpole endeavours to put his ideas into practice by admitting to the warmth and shelter of St Jim's every boozy, bleary (and pilfering) tramp whom he encounters and, of course, things soon get out of hand: 'If I don't pick up a hundred quid tonight in this 'ere school, blow me tight, that's all.'

Skimpole's counterpart at Greyfriars is Alonzo Todd of the Remove, who gathers his pearls of wisdom from the fuddled outpourings of his Uncle Benjamin. Alonzo was less concerned with politics than with social and educational causes: 'Alonzo Todd had received a remittance that morning from his Uncle Benjamin and . . . wished to send it to the Society for Providing Tracts and Trousers for the Borriobungo Islanders.'

Skimpole at least stays the course at St Jim's, but Todd was dropped as a permanent inmate during 1916. (He made one or two reappearances during the 1930s, which proved that he was still good for the occasional laugh.)

If ever there was an oddball collection at Greyfriars it was, in Alonzo's time, at Study No. 7 in the Remove passage. This was occupied by Billy Bunter and Alonzo Todd and the latter's cousin Peter – a more balanced character – with Tom Dutton making the fourth of the quartet. Tom had the misfortune to be deaf, and his only part in the stories is to become involved in would-be comic misheard dialogues with Bunter and others: ' "Dutton!" roared Bunter, shaking the deaf junior by the arm. "I say, Dutton, I want you to back me up!" "Crack you up!" said Dutton, with a sniff. "Not likely! I don't think much of you, Bunter, and I'm jolly well not going to crack you up!" ' Such frustrating exchanges generally continue until Dutton eventually tells Bunter to 'stop shouting', because he's not really very deaf at all. Of course he is, and this makes his exploitation as a figure of fun rather tasteless, and untypical of Frank Richards. We are probably seeing an example of a bit of buffooning calculated to tickle schoolboy readers' taste for slapstick, but it is surprising that Frank and the *Magnet* editors felt that the Dutton set-piece dialogues were amusing enough to be allowed to recur. Usually Frank had a surer touch with his fearful freaks and outsiders.

CHAPTER FIVE

'SUBS', SWEET HEROINES AND SHRIEKING SUFFRAGETTES

'I don't approve of the Suffragettes,' said Bob Cherry. 'I don't know much about them or their opinions but I strongly disapprove of them.'[1]

In 1909 Frank discovered what he called some rifts in the lute in relationships between the Amalgamated Press and himself. Percy Griffith, editor of the *Gem* and *Magnet*, handed him an uncompleted manuscript about Tom Merry & Co. and suggested that Frank (wearing his Martin Clifford hat) should go through it and 'knock it into shape here and there'. Dazed, Frank barely took in all the details, but he gathered that a journalist friend of Percy's had tried his hand at a St Jim's story, which the editor wanted to publish in the *Gem*. The story was called 'The Terrible Three's Air Cruise', and it was written by Harry Harper, a flying expert and former *Daily Mail* war correspondent. Frank was appalled, both at the quality of the story and at the situation. Without thinking things through, he agreed to Griffith's request, though the whole business left a nasty taste in his mouth. He did not seem to realize at the time that the *Gem* had already published eight St Jim's stories by other writers – some from the pen of 'the pushful Percy', others from Down and H. Clarke Hook. (Frank's vagueness about financial matters may have accounted for the fact that he failed to appreciate that in certain weeks he received only one cheque, instead of two, for the *Magnet* and *Gem* stories; in such cases a 'substitute writer' ('sub') had written and

received payment for a story.) Profoundly irritated at having his
characters and pen-name temporarily appropriated, Frank brooded
about this incident for some time afterwards. Over the years he was
gradually to realize that further sub-stories were appearing. Because
Frank spent so much time on his travels in Europe, there was always
the possibility that manuscripts would not arrive in time – even
though the international postal services before the First World War
seem to have been much more rapid and efficient than they are
today. His suggestion that other authors might be commissioned to
fill any gaps, using their own names and non-St Jim's characters,
was turned down. Griffith pointed out that boys who paid their
pennies for the paper expected to buy tales of St Jim's. One sym-
pathizes with both the author, whose busy schedule would never
allow him time to stockpile scripts, and the papers' editors, who had
at all costs to maintain the continuity of their publications.

Frank was so irritated by the whole business of the sub-writers
that in 1909 he decided to get away as far as possible from Griffith, so
he took off for Paris. He spent nearly half the year abroad, but,
although he could put distance between himself and his editor, he
could not put the affair of the sub-stories out of his mind so easily. It
continued to rankle even decades later, as is apparent in several of his
letters of the 1940s: 'I am quite vague about the number of *Magnets*
which were interpolated by the toads. They used to irritate me too
much for me to keep them or even look at them.'[2] (Lofts and Adley
state that the real Martin Clifford wrote approximately two-thirds of
all St Jim's stories in the *Gem*; the proportion of Greyfriars episodes
produced by the real Frank Richards was considerably higher.) It
should be noted that some of the *Gem*'s and *Magnet*'s young readers
could spot the difference between genuine stories from Charles
Hamilton and those by substitutes, even though literary critics like
George Orwell could not rise to this challenge. The Amalgamated
Press would frequently receive letters from schoolboys when sub-
stories had been used, asking when the 'real' Frank Richards (or
Martin Clifford) would be writing the tales again.

Frank enjoyed his wanderings on the Continent, sometimes on his
own, and sometimes in the company of Dolly and Percy Harrison.
He enjoyed the south of France particularly:

Life in Nice, with afternoon excursions up to 'Monte' and the
world of roulette, passed very pleasantly . . . Frank invented

systems which, on paper, showed vast profits for the punter. Tried out on the green tables, they showed considerable profits for the Casino. But he always had a hopeful nature: and when, at last, he left, it was with the fixed intention of coming back for a really serious campaign, to break the bank.'[3]

Frank made several attempts to fulfil this ambition.

Much of the atmosphere and event of his travels is reflected in the *Magnet* and *Gem* stories of the period; these have an idyllic innocence and a feeling of the calm before the storm, which seem to characterize many aspects of the pre-1914 European scene. Frank sold the bungalow he had bought on Canvey Island and in 1910 visited Switzerland, then Germany, where he was accompanied by Dolly. She and Percy Harrison married in June of the following year, and, because of the closeness of brother and sister, invited Frank to join their household, to which he agreed with delight. Still the wanderings continued, and Frank completed his word-quota every day and dispatched his copy to the Amalgamated Press from postal bureaux all over Europe. At some time during this period he considered the possibility of learning shorthand so that he could turn out his stories more quickly and then hire a professional typist to transcribe them. It is doubtful whether this system would have worked to his deadlines, even if he had mastered the intricacies of shorthand; in the event, these defeated him. 'Frank saw himself out of doors all day long, on a lovely Italian lake, with a fountain pen in his hand, a notebook on his knee, his output perhaps doubled, and his income along with it.'[4] But, he comments ruefully, with shorthand he met his Waterloo, even when later on he again tried to master it with the aid of a skilled instructor in London.

In 1912 Frank and the Harrisons were in Italy, where Rome, Naples, Capri and Pompeii provided some particularly colourful copy for the Greyfriars and St Jim's stories. A hoped-for visit to Greece never took place, because Frank's and Dolly's mother, Marion, had been taken ill, and they returned to London to look after her. Frank insisted that they should rent a house in the Hampstead area, which should be, for London, a healthy spot, and he stayed with his mother until she died in November 1912.

Afterwards, depressed at his loss, he took off for Nice; it was here in 1913 that he met Agnes (whose surname is not recorded), and became romantically involved.[5] His autobiography makes no mention of the relationship, though they became engaged; he does give details of his friendship with a young American woman, whom, for obvious reasons, he calls Miss NY, but he is at pains to stress that there was nothing romantic about this:

> It is often said that men and women cannot be pals: the eternal sex aspect is bound to crop up sooner or later. But it is not so. If there was a spot of romance in Miss NY – as doubtless there was – Frank never saw anything of it. Perhaps he was not the man to evoke it. No inexpressive she ever fell in love with Frank, so far as he knows. Certainly Miss NY didn't.[6]

This chummy relationship with Miss NY (which seems at odds with the anti-American flavour of his stories at that time), must certainly have been a very energetic one; she would ask Frank to 'step over from London to Lausanne, as one might have asked him to step over from Hampstead to Golders Green'. And when they were together, they saw all the sights, walked and took train trips at a frenetic pace, set by the dauntless Miss NY. It seems to have been quite a relief to Frank when she finally returned to the United States; she invited him to visit her there, but he never did: 'He rather dreaded being taken on a walk from New York to San Francisco: perhaps without being allowed to sit down and rest for a few minutes on the Rocky Mountains!'[7]

But to return to the shadowy Agnes – the engagement was short-lived, and terminated without rancour on either side. Possibly Frank had entered into it as a reaction to his mother's death, and, though drawn to female company, was apprehensive of undertaking marital responsibilities. (Apparently he once withdrew from the brink of an engagement to one of Dolly's best friends, and was obviously not ready for the commitment.) Certainly, if he had married and become responsible for children at this stage in his life, it is unlikely that he could have continued to produce his stories so prolifically. His experience of family life was to be through his sisters and brothers and their children, and, generally speaking, this degree of involvement suited him admirably, as it allowed him the psychological space he required.

It is probably significant that his best stories featuring girls and women focus either on the young and innocent or on the elderly and fiercely determined. When he writes about relationships between the sexes, it is adolescent 'romance' that inspires his wittiest, and his most touching, prose. With both St Jim's and Greyfriars, the formula for the associated female characters is an alternation of charm and the cartoon-like.

At one extreme at St Jim's we have Gussy's Cousin Ethel, who is pretty and gracious with just sufficient touches of mischief to make her likeable and convincing. In complete contrast comes Miss Priscilla Fawcett, Tom Merry's smotheringly protective old nurse, who is the archetypal funny, fusty old maid. Ethel Cleveland was an idealized embodiment of the quiet strength that Frank seems to have admired so much in women. Miss Priscilla, however, seemed mainly of interest to him as a comic device, though she was never treated in quite the same knockabout manner as Aunt Judy and Miss Bullivant in the Greyfriars saga. Cousin Ethel's presence glowed gently through the *Gem* from its early days to its end. She soon became so popular with readers that she was given a school career of her own in *Cousin Ethel's Schooldays* (originally serialized in the *Empire Library* and reprinted in the *Boys' Friend Library*). Ethel's physical appearance was frequently and enthusiastically described. In 'The D'Arcy Cup' we see her as 'a wonderfully pretty girl . . . dressed in some sort of a white, summery attire which the juniors would have found difficult to describe, but which one and all were ready to admit was ripping'.[8] In the same year (1909) there is a gracious vignette of her in a long pink frock and flowered hat, taking a turn around Dr Holmes's (the Head's) favourite rose-walk. She is the cynosure of all eyes. We are told of Ethel's smiles and dimples, and her blue eyes, glimmering with fun.[9] It was not only Gussy, Figgins and their chums who appreciated her attractions. Dr Holmes, 'wise in his thirty years' experience with young people', knew that the occasional presence of D'Arcy's cousin at the college had a refining influence on his charges, who, in his eyes, were 'more or less untutored savages' in their natural, boyish state.

Ethel is more than just a 'sweet young face'; as Tom Merry declares, she is no 'namby-pamby'; she can handle a boat with skill; we are told that she understands cricket and football as well as any boy and cuts a splendid dash on horseback. Her vigour, however, is most clearly expressed in all that cycling that she did with her St Jim's companions. In her boater and 'very charming' blue-serge long-skirted costume, she was a fetching figure of Edwardian elegance.

TALLY-HO! Cousin Ethel took the jump in splendid style, with Arthur Augustus D'Arcy close behind.

Her importance in the saga is her effect upon the fellows. Even the mocking and generally unrepentant Cardew can, simply by seeing her, uncover finer feelings in himself. On one occasion Ethel discovers him smoking in one of the studies, and he is extremely disturbed:

> as he went down the passage towards the stairs he gritted his teeth, and his brow darkened. 'Fool!' he muttered, addressing himself. 'Goat! Triple ass! Caught smokin' – like a silly little fag of the Third! She must think me a thumpin' duffer!' He shrugged his shoulders angrily. 'After all, what does it matter what she thinks?'
>
> But somehow it did seem to matter, for Cardew's brow was dark as he swung out of the School House and tramped away moodily towards the cricket ground.[10]

Ethel's effect on George Figgins ('Figgy') of the fourth is even more profound. It sometimes has comic results (as when she makes him promise not to fight, and the odious Baggy Trimble takes advantage of this), but frequently it is touching. Figgins's devotion to Ethel and her protective feeling for him are on a par with the relations between Bob Cherry and Marjorie Hazeldene in the *Magnet*. Like Bob, Figgy is rugged, straightforward and modest about his own shortcomings in his relationship with his dream girl. Just as Bob's countenance glowed even more ruddily than usual whenever Marjorie wheeled her bicycle into the Greyfriars precincts, so 'Figgy's face lit up like a blessed sunset at the thought of Ethel'.

Gussy has to admit that his Cousin Ethel is 'weally an awfully intelligent gal', and at a time when the issue of votes for women was looming large, he fears that she will become involved in political activity, which might necessitate her having to rub shoulders with a 'dweadful' lot of masculine 'boundahs'. When Skimpole asks Ethel if she is a suffragette, she does not get a chance to reply, but her St Jim's protectors do: ' "Ha, ha ha!" The idea of Cousin Ethel being anything of the kind at all struck the juniors as very funny.'

However, although Ethel is not involved in the women's suffrage campaign, she is inspired to join another all-girls-together group – the Girl Scouts – in 'The Boy Scouts' Rivals'.[11] This was in 1909, before the Guide movement had been officially recognized or set up. Girls had gatecrashed the boys' organization and adapted the name accordingly. Arthur Augustus thinks it is all rather unfeminine and tries to talk Cousin Ethel out of the 'Gal Scouts': 'There is an old maxim about wesistin' the beginnin's . . . I wegard it as necessawy for a woman to wemain in her place . . . it would be absolutely howwid for women to get into Parliament, you know, when you considah what kind of boundahs they would have to mix with there.' He confides to his chums: 'A man bein' so much supewiah to a woman in intellect is bound to look aftah her and give her fwiendly advice.'

Gussy's attempts to point out to Ethel the error of her (slightly) feminist ways are somewhat emasculated by the fact that, when going to meet her in Rylcombe woods, he is attacked by boys from the nearby rival school and has to be rescued ignominiously by Ethel and her Girl Scout Patrol. Gussy explains to Ethel that she should stay quietly at home and set a good example to her sex; she suggests spiritedly that she can best judge her own needs and challenges the St Jim's juniors to a scouting contest. The girls win, which is a strange, but satisfying, result in a paper of that period designed for boys. At the end of the episode, Gussy has become 'an assuahed and convinced supportah of the idea of patwols of Gal Scouts'. (Charles Hamilton was breaking new ground with this story, as it seems to be one of the very first Girl Scout adventures ever published. He was a great admirer of the Boy Scout movement and, although we do not often see the St Jim's and Greyfriars juniors in their shorts and wideawake hats, there are some memorable scouting moments in the stories.)

Gussy's further struggles with the fair sex are described in 'D'Arcy the Suffragist!', which was written during a period of intense militancy in the campaign.[12] Arthur Augustus is now a convert to the cause, and he persuades his chums to accompany him to the normally orderly market town of Wayland to watch a procession by members of the Feminine Liberty League. They arrive to find that

windows had been broken, pillar-boxes had been raided, policemen had been scratched and even bitten – in fact, there were all the signs of progress.

The wretched tools of a corrupt Administration – thus Mrs Jellicoe Jellicott [the league's leader] described the local bobbies – had been made to feel that their employment was no sinecure.

THE GEM LIBRARY 1d

VOL. 2.
NO. 72.

Grand Long, Complete Tale by

THE BOY SCOUTS' RIVALS.

MARTIN CLIFFORD.

Also a Grand War Story, "BRITAIN AT BAY!"

JACK BLAKE DREW BACK IN DISMAY!

The procession is riotous, and Gussy's loyalties are somewhat stretched when his brand-new silk topper is ruined in the affray. However, he sticks to his guns and calls a meeting of the juniors to debate the subject of votes for women, during the course of which he reveals that the 'weason why' he has become a 'Suffwagist' is because it seems 'wude to wefuse the deah cweatures anythin' they want'. On his way to a suffragette meeting later on, he is ambushed by Figgins, Kerr and Wynn, who, heavily disguised, claim to be Asquith, Winston Churchill and Lloyd George. They strip Gussy of his clothes, making him put on a weird assortment of feminine attire, daubed with suffragette slogans. He is pelted with rotten eggs and thrown into the horse-pond by local residents, who resent the window-smashing and letter-box-burning activities of Mrs Jellicott and her league. All that is mild, though, compared with the shrieking vehemence of the suffragettes, who consider that Gussy, a male impersonating a female, must be a spy. The straw that breaks the back of Gussy's resolve is the fact that a 'fivah' he has been eagerly awaiting from his pater, Lord Eastwood, arrives at St Jim's in charred fragments, because there has been a suffragette outrage at the Wayland post office, in which many letters awaiting delivery were destroyed or badly damaged. 'Arthur Augustus laid down the charred fragment. "Gentlemen," he said – "gentlemen, chaps, and fellows – On full considewation, I have decided to dwop the cause of feminine Suffwage, and to let the movement get on the best it can without my assistance." '

Gussy may leave the suffragettes alone, but sometime afterwards he has to tangle with another hefty harridan in 'Gussy Among the Girls'.[13] On this occasion he has temporarily 'wetiahed' from St Jim's, to avoid the indignity of an unjustified flogging. Cliff House School is one of his several refuges, where, concealed in a woodshed, he is discovered by Bessie Bunter, who has ventured there to devour a bag of jam tarts appropriated from Clara Trevlyn. Bessie's screams rend the air and bring the gym mistress to the scene. 'Miss Bullivant was a determined character. In younger days she had helped to wring the Vote from terrified Cabinet Ministers, whom she had waylaid with golf clubs.' Now, with her club at the ready, the Bull commands Gussy to come forth:

Arthur Augustus did not come forth.
    'Oh dear! S–s–suppose he rushed at you, Miss Bullivant?'

exclaimed Barbara. 'Hadn't we better all go away, and – and send the porter . . .'

'Nonsense! What a mere man can do a woman can do – better!' said the Bull.

When her repeated commands to the 'ruffian' to come forth are ignored, Miss Bullivant announces her intention of stunning him with one blow, and, swinging her golf-club through the air, she crashes it down on the stack of faggots sheltering D'Arcy. Crumpled and dishevelled, he emerges to a chorus of laughter from the girls and fury from Miss Bullivant. At first she suspects him of criminal intent, and then of 'holding surreptitious communication with a girl belonging to this school':

'You are a young rascal! . . . An unscrupulous and precocious young scoundrel!' continued Miss Bullivant, who had learned a fine flow of language in her early days of the struggle for the Vote. 'Well may you cringe before me . . .'

The grip on Gussy's collar was like iron, as Miss Bullivant marched him through the gateway into the road.   " Now go ! " she cried.   " Reappear here at any other time, and I shall hand you over to the police : Wretched boy, take that as a punishment ! " " Yawoop ! "   D'Arcy staggered to one side as Miss Bullivant gave him a powerful box on the ears.

'Bai Jove! I was not awah that I was cwingin' . . .'
'I look upon you with disgust, detestation and abhorrence!'
said Miss Bullivant. 'Wretched interloper!'

Gussy's gorgeous manners and niceties are utterly lost on the Bull,
who propels him protesting to the gate. With an iron grip on his
collar, the ex-suffragette yanks him along so vigorously that he has to
trot to keep pace with her.

'Wretched boy, take that as a punishment!'
Smack!
'Yawoop!' roared Arthur Augustus, staggering to one side as
Miss Bullivant gave him a powerful box on the ears.
Smack!
A box on the other ear righted the swell of St Jim's.

D'Arcy, discomfited and muttering about the 'feahful thwashin' ' he
would administer if only Miss Bullivant were a man, 'stood not upon
the order of his going – but went!'
    Frank Richards's (and Martin Clifford's) assorted images of
'liberated' women in the Amalgamated Press boys' papers probably
had a conditioning effect on readers, as well as raising a laugh. It is
noteworthy that the farcical and dismissive tone was applied to the
suffragettes mainly during and after their period of militancy. Frank
was doubtless horrified by the suffragette who took a horsewhip to
Mr Churchill in 1910, and presumably appalled too at the beating
up of Mrs Pankhurst by roughs at an election meeting in 1908.
Ironically, a few weeks after 'D'Arcy the Suffragist!' was published
in May 1913, the climax of violence came. Emily Davison, just
released from six months in prison for setting fire to a letter-box,
went straight to the Derby and threw herself under the King's horse;
she died a few days later.
    The campaign for women's suffrage is given a far more sympath-
etic voice in the *Magnet* than in the *Gem*, almost certainly because
these stories were written before the peak of militancy had been
reached. The main proponent of votes for women is Miss Amy
Locke, sister to the Headmaster of Greyfriars and a Girton girl, who
becomes Mr Quelch's temporary replacement for a brief period in
1908.[14] We are told that 'there was nothing of the blue-stocking, the
learned miss about Amy Locke . . . a young and graceful girl with a

An amusing incident in the Grand School Tale in this issue.

sweet face and soft brown eyes', from which we gather that independence in women was approved by Frank, so long as they were
young and pretty. Miss Locke reappears at Greyfriars a few months
later in 'Harry Wharton's Campaign'.[15] The attractive Girton girl
has now blossomed into a fully fledged suffragette, and the cover
picture shows the wasp-waisted Miss Locke arguing the cause of
women's suffrage with the Head. Overhearing her talking down her

illustrious brother on the injustice of denying women the vote, members of the Remove react in a manner which could hardly be called progressive: ' "My only chapeau!" murmured Bob Cherry . . . "Miss Locke has become a Suffragette." "The Suffragettefulness is terrific!" "Never mind," said Harry Wharton. "She's a ripping girl, all the same, and the right sort; and we all have ideas at times." ' Bully Bulstrode, as expected, voices the most reactionary view: 'a woman ought to get her opinions from her father or brother, and stick to them. It's utterly absurd for a woman to start thinking on her own.'

It soon becomes apparent that any campaign in support of female suffrage launched by Miss Locke in the tradition-ridden confines of Greyfriars must be doomed, but Wharton, chivalrous as ever, is determined that she should receive as fair a hearing as possible. A discussion is arranged at the school Debating Society, in which Miss Locke maintains her dignity, despite vociferous insults from some of the tougher spirits of the school. Among the speakers is Blundell of the fifth, who makes a colourful, but completely erroneous, prophecy:

> 'Imagine to yourselves feminine Members of Parliament! . . . I foresee that debates will be interrupted by discussions on the latest thing in hats . . .'
> 'Ha, ha, ha!'
> '. . . that the Honourable Leader of the Opposition will in all probability scratch the Speaker if he interrupts her . . . And the Premier – I mean, la Première, if we get a lady Prime-minister, will go into hysterics in the House if she can't pass her measure.'

Miss Locke is allowed to make a moving indictment of the established order:

> 'Men have governed this country for the whole period since the English have been a nation, considerably more than a thousand years. They have not abolished sweating, and child and woman labour in factories. They have not yet abolished poverty. They have not yet abolished still more terrible evils. Give the women a chance . . . Men have tried for a thousand years, and failed miserably . . . During that time the women have waited. Can you wonder at it that they are tired of waiting?'

"Good gracious me!" gasped Miss Penelope Primrose, as Nugent's hat and wig came off in her hand.   "It's not a girl at all!   Good gracious me!"

Frank, however, allows farce to triumph, with Temple & Co. of the fourth wrecking a public lecture that Miss Locke gives a little later. Votes for schoolboys are proposed, instead of votes for women – a twist that must have given considerable satisfaction to many *Magnet* readers.

Miss Locke becomes Miss Penelope Primrose's second in command at Cliff House, though it is baffling to consider such a progressive character working in close co-operation with someone as old-fashioned and out of touch as the Cliff House Head. Amy Locke reappears at Greyfriars in *Magnet*, nos. 68–70 (1909) when 'there is something amiss with the foundations of Cliff House – something that seems to have been overlooked by the architect'.[16] While – presumably – the erring architect is putting things right, the Cliff House girls come to live temporarily at Greyfriars and to take lessons with the Remove. In 'The Invasion of Greyfriars' their presence causes some embarrassment to the boys, especially Bob Cherry, who 'was blushing rosy red in anticipation before he reached the door' of the form-room.[17] Frank emphasized that 'there was no doubt that the girls' bright faces and curls and bright dresses gave the room a touch of colour that improved it very much'. Marjorie's chum, tomboy Clara Trevlyn, is determined to 'make things hum', in spite of Marjorie's sedately murmured 'Oh Clara!' in disapproval, and Mr Quelch's nerves are torn to shreds after a couple of coeducational classroom sessions. He is impotent in the face of Clara's teasing and the 'tempests of tears' that the Cliff House girls seem able to tap at will. Fortunately, Miss Locke offers to take over the teaching of the girls.

The spirited Clara challenges Bulstrode to a fight because of his insulting behaviour towards the girls. She knows, of course, that she has him at a disadvantage, because he would not dare to fight a member of the opposite sex and thus 'incur the mortal fury of the Remove'. He is therefore forced instead to apologize, and Clara says, with infuriating magnanimity, 'I will let you off this time, but you must not be a naughty boy again!'[18] (Later she admits to her chums that if Bulstrode had accepted her challenge and fought, she would have countered this by tears. Female duplicity in evidence!)

In the boys' world of the *Magnet*, masculine supremacy, of course, has to be reasserted, and who better to do it than Harry Wharton? Anxious not to be outdone by the boys, the girls decide to buy supplies for a midnight feed in 'The Cliff House Party'.[19] Marjorie is selected for this purpose, but 'before she had gone a dozen yards from Greyfriars, Marjorie realized with great clearness that, whether boys could break bounds at night or not, it was no task for girls'. The poor girl is soon clinging to Harry (who happens to be around at the right moment) and 'crying softly', after being waylaid by one of those foul-smelling, unshaven, typically Hamiltonian tramps – savage oaths, evil drink-distorted eyes and all – with the usual thievish designs. Marjorie proves herself thoroughly inept at this breaking bounds business. In her panic-stricken flight from the tramp she has 'dropped her little purse . . . all her money was in it – her own as well as the ten shillings subscribed by the Cliff House girls for the surreptitious feed'. Meanwhile, back at Greyfriars, Clara, the bold tomboy, has been reduced – with Milly – to a state of tears and terror, because Bulstrode has locked them out of the house. Marjorie rather pitifully tries to keep her end up with Harry, as she endeavours to convince him that she is not really afraid of darkness, or dingy, drunken tramps. ' "Girls are as brave as boys, you know," said Marjorie. "Of course they are," said Harry [assuming the role of the all tolerant and understanding male] "but in a different way. This sort of thing isn't in a girl's line." ' It certainly is not for Marjorie in these early *Magnet* stories, even though at other times in the saga she will gamely go through (metaphorical) fire and water to prop up her weak and wayward brother Peter.

There is one other female who has played a key role at Greyfriars, though her appearances are brief and spasmodic: Coker's besotted Aunt Judy, a lady of uncertain age, who wears voluminous Victorian dresses and intimidates everyone from the Head downwards. With her endless chat, her obsession with her darling Horace, and her ancient umbrella, which makes a nifty weapon when occasion demands, Aunt Judy is the female buffoon of the *Magnet*.

Marjorie is the feminine star, and her frank integrity struck the right note with Harry Wharton and Bob Cherry from the moment they first met her in 'Kidnapped'.[20] She became their 'ripping' girl chum and, because of their state of permanent adolescence, their author probably thought, at first, that no further definition was ever

" Gosling ! " roared Prout.   " Go and tell Coker that he is excused from detention, as his aunt has called, and take Miss Coker to the visitors' room."   " Thank you so much, Mr. Snout—I mean Stout ! " said Aunt Judy.   " My name is Prout, madam ! "   " Thank you so much, Mr. Sprout ! "

to be required. He would never, for example, have dreamed then that boy readers might have had fantasies about one day marrying Marjorie, or that girls weighed up the comparative states of marital bliss with Harry on the one hand or Bob on the other, and that readers of both sexes would speculate quite seriously about whether Harry or Bob was the front-runner with Marjorie in their curiously triangular, but chummy, relationship. Readers' letters, however, were to provide indications of the strong interest in Marjorie that was felt by a fair proportion of readers. (Boys' papers before the *Magnet* and the *Gem* had tended to ignore the female sex altogether; it is often said that in the early decades of its existence the *Boy's Own Paper* did not contain a single mention of women or girls.) It is interesting that Frank, no doubt prompted by his feelings for his sisters and their influence on his own boyhood, quite consciously built up the characters of Marjorie in the Greyfriars saga and of Ethel at St Jim's. Some of his stories might send up what he considered to be the (un)fair sex, but on the whole they suggest his adherence to the conviction that girls, in fact and fiction, had a good effect upon adolescent boys.

He was, of course, acutely aware that idealistic romantic stirrings could be expressed only if they never spilled over into 'soppiness', which would disrupt the papers' bracingly boyish mood. So, despite the special interest shown by Marjorie and Ethel in certain boys, safety in numbers seems to have been the watchword of these fearfully pretty and capable young heroines. Marjorie, for instance, could at times be seen as the wholesome 'girl chum' (as distinct from the sexier term 'girlfriend') of the whole of the Greyfriars Remove; however, within this determinedly healthy context, her marked partiality for Harry and Bob was allowed to develop. In the *Magnet* Frank fairly seriously manipulates this three-sided relationship, while in the *Gem* he often uses the triangle of Ethel, Gussy and Figgins for comic effect.

Marjorie's friendship with Harry and Bob shines through the *Magnet* from beginning to end. In spite of the strength of character that she demonstrates when having to extract her feeble and erring brother from his frequent predicaments, Marjorie of 'the sweet, girlish face' has a curious passivity. This is illustrated by the fact that we know her more from the way she is spoken of by the other characters than by her own actions and attitudes. Wharton decides at his first meeting with her that she is 'stunning', and his opinion remains unaltered through the years. As early as 1908, in *Magnet*, no. 17, Bob is wistfully commenting to Harry about how 'ripping' she is, and by 1915, in no. 410, we are told that 'Marjorie represented perfection in Bob's eyes'. Harry solemnly and 'with flashing eyes' warns Bulstrode, 'If you utter a single word that might cause Marjorie Hazeldene pain if she knew it, I will thrash you within an inch of your life.'[21] Bob is prepared to go even further for his dream girl: in 'The Bad Hat of the Remove' the evidence of his own eyes suggests that Marjorie has appropriated Lord Mauleverer's lost tenner.[22] Bob, however, 'still believed in his girl chum, because he could not doubt her without doubting his own senses'. His efforts to shield her bring suspicion on himself: 'He choked. Even if his own pals thought the worst of him, not to save his good name, not to save his life, not to save a thousand lives, would he utter a word.' Somewhere along the lengthy line of stories, Bob's special claim on Marjorie's affections seems to be recognized, and Harry tacitly acknowledges this by standing back somewhat from the trio. His special feeling and intense respect for Marjorie continue, and he is ever ready with manly advice and muscle when occasion demands, but, inwardly stronger and more independent than the sunnily conformist Bob, he nobly leaves the field clear for him.

Marjorie, in common with his pride, is Harry's weak spot. Bob is not alone in sacrificing himself for Marjorie, for in the same story Wharton also puts his reputation on the line for her sake. He has given Peter Hazeldene a place in the team for a cricket match against Highcliffe School. At first Hazeldene rides the crest of the waves, because – unknown to the chums, of course – he thinks that a horse he has backed is a dead cert, and he shines during the first innings: 'So long as Hazel was keen on cricket and on friendly terms with the Famous Five, he was safe from the dingy scrapes into which he was likely to fall . . . At least, so it seemed to Marjorie, little guessing what was in her brother's mind.' But, alas for this sisterly trust, Hazel collapses completely in the second innings, having learned of the failure of the hotly tipped horse, which means that he now owes bookie Bill Lodgey ten pounds for his disastrous flutter. Once again Hazeldene becomes the slacker with a 'moody hang-dog look', and his inclusion in the team appears to justify the caustic comment of the Bounder, Herbert Vernon-Smith: 'I'd boot him out of the eleven if I were skipper! Catch me letting a man play ducks and drakes with the cricket just because he's Marjorie Hazeldene's brother.' The narrative reinforces this point: 'A cricket captain, of course, could not be influenced by considerations of that kind. Wharton had an uneasy feeling that it had influenced him just a little.'

'Honest, clumsy old Bob' suffers in silence on several occasions in the process of protecting Marjorie from a variety of physical and psychological hazards. He is always 'the happiest man in the County of Kent' when misunderstandings with Marjorie are eventually resolved: in the words of Hurree Jamset Ram Singh, 'when the infuriated frown has given place to the idiotic smile of absurd friendship, the rejoicefulness is preposterous'. Bob's highest rewards from Marjorie for all this trust and sacrifice are soft smiles and discreet hand-holding:

> Marjorie lingered in the old gateway and Bob remained with her. His face was red.
>
> 'I – I – say,' he stammered, 'I never – I mean, I wasn't – I hope you don't think – I mean – that is –'
>
> Marjorie smiled softly . . . 'You saw me – I know now – drop that banknote out of the study window, and you knew it was Mauleverer's! What could you think?'

"I say——" said a fat voice. Marjorie Hazeldene was holding out her hand to Bob Cherry, when a fat figure rolled into view. "I say, I hope I'm not too late for the picnic," said Bunter. "I suppose you've only just got here, Marjorie, as you're shaking hands with Bob!"

'I just couldn't think at all,' said Bob. 'I tell you, I was flummoxed . . . But if you think I doubted you for a single instant –'

'You must have had a lot of faith in me, Bob, if you didn't.'

'Well, so I have – lots!' grinned Bob. Marjorie smiled . . . Impulsively she held out her hand to Bob. It disappeared in Bob's, which was about twice as large.

'I say –' said a fat voice.

The clasped hands dropped as Bob and Marjorie looked hurriedly round. A fat figure rolled out of the path in the wood into the old gateway . . . Billy Bunter bestowed an ingratiating smirk on Marjorie. 'I say, I hope I'm not late,' he remarked. 'I suppose you've only just got here, Marjorie, as I saw you shaking hands with Bob –'

'Eh! Oh! Yes!'

'Then the picnic hasn't started! Good! I was afraid I might be late.'[23]

Thus the gatecrashing Bunter shatters Bob's beautiful moment.

George Figgins is similarly capable of tremendous self-sacrifice for Ethel. As Cardew succinctly comments: 'That's Figgins all over . . . He would let himself be chopped into little pieces to save Ethel from a pain in her little finger.'

One has to hope that, with all this male chivalry around, the boys who devoured the *Magnet* and *Gem* would eventually become extremely upright and romantically idealistic young Englishmen. But what about girl readers? Females in the stories were often presented more quirkily, with tomboy Clara Trevlyn putting down the heroes illogically and unmercifully ('That's a boy all over – no gumption!'), and even Marjorie and Ethel huffily misinterpreting events from time to time. Boys were expected to live up to Harry Wharton & Co.'s high standards, but something short of honour or even, occasionally, reasonableness was demanded from the girls: 'Miss Bunter's eyes gleamed through her spectacles. "Let's go over to Greyfriars and smack their faces!" she suggested.'[24]

Supposed differences between masculine and feminine moral codes constantly crop up in the papers; a good example occurs in 'The Girls' School Challenge', in which the Cliff House girls challenge the Greyfriars boys to a snow fight; despite the fact that the girls cheat, the boys manage to win.[25] Female foul play prompts the author to state ironically: 'as is well known, ladies may do anything they please, from punching Cabinet Ministers to biting policemen, but they must not be punched or beaten in return, or what becomes of chivalry?' (In this context Frank finds it appropriate to ignore unchivalrous trifles like the torture of forcible feeding inflicted on suffragettes in prison at the time of the story.)

Frank Richards's handling of the relationship between Ethel and Figgins is masterly. His own taste made it easy for him to conform with Lord Northcliffe's taboo on sex as a topic for the Amalgamated Press's juvenile papers. Nevertheless he managed to suggest convincingly and without excessive sentimentality the idealism and the ironies of young love and a hint of its potential when the parties involved matured into adults. Figgins

> was too young to have thought about such matters as being in love, of course, and he was not so absurd as to let such ideas come into his mind. But he had a great regard for Cousin Ethel . . . And Ethel liked Figgins very much. She seemed to see more in him than in the other fellows, somehow, though he certainly was not so good-looking as Tom Merry, or Arthur Augustus D'Arcy, or Lowther or any of the chums of St Jim's, in fact. Perhaps Cousin Ethel valued other qualities higher than good looks.[26]

What splendid encouragement this kind of comment must have given to boy readers who knew that they did not exactly slot into the category of handsome heart-throb.

Figgy's modesty about himself with regard to Ethel is often stressed: 'Mellish, the cad of the Fourth, had once referred to Cousin Ethel and Figgins as "Beauty and the Beast", and Figgins had been cut too deeply by the remark even to resent it. Like many big, kind-hearted fellows, Figgins had a diffidence and lack of confidence in his own personal qualities.'[27] This diffidence, however, did not always hold him back. That he could be assertive about Ethel is often illustrated in the stories. He frequently steals a march on Tom Merry & Co. (his School House rivals) by getting in first with invitations to Ethel to join some expedition or another, or a study tea-party at the school. And in 'Figgins' Folly', when she and an aunt set off on a trip to France, he asserts himself to the extent of going beyond seeing Ethel into her train and suddenly decides to travel with them.[28] He has the exquisite fulfilment of saving Ethel's life in a continental train crash, but the story also provides a compelling description of how jealousy can affect the behaviour of a normally genial character.

Figgy's hostility is provoked by a French gentleman whom they encounter on the train. He is a typical Frank Richards foreigner, and his greasy appearance and ingratiating Gallic gallantry towards the ladies are described with considerable relish. The extroverted and voluble Frenchman is in complete contrast to the unassuming and straightforward Figgins. He has carefully arranged balding hair, an over-waxed moustache, a dyed beard, tight patent-leather shoes, fastidiously cared-for clothes and – the greatest affront of all to any right-minded British boy – corsets, the presence of which is betrayed by a slight creaking noise. Ethel and her aunt, of course, are polite to the stranger, which increases Figgy's antagonism towards the Frenchman, whom he sees as a rival for Ethel's affections. The poise of the ladies and the practised courtesy of the corseted gent throw Figgy's phlegm and awkwardness into sharp relief, and, insecure and resentful, he begins to behave quite boorishly towards Ethel. To escape the coolness that then develops between them, he sulks off into the corridor and curses himself 'with the bitterness of death in his heart'. Fortunately, however, it is not too long before his good relationship with Ethel is restored and, in a favourite phrase of the author's, 'all is calm and bright' again.

There are many other incidents of Figgy's assertiveness in connection with Ethel. Even when she is with a large group of the juniors, he generally manages to have a private and pleasing conversation with her or to be the one who offers his arm. Tom Merry, Jack Blake and most of the others, although themselves very fond of Ethel, are always tolerant of Figgy's desire for a special place in her affection. But Gussy from time to time resents this. When Figgins reminds him, for example, to send her a telegram to invite her to a picnic with the chums, D'Arcy replies coldly, ' "Pway leave the mattah to me. I shall not forget to wiah to my cousin." There was unusual emphasis on the "my".' Gussy's possessiveness, of course, springs less from the fact that he and Ethel are related than that he too is sweet on her. Tom Merry, as well as Figgins, has to take him to task occasionally for his persistence in 'ramming the fact' that Ethel is his cousin 'down everybody's throats', and Blake heartily concurs: 'Hear, hear! Good for you, Tommy! . . . Miss Cleveland is the cousin of every decent member of St Jim's.' Gussy's part in the eternal triangle is used by Frank as a comic motif throughout the *Gem* saga.

His feelings for Ethel, however, do not prevent him from falling frequently and farcically in love with a string of other girls. Perhaps his earliest infatuation was chronicled as early as 1907.[29] His lady-love then is the Head's niece – another Ethel – whom he has to meet at Rylcombe station. On this occasion the extreme elegance of his attire is too strong a provocation for a trio of village boys, who roll him, on his way to the station, in a six-foot-deep ditch of muddy water. Later he risks further sartorial damage when, sighing like a pair of bellows and wearing a white flower in his buttonhole, he endangers the immaculate appearance of his fancy waistcoat by going out in the rain to buy flowers for his beloved. However, she is eighteen while he is only 'coming up for fifteen', a discrepancy that his chums, weak with laughter over his love affair, feel at pains to point out. This infatuation, like most others of Gussy's, quickly peters out; in this case the object of his affections, after receiving a worshipping letter from him, patiently and gently explains that she is already engaged to a handsome army captain. D'Arcy, with true aristocratic grit, hides his temporarily 'bwoken heart' by announcing his intention of sending her, eventually, 'a weally wippin' weddin' pwesent'.

Gussy's flirtations are fair game for Frank, but nevertheless he takes seriously the idealism in these infatuations and in the rather more earnest romantic responses occasionally aroused in some of the older boys by female pantomime-, opera- or circus-performers.

Whether Frank was portraying the idealized and utterly feminine Marjorie and Ethel, funny old sketches like Priscilla Fawcett and Penelope Primrose or mannish martinets like Miss Bullivant and Aunt Judy, his female characters always added style and sparkle to the stories.

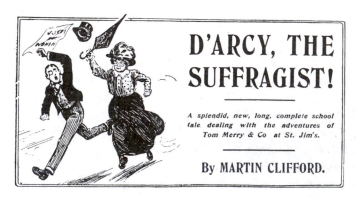

D'ARCY, THE SUFFRAGIST!

A splendid, new, long, complete school tale dealing with the adventures of Tom Merry & Co at St. Jim's.

By MARTIN CLIFFORD.

CHAPTER SIX

THAT UNBREAKABLE BANK AT MONTE CARLO

I used to visit, and revisit, and re-revisit the place, like a moth going back to the candle.[1]

Frank played the gaming tables at various continental resorts, but Monte Carlo was always the most seductive. With its splendid setting and alluring prospect of the glittering prize, Frank found it delightful and quite unreal: 'At Monte you have left the common earth – and commonsense – behind you. You live an airy, fictitious sort of existence, in which money has little meaning, and hardly any value.'[2] Frank explains in his autobiography that when a cabby in Nice overcharges by ten francs, one reasons with him; however, once in Monte 'the bare idea of bothering about ten francs would make you laugh . . . if you play for small stakes, ten francs goes in a whisk. If you play for large, you lose enough in an evening to buy the cabby and his horse, and everything that is his.'

In his autobiography and letters Frank provides fascinating insights into the mind of a truly compulsive gambler. He was bitten by the bug when young, and the addiction remained with him through middle life into old age. For many years it dichotomized his world: on the one hand he was recklessly throwing away large sums of money, while on the other he was deeply and sincerely, as a mentor and protector of youth, inculcating his readers with ideals of upright and responsible living, which certainly did not include gambling at Monte Carlo. There was a serenity about him that suggested that he had learned to ride this conflict of views, and, indeed, of passions; it was possibly to salve his conscience that he wrote several excellent,

EVERY MONDAY, The "Magnet" LIBRARY. ONE PENNY.

Vernon-Smith touched Hazeldene on the arm. Hazel turned round savagely, and started violently as he saw the Bounder. "You again?" he muttered. "Turned up like a bad penny, you know!" said the Bounder coolly. "How is the system going?"

atmospheric and admonitory *Magnet* and *Gem* stories that focused on the grisliness of the gaming addiction.

Frank's major campaign for breaking the bank took place towards the end of 1913 and at the beginning of 1914. He confided to the readers of his autobiography that he 'would try systems: many and varied. Or he would rely on his luck. In either case he came out, in the long run, at the little end of the horn, as the Americans say.' He had already made several attempts, taking the occasional trip from Paris to test a new system or staying near to the casino and 'blue-ing' his money at an alarming rate. 'Hope springs eternal in the punter's breast. Really and truly, at the bottom of his heart, he knows very well that he will never trim the tiger's claws, and that the tiger will devour him. But he refuses to know it. He doesn't want to know it, and he won't.' Frank mentioned too how difficult it is to stop wooing 'the smiles of the fickle goddess of Fortune', and the ever alluring mirage. What he did not voice in the book were his doubts about the way in which the tables at Monte Carlo and elsewhere were operated; this is left to the Bounder, when he is questioned by Peter Hazeldene in 'The Greyfriars Trippers':

'You don't believe in a system?'

'Yes, I do,' said the Bounder unexpectedly. 'I've looked into it. There's not one system: there are half a dozen that would be certain to win if the game were played fairly. That alone is a proof that it isn't played fairly, for lots of people go there with good systems, and the casinos don't go broke that I've heard of. I shouldn't wonder if your system's all right, given a fair game. But given a game in the hands of the most unscrupulous set of swindlers on the Continent . . . it's the duffiest wheeze I ever heard of.'[3]

In '*Faites vos jeux!*' Roger M. Jenkins perceptively discusses Frank Richards's clutch of gambling *Magnet* and *Gem* stories, in which the author was 'wryly analysing his own weaknesses'.[4] On the same theme Frank wrote in his reply to Bagley's questions:

I certainly . . . like all other punters . . . had bad luck at Monte Carlo, in a financial sense . . . but considerably enriched my experience of human nature, and subhuman nature. I think it was worth while: especially as Monte, from what I now hear, is only a shadow of its former self . . . small stakes, and counters instead of hard cash, on the tables . . . I have very strong doubts whether the bank ever was 'broken' except for publicity purposes. Whenever I have seen a player raking in huge winnings, there has always been some little dubious circumstance which gave the impression that he was a 'stooge' put up to make the mob believe it could be done.

As Jenkins points out in '*Faites vos jeux!*', Frank's *Magnet* and *Gem* gambling stories indicate how the addiction can lead to worse depravities, such as theft and violence: 'Such players, it is true, are

rare – and yet outside the Casino they appear to be in possession of
their senses and not fit subjects for a lunatic asylum. Upon habitual
players the game exercises a fascination which seems to rob them of
all common sense.'

It was fortunate for Frank that, at the period in his life when he
could most easily slip over to the Continent to have his flutters on
roulette or *petits chevaux*, his earning capacity was high and steady
enough to replenish the pockets he so quickly emptied. Even so, he
often found himself wondering how many extra pages of typescript
he would have to produce to get his finances back into order again.
Fortunately, his habit of slogging over his typewriter for two or three
hours almost every morning, whatever circumstances he might be in,
ensured that at least he attended to business before embarking on the
dubious pleasures of the casino. Frank also knew when the moment
had come to pack up and go – 'unless you have, like some extreme
cases, a fancy for a gun and the Suicide's Cemetery. Millionaires
may carry on as long as they like – ordinary mortals cannot.'[5]

In a sense his stories for schoolboys about the Edwardian splen-
dours and horrors of Monte Carlo are curiosities. To get into the
casino, Tom Merry & Co. have to disguise themselves as adults;[6]
and Harry Wharton & Co. have to don false moustaches in order to
gain admittance to a Swiss casino.[7] This gives the stories an air of
cloak-and-dagger amateur theatricals. A later story, 'Bob Cherry's
Chase', provides a more realistic atmosphere, a sense of the Monte
Carlo dash and dazzle, and details about the application of systems
that are optimistically expected to beat the bank.[8] A disgraced
relative of Bob's is thrown in for good measure to provide the
character conflict that is quintessential to Frank's best stories.

'The Greyfriars Trippers' has the bonus of including Marjorie
Hazeldene and Clara Trevlyn, who accompany the Famous Five,
Peter Hazeldene and Vernon-Smith on a Founder's Day trip to
Boulogne, which the now semi-reformed Bounder is financing.[9] The
story starts on Little Side at Greyfriars, where Wharton's team is
locked in battle with Redclyffe School and losing wickets too easily
for comfort. The always unpredictable Hazeldene, whom Wharton
has given a chance in the team partly to please Marjorie, keeps the
field waiting when he is due to start his innings. This is because he is
absorbed in studying a gambling system, which he has been working
out for many months and hopes to put into practice on the forth-
coming day trip to France.

Hazel goes to the wicket, but, with his mind more on winning money than winning the match, he hardly justifies Wharton's decision to give him a place in the team. Nevertheless

Marjorie's face had brightened as she saw her brother go to the wickets. She was very fond of her moody, wayward brother, though what she could see in him to be fond of was a puzzle to the Remove fellows. Perhaps it was partly because he was weak and wayward, and incessantly getting himself into scrapes, and requiring to be got out of them, that the girl concerned herself so much about him. It was through her influence that he had devoted himself to cricket, instead of slacking about on half holidays with Skinner and Snoop, and smoking cigarettes. And Harry Wharton & Co. had been only too willing to help in the good work.

Before the chums take off for Boulogne, there are some intriguing exchanges between Hazel and the Bounder (both bad hats in their different ways) about the possibility of fitting a bout of gambling into the trip. The Bounder is shocked that Hazel should even consider this with his sister in the party, but Hazeldene sullenly makes it clear that he intends to slip away from the others to the tables at Le Coin. This is why he wants the Bounder's advice about his proposed system; he points out that lots of English people *do* cross the Channel in order to play roulette or *petits chevaux*:

'Yes, I've seen 'em . . . Boatloads of silly duffers come over from Dover or Folkestone,' said Vernon-Smith with a sarcastic grin. 'Awfully respectable people at home; but the minute they set foot in Boulogne they make a beeline for the casino, and stand there being swindled till it's time to catch the boat back. Those foreign thieves must make thousands and thousands out of English mugs.'

Once on the steamer to Boulogne, Hazel wants to drink champagne, and neither the Greyfriars juniors nor Marjorie's powers of persuasion can divert him from this indulgence. Unusually, it is the outspoken Clara who brings him to heel: 'Don't play the giddy goat, kid . . . it doesn't suit you. If you order champagne, I'll box your silly ears – so there!'

There is a dramatic build-up of suspense, as Vernon-Smith tries to keep Hazel away from the gaming tables without letting Marjorie discover her brother's intentions. But Hazel does get to the casino, where, inevitably, he is cleaned out; he steals and loses again, and, when the Bounder tries to stop him, he crashes a large stone against the Bounder's head and knocks him out. All – ultimately – ends well, because the Bounder and the Famous Five close ranks to save Hazel from himself – for Marjorie's sake, of course. Incidentally, the differences between the Bounder's and Hazel's kicking over the traces are intriguingly shown in this story. The flamboyant Bounder can exercise self-control, whereas the dingy, easily led Hazel does not know the meaning of self-understanding and restraint.

In the Hamilton canon, gambling and betting come in the same breath as smoking and pub-haunting. (It was never entirely clear whether the fellows who engaged in the last named actually drank hard liquor, or whether they simply frequented pubs in order to play cards or billiards and to absorb the generally smoky and seedy atmosphere.) However, in the stories the most unlikely schoolboys occasionally demonstrate aspirations to become 'rorty' or 'gay' dogs. (Frank used 'rorty' in a dingier sense than 'cheerful', its dictionary definition.) Whenever Billy Bunter can snaffle someone else's smokes or a racing-tips paper, he likes to think of himself as 'no end rorty', unlike those stick-in-the-muds from Study No. 1, the Famous Five. At the beginning of 'The Vanished Sovereigns' he has sought the seclusion of the woodshed in order to smoke some purloined cigarettes, away from the gaze of their owner and of any of the schoolmasters:

> He was half-way through his first smoke, and he was – or at least was determined to believe that he was – enjoying himself no end. Had he been half-way through the third or fourth, he would have been undeceived. There had been sardines for tea in Toddy's study, and after tea – all the fellows being out of the House that fine day – Bunter had found a bag of doughnuts in Harry Wharton's study, and a dish of jam-tarts in Bob Cherry's study, and a pot of jam in Johnny Bull's study ... The doughnuts, the tarts, and the jam were packed away inside Bunter, and it was rather a full cargo. A few cigarettes would certainly have caused the cargo to shift.[10]

"What are you doing?" said Vernon-Smith, catching Bunter standing by the open table-drawer. "Oh, nothing!" said the fat junior, putting both hands behind him. "I haven't bagged your smokes. I—I don't smoke!"

Gosling, the porter, discovers Bunter and looks forward to doing his 'dooty' and reporting the Fat Owl to Quelch. It is Gosling's fixed opinion that all boys should be 'drownded' at birth or, failing this, flogged frequently. Bunter makes many other efforts to be a 'rorty dog' or a 'doggish card', though he is likely to collect kicks from his studymate Peter Todd in so doing, for letting down the honour of the study.

Another fatty who casts himself in a doggish role when he can is Tubby Muffin of Rookwood School, which Frank created for the *Boys' Friend* in 1915. In the *Greyfriars Holiday Annual 1938*, in an exuberant tale called 'Tubby Muffin Goes Gay', Tubby surprises Jimmy Silver & Co. by imitating the bold, bad blades, arranging to place bets on horses and trying to set up games of nap or banker. It turns out that he is acting up as a gay dog to impress a rich uncle who is to visit the school – an uncle who, many years earlier, had been expelled from Rookwood for precisely similar activities. Uncle arrives; Tubby continues to maintain his knutty stance until, unable to

stand any more, his uncle yanks Tubby off to Dr Chisholm, Rookwood's august and somewhat frosty Head:

> I am Muffin – the one you expelled years ago. On that occasion,
> sir, you did me a good turn for which I shall always be grateful to
> you. You brought me to my senses. Now, I want you to do a
> similar good turn to this wretched nephew of mine by flogging
> some sense into him before expulsion becomes necessary.

Later, when the misapprehension is cleared up through the intervention of Jimmy Silver, Uncle George has strong words to say: 'The
schoolboy who apes grown-up weaknesses in order to look manly is
heading for trouble. I learned that lesson in time. But that is not
everybody's good fortune.'

Frank may have enjoyed gambling and betting, but he was
determined to remove all glamour from these activities to dissuade
readers from following in his footsteps. (The worlds of boys' and
girls' papers and horse-racing did occasionally overlap: in 1957
Frank wrote to the editor of the *Collectors' Digest*, quoting from a
sporting paper that 'a geegee named Bessie Bunter' was running in a
race.[11] He added, 'It would have been interesting to see Bessie a
winner: but no doubt she had too much weight to carry!')

Frank harked back to his trips before the First World War to
Monte in 'The Girl from Monte Carlo' (written under the pen-name
of Winston Cardew).[12] This is intended for adults rather than

children, but the language is far less demanding and stylish than that of the *Magnet* and *Gem*. At its atmospheric opening the punters are staring as if mesmerized at the ivory ball that whizzes and dances in the revolving bowl, the piles of stakes on the yellow numbers on the green cloth, the long rakes in the hands of the croupiers, which pull in a fortune at every spin of the wheel. A violet-eyed British girl ('wedged between a fat Frenchman and a shiny Italian') has just about lost her all and she is too preoccupied to notice the young man who turns out to be the hero of the book: Ronald Vane, 'a clean-looking, upstanding Anglo-Saxon, among so many dark, greasy Latins'. It seems that by this time Monte Carlo has lost its fine careless rapture for Frank. All that is left of the Edwardian mood of his own experiences there is the language: 'You dastard!' breathes the heroine to an importunate male, and 'Get up, you cur!' Ronald says hoarsely to the same foreigner, after he has knocked him down.

Back in the early months of 1914 Frank left the south of France, with the bank at Monte Carlo still intact, and soon afterwards met up with Dolly and Percy in Italy. They were in Bellagio when the Archduke of Austria was shot at the end of June, but, suspecting sabre-rattling instead of hostilities in earnest, they continued their travelling. War was declared at the beginning of August, but they still did not take it seriously, and booked in at the Hotel Hirsch in Spondinig in the Austrian Tyrol.

Here Frank revelled in the scenery, walked in the mountains with the dog, Mickey, who had 'found' him some time ago in Marseilles, and produced his daily quota of copy (which, presumably, was taking far longer than usual to filter through the war-disrupted international postal system to the London offices of the Amalgamated Press). Frank failed to see how 'the shooting of some archduke or other' could be very serious, but, with every meal, the head waiter at the hotel gave Frank, Dolly and Percy more and more dramatic news of the progress of the war. They decided that they should get out of Spondinig as soon as possible; Germany and Austria were allies, and Frank & Co. were 'perched high in the mountains' of Austria, with Germany not far away. The snag was that before they could travel further, they needed money, and they had been waiting for a while for an overdue remittance.

Every day when they went to inquire at the post office about the expected remittance, the locals were amused at the sight of '*die drei Engländer!*' while their own companies of departing recruits were

"Halt!" Tom Merry jumped back as a bayonet gleamed before his eyes. In the corridor outside the room a Tyrolese conscript was on guard. "Am I a prisoner?" demanded the junior.

marching through the streets. Still the money did not arrive, so every morning Frank sat at his typewriter in his hotel room churning out stories of Greyfriars and St Jim's. Just before the war started, there had been much talk of Zeppelins, and Frank, ever topical, had introduced one into a Tom Merry story he wrote at Spondinig. In his autobiography Frank tells how one morning when he was working, two men in uniform appeared in his doorway and informed him that '*die drei Engländer*' were under arrest. A young soldier was posted at the door, with his rifle at the ready, and he seemed deaf to every remark Frank made, in whatever language. Hoping to go along and speak to his sister further down the corridor, Frank moved to the door, only to have the soldier's bayonet thrust within a foot of his waistcoat. So, forced to remain in his room, Frank decided not to waste his time: 'Military fatheads might come and go, but Billy

Bunter went on for ever.' Within a few minutes the guard was forgotten and Frank was at Greyfriars again, churning out his copy. All went well until he crossed the room to his suitcase, opened it and put his hand inside to find a paper-clip. The soldier this time pushed the bayonet point to Frank's ribs, thinking that he was groping in the suitcase for a weapon.

Later on that day Frank and his sister and brother-in-law were interrogated in the hotel by an Austrian army officer. Meanwhile their belongings were being searched upstairs in their rooms. A man came down with some of Frank's typed sheets in his hand, and the interrogating officer looked askance as he studied them. 'That fatal word ZEPPELIN stared at him from the pages . . . It was a tense moment.' Could it be that the three Britons, who had hung on when all the other tourists had left, were spies, who were making out reports on that busy typewriter? If not, why did the word Zeppelin recur on so many pages? Luckily, the head waiter could read English, and he was able to explain the circumstances to the officer. This was no spy's report, but a story written for English schoolboys. (The story in question, 'The St Jim's Airmen', was published in 1914.[13] It has a pre-war setting, and in it a Zeppelin lands on the cricket field at St Jim's; Tom Merry & Co. find themselves on board as unwilling passengers when it suddenly takes off. They land eventually near the Italian–Austrian border, and in returning to St Jim's have similar adventures to those that overtook Frank, Dolly and Percy.)

The money came through later that day and the party was allowed to go. At last they packed themselves, their luggage, Frank's typewriter and his dog into a hired car, and set out for England. The trip home by car, train and boat was slow and complicated. Frank separated from Dolly and Percy in Paris, where he stayed for a few days while they went on to England. Frank arrived in Dieppe at the end of August, ready for the last lap of his journey. Already Calais and Boulogne had been cut off by the German armies, so it seems that Frank was lucky to get back to England for the duration. One thing was certain: the period of his intensive travelling had come to an end.

CHAPTER SEVEN

HEROISM, HUMBUG AND SUPERSLEUTHS

'Let them do as they like! They shan't see us show the white feather.' Tom Merry's voice rang out clearly.[1]

Charles and the Harrisons had managed to return safely to England, but one member of the party was not so fortunate. This was Mickey. Bureaucratic problems made it impossible for Frank to bring the dog back with him, so he arranged for Mickey to be temporarily boarded in France with a country couple. Believing like almost everybody else that the war would be short, Frank intended to nip back to Dieppe in the near future to collect him. He therefore decided to find somewhere to live in the Folkestone area for the time being. In this way, when Mickey was eventually brought to England, Frank would be near at hand for the period of his incarceration in the local quarantine kennels. In the event, of course, his reunion with his pet was to be put off for those four fateful years of war. Frank collected him as soon as possible when hostilities had ended; Mickey was quarantined; the faithful Frank visited him regularly during this time, and then master and dog settled down happily together in the village of Hawkinge.

Altogether, Frank's relationship with Mickey seemed to demand far more devotion from the master than the dog. Frank's loyalty is particularly touching in view of the fact that he did not seek the relationship in the first place but was 'found' by Mickey. If anything, he was a cat person rather than a doggy one, relishing the feline's greater independence and fastidiousness. His correspondence (after the Second World War) made frequent references to Sammy and other cat companions; for example, in a letter to Margaret Wark, a small girl reader, in the early 1950s he says:

Sammy is in the pink . . . a big cat now . . . with an appetite on Gargantuan lines, and still the dearest old animal in the world, excepting of course Midge! and perhaps Dinkie! . . . As Sammy was on my knee when I opened your letter, I showed Midge's picture to him, and he mewed – though whether that was a greeting to Midge or not I wouldn't be certain!

There is little in Frank's writings to suggest a strong feeling for dogs; indeed, they appear as mixed blessings in the *Magnet* and *Gem* stories, doted on by their owners but occasionally cursed by the owners' chums. Wally D'Arcy (Gussy's younger brother) lugs Pongo across America in the 1909 Western series, but his canine pride and joy causes irritation to most of the St Jim's party by his habit of taking off and disappearing for hours, even days, at a time. Here Frank gives us a comparative study of two kinds of emotional loss – and it is interesting that grief for a supposedly lost dog is shown as more dire and durable than that for a lost human love:

At breakfast Arthur Augustus had somewhat recovered his spirits, sufficiently so to make a good meal. He was, of course, still in love, and would probably be in love for some days to come: but an undying affection and a never-fading memory were his consolation for being rejected. Wally, however, refused to be comforted. Pongo was gone, and without Pongo D'Arcy minor was disconsolate.[2]

The most frequently featured dog in Frank's stories must be Towzer, the bulldog pet of Herries of the St Jim's fourth form. Naturally, his owner thinks he is top dog in every respect, though the action of various plots suggests that Towzer is actually pretty stupid. Nevertheless his ferocious appearance stands Herries and his chums in good stead on occasions when they have to confront burglars or other baddies; the trouble is that Towzer is as likely to take a lump out of the trousers of one of the St Jim's juniors as those of characters with felonious intent.

Frank went to Hawkinge immediately on his arrival from Dieppe at the beginning of September 1914, asking the taxi-driver who collected him off the Channel ferry to take him somewhere nearby where he could find pleasant accommodation. He became the paying guest of Mr and Mrs Hunt, who ran the Hawkinge post office, and,

as a stranger to the village, was at first suspected of being a spy. The
Hunts' small daughter Sylvia and nine-year-old Edith Hood sometimes helped in the shop and did little errands for Frank, who
befriended both girls. (Several years later, when Edith had grown
up, Dolly and Percy Harrison, at Frank's suggestion, employed her
as nursemaid to their new baby, Una – who, like her mother, was
named from Spenser's *The Faerie Queene*. Later still, Edith became
Frank's housekeeper.)

Though largely based at Hawkinge, Frank spent quite some time
in London visiting the Amalgamated Press editorial offices and
seeing the Harrisons, who had taken a house in Hampstead Garden
Suburb. Dolly had acquired another house in the same road
(Midholm), and it was agreed that Frank would occupy this. The
arrangement suited him very well, but he decided to rent a cottage at
Broughton Farm, between Aylesbury and Tring, as a safe haven for
himself and the Harrisons that was beyond the expected reach of
Zeppelin raids. So, although trips to the Continent were out of the
question, Frank moved around during the war years between these
locations, often with Miss Beveridge, who was then his housekeeper.

It seemed strange to Frank to be sitting in the familiar room 57 in
the Amalgamated Press's Fleetway House, just as he had done so
often before the war. After his experiences in Austria, London
seemed miles away from the action. There had, however, been
changes in personnel at the Amalgamated Press. Griffith had left,
quite suddenly, in 1911: Herbert A. Hinton was now editor in chief of
the department and Down had become chief sub-editor. This com-
bination appealed very much to Frank, as he had always got along
well with Hinton (the inspiration for Figgins of the St Jim's fourth)
and Down (the model for Gussy). Down, however, was quickly out of
action, for he enlisted early on in the war, and was commissioned in
the 1st Hertfordshires, an infantry regiment. He was later seconded
to the Royal Flying Corps.[3]

Hinton had recently added the *Boys' Friend* to the papers under his
control, and in order to boost its circulation he asked Frank to
produce a new fictional school for a series of stories. Writing as Owen
Conquest, Frank obligingly produced Rookwood, a school set in
Hampshire, which had Classical and Modern sides (for japes and
rivalries). It was popular from its inception (1915) and ran until
1926. The stories were about half the length of the average *Magnet*
episodes, and Frank could often produce one at a sitting. There was a

A few of the well-known characters you would meet in the course of a ramble round Rookwood.

pleasant sense of intimacy about the Rookwood adventures, and,
because they were started during Frank's writing prime, the stories
and characterizations were always well developed and convincing.
Jimmy Silver, the junior captain, was likeable and not easily put out;
he was, perhaps, a trifle lightweight when compared with Wharton
and Tom Merry. The rest of the cast were in essence variants of
characters already established at Greyfriars and St Jim's, but with
his customary skill Frank injected them all with individuality. It is
interesting that several of his most successful plots were first used at
Rookwood, later to be adapted, with variations, for St Jim's and
Greyfriars. Perhaps because the stories were fairly short (about
10,000 words), many stand out as fascinating cameos.

'The Amazing Proceedings of Timothy Tupper' is a sparkling
episode about the turning of the worm, or rather of the Rookwood
house page, Timothy Tupper.[4] Tupper has a slight tendency to be
work-shy, but is usually kept in line by his superiors on the domestic
staff. There is no holding him, however, when he receives a letter
from his father explaining that Timothy's Uncle Bill has 'pegged
out', leaving his pub, the Peal of Bells, to Timothy's father. On the
strength of this Tupper rises in his own estimation from bootboy and
general dogsbody to being the equal of anybody at Rookwood,
including the Head. He is walking in the quad when he should be at
his duties, and Dr Chisholm, the Head, throws up his window to
address him:

'What does this mean, Tupper?' asked Dr Chisholm, fixing his
eyes upon the heir to the Peal of Bells.
'What does what mean?' retorted Tupper.
'I rang for you, Tupper.'
'Ho!' said Tupper.
'Why are you not attending to your duties, Tupper?'
'Can't a bloke take the hair if he likes?' asked Tupper.
'The – the what? Oh, the air!' ejaculated the Head. 'Certainly
not, Tupper, at this time or in this manner. Is it your intention
to be insolent, Tupper?'
'Is it yourn?' asked Tupper.
'What!'
'You asks me one question, and I asks you another,' said
Tupper independently. 'Don't you cheek me, and I won't cheek
you, see?'

'Bless my soul!'
'You be civil, old Chisholm, and I'll be civil!'
'Old Chisholm!' murmured the Head dizzily.

Tupper is for the high jump after this, which does not upset him, as he is now a person of independent means and intends to leave Rookwood anyway, to lord it at the Peal of Bells. Of course, having burned his boats, he then receives another letter from his father, urging him to do nothing to prejudice his job at Rookwood, because the Peal of Bells turns out to be so heavily mortgaged that there is not even sufficient money to pay Uncle Bill's debts. Poor Tupper; he has to eat very humble pie, and even then gets his job back only because Jimmy Silver pleads with the Head on his behalf.

Frank was glad to have the extra weekly cheque that came his way for writing the Rookwood story, for he was keeping three homes going (one at Hampstead, one in the Chilterns and Clyde Cottage at Hawkinge, which he bought sometime during the war). According to his autobiography, packing parcels for prisoners of war was one of his regular leisure-time activities, but he soon reached the point when giving time and money for this did not seem enough. The war was turning out to be a longer, slower and more agonizing business than almost everyone had expected. Walking with Frank one day, Dolly showed him a letter from a cousin, who had since been killed in action. On the spur of that moment, Frank decided to enlist. He went straight to the recruiting office at Kilburn but, as it was just after 6.00 pm, found the office closed. The next day his impulse to enlist was less urgent. However, he eventually got as far as having a medical examination to assess his suitability; he was then forty-one years old, and his army discharge certificate records that he was 'found permanently and totally disabled for Service'. The details are not given, and Frank did not produce these in his autobiography; he simply says that 'Frank Richards has no military experiences to relate. His contact with the War, from that angle, was brief, distant, and not without an element of the comic.' It seems likely, however, that he was rejected because of his poor eyesight.

Frank was unable to do his bit in what he thought was the most direct way, but there is no doubt that through his writing he was able to influence many boys who were at an age to volunteer (conscription was not introduced until the war had been in progress for some time). In 1914 many of the first generation of readers of the *Gem* and

Magnet were at the age of considering enlistment; readers who were too young might well have considered that the war would still be on when they became old enough to join up. As Tom Merry says to Gussy in 'The Patriot of St Jim's', 'My dear kid, the war is a permanent institution. Under the new law, we're going to be conscripted when we grow up, and then we shall have to take our turn in the trenches. We've got to keep ourselves fit, or we shan't be allowed to go out and get killed!'[5]

Frank's wartime writing reflects his own conflicting moods. On the one hand he was a great patriot, prepared to do anything to uphold many deep-rooted national attitudes and traditions. At the same time he could see through the humbug of a great deal of the recruiting propaganda that was then going on. He tackled this ironically and satisfyingly, particularly in the *Gem*, where Gussy's naïve, but sincere, patriotism often sets the mood. In the story mentioned above Gussy comes up with the 'bwilliant' idea of conscripting wealth, particularly that of people who are either too old or – as in the case of the St Jim's juniors – too young to fight:

'When we look awound us, we see the best fellows in the countwy backin' up against the Huns like anythin'. But we also see a lot of selfish wottahs who are makin' money out of the wah. It is vewy humiliatin' for a Bwiton to have to admit it, but there are wottahs in this countwy who bloat and fatten on wah-pwofits!'

Gussy also comments that 'the wah has been dwaggin' on long enough', because 'our gweat statesmen are so busy lookin' aftah their jobs and their salawies that they haven't weally time for weflection'. Gussy's scheme to make the St Jim's fellows attest and then hand over their surplus wealth for the war effort falls flat on its face, for, when it comes to the crunch, no one wants to part with the cash and trappings over and above what is needed, as these help to make life not merely tolerable, but pleasant. (D'Arcy is reluctantly forced to acknowledge that his own family is a case in point; he talks blithely about millionaires handing over all their excess wealth, but considers it quite impractical that Lord Eastwood, his father, should run his house and estate without a full complement of domestic staff.)

In contrast to many other popular fiction writers of the period, Frank combined sincere patriotism with a lively critical attitude towards jingoism. In a climate of anti-German fanaticism, which even persuaded some people to have their pet dachshunds destroyed, he maintained a distinction between 'good' and 'bad' Germans. Harry Wharton points out in a 1916 *Magnet* that 'there are some decent Germans – Handel and Beethoven were Germans, you know, and it would be idiotic to call them Huns'. Harry is really concerned about the persecution of Herr Gans, the hysterical, but harmless, German master of Greyfriars. Some of the nastier chaps in the Remove are systematically scheming to 'make him think that he's really off his dot', while even the more tolerant boys jeer at him, put kippers in his Sunday hat and glue in his slippers. Herr Gans breaks down when he discovers a drawing of himself dressed as a German soldier, impaling a baby on a bayonet: 'I veep mit shame tat men of Cherman blood shall do tose tings.' He is allowed to demonstrate his almost British decency by intervening on behalf of his persecutors to save them from a flogging, and also to prevent the much deserved expulsion of Skinner, his most odious tormentor.

Many of Frank's wartime stories *were* intensely patriotic, for he wrote of embezzlers, petty criminals and weedy, frowsting rotters who were incredibly quick to answer their country's call. Once at the front, they obliterated past misdemeanours by covering themselves in glory. Leading Greyfriars and St Jim's juniors, too, proved their pluck on numerous occasions when they skirmished with the enemy. Early in the war, Harry Wharton, Peter Todd and Herbert Vernon-Smith are 'Looking for Alonzo', who has managed to get himself stranded on the Continent.[6] (Perhaps Frank is having a dig here at himself.) This is rather a gruesome episode. With their usual resourcefulness, the juniors have little difficulty in getting behind the German lines. The Bounder and Peter Todd are captured and almost executed. Their response is satisfyingly game: ' "Keep a stiff upper lip," said the Bounder. "If we've got to face it, it's no good whining. Don't let the curs have the laugh of us." '

The juniors witness a great deal of shooting and bayoneting behind the lines, as well as another depressing result of war – the long trail of dispirited refugees 'with laden hand-carts and heavy bundles'. When they eventually manage to get to Switzerland, they are exploited by smug neutrals. In fact, foreign boys are quite often referred to as 'those rotten neutrals' in the wartime *Magnet*s and *Gem*s. By 1916 Fisher T. Fish from the USA had collected a certain amount of opprobium, springing from President Woodrow Wilson's

unfortunate comment that America was too proud to fight.[7] Stories
featuring the 'Noo Yark' junior become so sourly edged that, for a
period, they made heavy reading. It was only after America entered
the war in 1917 that Fish was allowed to revert to his normal degree
of comic brashness and business manipulation. Anti-German feelings brought some new epithets into the juniors' vocabulary, including 'That feahful Pwussian!' and 'The Hunfulness of the esteemed
rotter is terrific!'

Apart from amusing his readers, Bunter made no contribution to
the war effort. He is taken to task by his indignant form-mates for
unpatriotic gorging (at a time when food was short) in 'Bunter's
Anti-tuck Campaign'.[8] He is paraded unceremoniously around the
quad, bearing a placard that invites all and sundry to throw something at him for being a 'prize hog'. The Fat Owl's revenge is a

pretended fast, in which most of the Removites feel compelled to join. Bunter, however, with no intention of going hungry, has access to secret supplies of food, which his fellow fasters discover only when they are almost famished.

Coker of the fifth really does try to do his bit. In 'Coker the Joker' he has the dreadful idea of becoming a comedian to alleviate people's irritation at food shortages and other discomforts.[9] His facetious jokes certainly do not go down well at Greyfriars, and when he decides to cheer up the villagers in the 'margarine and bacon queues', the outcome is even less successful. His smug reassurances and well-fed, well-clad appearance infuriate his hard-up captive audience, and 'a big bargee' knocks Coker down and hurls him into a water trough. This story includes an entertaining reference to the portly fifth-form master, Mr Prout, who is badly hit by food restrictions: 'Like many warlike gentlemen, he had always thought of war as an affair of flashing sabres, bursting shells, pride, pomp and circumstance. He found out that war really meant bread which took no end of chewing, and no butter therewith, and the glory departed from the war in his eyes.'

Frank was sickened by the hypocrisy of wartime politicians and the popular press. He obviously felt that there was a particularly revolting smugness about stirring speeches and articles that exhorted *other* people to go and fight, and his fiction ironically reflects this kind of humbug: 'Some had come to the Anti-Conscription meeting to cheer, and some had come to "boo", and there was a party of determined-looking old gentlemen – over military age – who were there to heckle the speakers.'

A masterly story on the theme of vicarious recruitment is 'The St Jim's Recruit', which is ironic and sincerely patriotic by turns.[10] Gussy hears that Mr Railton, the popular School House master, is to attend a local football match that afternoon, and the junior questions whether such public games should be encouraged in wartime. His idea is that 'when the countwy is engaged in a gwapple with a barbawous horde of howwid Pwussians', all professional footballers should forsake the game and enlist. When he puts this to Mr Railton, to try to dissuade him from attending the football match, the master is not impressed, though he listens politely:

> 'You see, sir, all those playahs could be fightin' at the fwont – they are all of militawy age, and men of militawy age are wanted. There are lots of othah men of militawy age who can't go – such as the undahgwaduates at Oxford and Cambridge, sir, who are pursuin' their studies – and actahs, sir, who are goin' on playin' in the theatres – and men who are employed in the cinemas – and footmen and butlahs, who are wanted to open cawwiage doors and serve dinners, sir – and journalists, who have to go on descwibin' murdahs and divorce cases in the papahs – all these men can't go – at least I suppose they can't, as they don't – so at a time like this, sir, I think all the pwofessional footballahs ought to go to the fwont.'

Mr Railton points out that his attending the football match is no business of Gussy's, but that, in fact, he will be there to make a recruiting speech to the crowd. Gussy is reassured, but he gets two cuts with the cane for interference and impertinence.

Frank carries through to the football match the theme, which Gussy is too dim to perceive, of there being one rule for the rich and dilettantish and another for the poor and hard-working. Mr Railton appeals to the football crowd as Britishers and sportsmen 'to back up our team – England's team in khaki . . . out there'. Railton particularly addresses himself to Benny, a young carpenter in the forefront of the crowd, asking 'as a friend' why he does not volunteer. However, the young man's spirited reply – 'May I arsk *you* as a friend, Sir, why *you* don't go?' – sets the St Jim's master thinking. The carpenter, with a family to keep, earns 'two quid a week', most of which he loses if he volunteers. Moreover, 'the loss of a leg or an arm was terribly serious to a worker who depended on his limbs for his daily bread', whereas a wounded schoolmaster could probably take up teaching again. Mr Railton's half-hearted resistance – 'I have no training. If I should apply for a commission I should be refused' – is

Mr. Railton raised his head proudly. "You are perfectly right," he said. "It is my duty to enlist as a private soldier, and I shall do so." "Gammon!" "Come orf!" "I shall show you that I am in earnest," said Mr. Railton. "Gentlemen, there is a recruiting office open in this town. Who will follow me there, and sign on with me?"

succinctly dealt with by Benny: 'Was you recommending me to apply for an officer's job, Sir? . . . And can't you go as a private if I does?' Schoolmaster and carpenter leave the pitch together for the recruiting office, followed by a score of other volunteers, to the satisfaction of the fictional schoolboys of St Jim's and real-life readers of the paper.

Hinton of the Amalgamated Press enlisted and obtained a commission in the Coldstream Guards. With Down already in the services, the editorship of the boys' papers was given on a temporary wartime basis to John Nix Pentelow, formerly a schoolmaster and Customs and Excise officer, and an expert on cricketing matters. Although most of his editorial colleagues speak well of Pentelow, Frank clashed with him on many occasions, especially over the question of substitute stories. Pentelow, who saw himself as a writer, told Frank that unless he accepted with a good grace that sub-stories must be used if his copy was late, he (Pentelow) was prepared to write all the stories for both *Magnet* and *Gem*. This was probably an idle threat, but it infuriated Frank. Pentelow's style was turgid, and too many of his stories would undoubtedly have killed off the *Magnet* and the *Gem*. He did, in fact, do away with one of Frank's Greyfriars characters. In 1918 *Magnet* contained a story by Pentelow (under the Frank Richards pen-name) called 'A Very Gallant Gentleman'.[11] It was a highly dramatic tale, in which Courtney of the sixth, through an act of heroism, is killed in a fire. Courtney was a fairly minor character, but in a sixth form where there were surprisingly few decent fellows to back up dauntless Wingate, the captain of the school, Courtney's absence created an imbalance. At any rate, as Frank had created the character and was the regular Greyfriars writer, he should certainly have been consulted. There was some slight reason for cutting short Courtney's fictional existence; readers sometimes confused him with Frank Courtenay of Highcliffe, another of Frank's schools, which was located near Greyfriars. But Pentelow's attitude over this and other storms in the Greyfriars teacup seemed cavalier, to say the least.

There was another piece of wartime sub-writing chicanery, which Frank did not hear about till nearly thirty years afterwards. If he had known of it when it happened in 1915, he might have been sufficiently angry to have severed his connections with the Amalgamated Press there and then. Hinton had announced a Greyfriars Story Competition, which seems to have been a bid to find more substitute writers;[12] furthermore, Hinton had stated that the winning effort would 'be selected by the Editor, in consultation with Frank Richards'. Frank, who never bothered (nor had time) to read the papers, remained in happy ignorance of this. Neither did he know that Hinton also published a letter addressed to himself and 'signed' by Frank Richards.[13] This was basically a plug for a forth-coming story, to be called 'School and Sport', on which, according to the letter, Frank had lavished his best energies: 'it is now finished entirely to my satisfaction, and I feel confident that "School and Sport" will prove an undoubted success'. Of course, the story – 'that muck', as Frank was later to call it – was not by the real Frank Richards, but by a substitute author.

A happier wartime innovation was the start of the Cedar Creek stories in the *Boys' Friend* in 1917. As mentioned earlier, these were written by Frank using the Martin Clifford byline, and purported to be tales about the Canadian schooldays of Frank Richards.

Herlock Sholmes

Another new series that Frank undertook was that of Herlock Sholmes, his send-up of the Conan Doyle character, which was to prove extremely popular. In 1915 Hinton launched a small paper called the *Greyfriars Herald*, which was supposed to be a Greyfriars school magazine, containing contributions from the characters who were so well known through the *Magnet*. Frank's spoof detective was ostensibly created by Peter Todd (who, it may be remembered, was one of Billy Bunter's studymates). The stories were extremely stylish parodies, written with affection as well as wit and by someone who obviously had a strong feeling for the genuine Holmes stories. Frank had long been a fan of Sherlock Holmes (whom he considered to be a popularized version of Edgar Allan Poe's Dupin, with 'Dupin, in his turn, being derived from an episode in Voltaire's *Zadig*'). Whatever their genealogy, the Herlock Sholmes 'misadventures' outlived the run of the *Greyfriars Herald* and continued in the *Magnet* and other Amalgamated Press papers.

Sidney Paget's illustrations, as well as Conan Doyle's stories, were parodied in these *Greyfriars Herald* episodes. The lean and lithe supersleuth and his short stubby assistant, Dr Jotson, were drawn by Higgins, the boys' paper editor who might – or might not – have been a partial inspiration for Frank's creation of Bunter. Chronicled by Jotson, the great detective's cases reach the point of resolution rather more quickly than those of the original Victorian duo, but a vein of the authentic atmosphere runs satisfyingly through the series. The Herlock Sholmes stories, apparently, have become collectors' items for many admirers of the Conan Doyle canon. It is interesting that these are the only examples of Frank's quintessentially English stories to have become popular in the USA. A collection of the first

eighteen adventures in the *Greyfriars Herald* (1915–16) was published
in 1976 by the Mysterious Press of New York. Several stories from
this period, such as 'The Munition Mystery', 'The Sham Huns',
'The Kaiser's Code' and 'The Captured Submarines!' have a wartime flavour, while others, like 'The Case of the Pawned Pickle-jar',
'The Missing Mother-in-law' and 'The Freckled Hand', are closer to
the classic tradition of Holmes stories. Fun and puns fly thick and
fast, and Frank's favourite hobby-horses are also much in evidence.

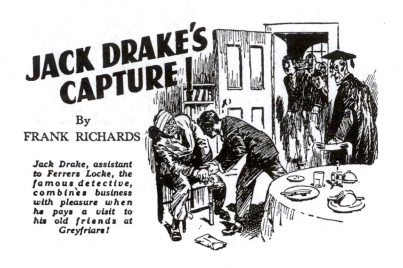

JACK DRAKE'S CAPTURE!

By
FRANK RICHARDS

Jack Drake, assistant
to Ferrers Locke, the
famous detective,
combines business
with pleasure when
he pays a visit to
his old friends at
Greyfriars!

In 'The Captured Submarines!', for example, which was originally
published during 1916, it is not surprising that the Germans are
represented as farcical figures; the author's irritation at the continued neutrality of America is also boisterously given rein. Sholmes
knocks out the crews of no less than twelve German submarines by a
cunning ruse: he secretly loads packing-cases of specially prepared
German sausages on to the submarines, and the sausages are
orgiastically devoured, rendering the crews helpless. Jotson, of
course, simply cannot understand what has happened, because, as
he points out to Sholmes, 'German sausages, though perhaps fatal to
civilized stomachs, are an accustomed article of diet among the
Huns'. Sholmes then coldly explains his master-stroke: each of the
sausages concealed a fragment of American potted beef, 'especially
imported from Chicago', and that mysterious compound – 'the
ingredients of which are known only to the American inventor' – was

too much for the Germans. They were completely overcome and were at the mercy of wind and waves, while submarine after submarine was snapped up by British patrols. Jotson can only gaze at his 'amazing friend in silent admiration'.

Herlock Sholmes was not the first detective to be created by Frank. He was writing about Denham Croft, 'the great London detective', for *Tom Browne's Comic Annual* in 1905, and several of his Edwardian 'romances' had sleuthing themes. In 1907 he had introduced a detective called Ferrers Locke (supposedly related to the Greyfriars Head) into the *Gem* stories; this character soon made occasional appearances in the Greyfriars tales, and in the 1920s he was given a boy assistant, Jack Drake (who had earlier been a schoolboy in other Hamiltonian series). The last of his fairly well-known detectives was another schoolboy, Len Lex of Oakshott School, who, as the nephew of a Scotland Yard detective inspector, was well equipped to solve mysteries about suspicious-looking new masters and safe-cracking petty thieves. Detective fiction may not have been Frank's forte, but he was no mean exponent of the genre.

CHAPTER EIGHT

SPIFFING SCHOOLGIRLS AND TETCHY TEACHERS

'Skinny girls are always jealous of a girl with a good figure,' sniffed Bessie Bunter.[1]

In spite of the fears of the St Jim's juniors that the war would go on for ever, it did, of course, eventually grind to an end in 1918. With the return of various staff members from the forces, there were changes and shake-ups at the Amalgamated Press, which had repercussions for Frank. As soon as Down was discharged from the army, he took over the editorship of the *Magnet* and *Gem* from Pentelow.

Reginald T. Eves had been a deputy wartime editor on the boys' papers, and a little while before the end of hostilities he realized that he might well be out of a job on the return of those who had been called to the colours. (Unlike some employers, Lord Northcliffe was insistent that all returning soldiers should be given their jobs back.) Eves's solution was a suggestion for a new juvenile paper, which he could edit. During the war he had shared an office with Pentelow and had been very impressed by the unabating flow of correspondence from *Magnet* and *Gem* readers. It was evident from this that girls, as well as boys, were avidly following the exploits of the heroes of Greyfriars, St Jim's and Rookwood. Eves realized that, although hardback books of girls' school stories had become extremely popular, there was not a single 'schoolgirl' weekly on the market. He decided that Frank Richards – who better? – should be sounded out about writing the lead stories for such a paper. There were several practical snags. First of all, could Frank cope with yet another regular writing commitment? Next, newsprint was still strictly rationed and in short supply, but as soon as more became available, he hoped to persuade the Amalgamated Press directors to launch a feminized version of the *Magnet* and *Gem*, which would be more than just another paper, as it would break new ground in the publishing field.

Eves went out to Hampstead Garden Suburb to discuss his brainchild with Frank who, incidentally, was at that time sporting a beard. (Perhaps this marked the beginning of his semi-reclusive tendencies? At any rate, the beard was never shown off by the author on any of his visits to the Amalgamated Press's Fleetway House offices.) Frank responded enthusiastically to Eves's suggestion, undeterred by the fact that he was at the time already producing between 50,000 and 60,000 words every week (on Greyfriars, St Jim's and Rookwood) and regularly writing other stories for the Amalgamated Press.

He had no difficulty in thinking up characters and locations for the stories in the proposed new paper, because he decided to round out Cliff House, the girls' school that he had established in the *Magnet* stories as long ago as in 1909. Everybody's dream girl, Marjorie Hazeldene, and her tomboy chum, Clara Trevlyn, were pupils there, together with more vaguely sketched denizens, such as Milly, Maud and Kate, who had not so far achieved the distinction of having

" Keep that basket shut, Bessie ! " called out Clara Trevlyn, as she pulled at the oars.   " I'm only counting the tarts ! " said Bessie Bunter.   " Think I was eating one behind this sunshade ? "   " I believe you'd eat the sunshade, if there wasn't anything else to eat ! " replied Miss Trevlyn.

surnames. Frank knew that in two shakes of a hockey stick he could unleash further adolescent heroines from his fertile imagination. Some thought, however, would have to be given to the funny-fatty role (quintessential to most of Hamilton's schools), which had originally been played by a gluttonous German girl called Wilhelmina Limburger, who had been dropped at some time during the war. In its aftermath a German character could hardly have been expected to pull in new readers, but a replacement soon bounced off Frank's typewriter in the shape of Bessie Bunter, the sister and skirted version of the celebrated Billy. Apparently Frank had almost settled on Bertha as her Christian name, but, with his usual flair for nomenclature, had switched to Bessie (Elizabeth Gertrude) shortly before this new character first went into print.

The *School Friend*, as Eves's paper was called, began on 17 May 1919. Six weeks earlier Frank had, so to speak, given Bessie a trial run in the *Magnet* in 'The Artful Dodger'.[2] The first ever picture of Bessie, which adorned the cover, appropriately depicted her sitting in a bun-shop, smiling smugly and looking every inch a Bunter. (C. H. Chapman was the artist for this issue, and thus can be claimed as Bessie's first illustrator. She was to crop up in many subsequent Greyfriars stories and her accepted likeness in the *Magnet* was the one eventually established by Leonard Shields's pictures. In the *School Friend* and its successor paper the *Schoolgirl* the Cliff House illustrators were G. M. Dodshon and T. E. Laidler respectively. Chapman's Bessie was almost a caricature, with corkscrew curls and fussy clothes; the other artists stuck more strongly to the velour-hatted, lisle-stockinged, gymslip-garbed between-the-wars British schoolgirl image.)

As Frank recorded in a much later *Magnet*, 'it was not only in looks that Bessie Bunter resembled her fascinating brother Billy . . . Their manners and customs were also wonderfully alike.'[3] Clara Trevlyn spells out this unfortunate resemblance even more clearly in 'The Girls of Cliff House School' in the first issue of the *School Friend*: 'Imagine everything that's fat, and unpleasant, and horrid and . . . she's like that!' From the beginning Bessie's conceit is unbounded; convinced that she exercises a fatal fascination over all comers (though the reverse is true), she constantly remarks accusingly to Clara and Marjorie that 'plain girls are always catty with pretty ones' who have 'good figures' like herself. Just as Billy does, she loves the sound of her own voice, rolls rather than walks, has 'fat paws'

A BOOBY-TRAP FOR BESSIE BUNTER! (An amusing incident from "The Rivals of the Fourth!" Complete in this issue.)

instead of hands and wears owl-like spectacles over cunning little eyes. She shares his gift of ventriloquism and his assiduousness in searching neighbouring studies for grub, ready to appropriate any that is there, with or without invitation.

The only way in which Bessie's behaviour differs from Billy's is that she bawls 'Yah! Cat!' instead of 'Yah! Beast!' through the keyholes of study doors that are locked against her tuck-pilfering activities. In spite of the wholesomeness in which he gift-wrapped Marjorie, Frank seems to have held the male misconception that the keynote of most girls' behaviour to each other is 'cattiness': 'Everybody who caused Bessie Bunter discomfort was, according to Bessie, a "cat". Sometimes it seemed that from Bessie's point of view, the population of Cliff House was entirely feline.' One is tempted to add that at times it seemed that from the *Magnet*'s point of view the female population of the British Isles was also 'entirely feline'. Here Frank must have been pandering to the supposed attitudes of boy readers. Although 'cat' was a persistent, obtrusive term of abuse in his Cliff House stories, it is significant that leading contemporaneous women writers of girls' stories (Angela Brazil, Elsie Oxenham, Dorita Fairlie Bruce, Elinor M. Brent-Dyer & Co.) rarely used this epithet.

As well as familiar characters from the *Magnet*, we find in the early *School Friend* characters like the hefty Miss Bullivant ('maths and drill') and Mademoiselle Lupin, who is a French teacher in the same incompetent tradition as Monsieur Charpentier and other Hamiltonian language teachers. Marjorie and Clara acquire a new chum and studymate, Dolly Jobling (shades of sister Una again), an amiable girl. Her great hobby was toffee-making, which she practised over many years with singular lack of success. Her toffee was usually burned to the proverbial cinder or far too runny, in which case some teacher or prefect would inevitably accidentally sit in it.

Dark-haired Barbara Redfern and blonde Mabel Lynn (Babs and Mabs) were introduced as chums and rivals of Marjorie, Clara and Dolly, while Bessie Bunter shuffled between the two factions according to the plentifulness, or otherwise, of their tuck supplies. Almost from the beginning Marjorie and Babs are locked in battle for the leadership of the form, with the latter, surprisingly, winning the crown. It seems unlikely that Frank would have allowed Marjorie to be an also-ran for very long, and almost certainly he planned further struggles for the captaincy of the fourth, from which his favourite teenage heroine would emerge successful.

Left: Frank Richards in his early thirties, in the garden of his mother's home at Chiswick (*c.* 1907)

Top right: This picture of Frank Richards was the only one ever to be reproduced in the *Magnet.* It appeared in the thousandth number in 1927, but was taken several years earlier

Bottom right: Wedding picture of Frank's brother Richard and Emma Mary Cluley in 1900. Richard inspired aspects of one of Frank's most celebrated Greyfriars characters, Horace James Coker

Left: Frank's birthplace at 15 Oak Street, Ealing. The house and street have now been demolished, but a plaque marking the birthplace of 'the creator of Billy Bunter' has been erected in the Ealing Broadway Centre, which now stands on the site

Below: The corner shop, Oak Street, where Frank and his brothers and sisters might have bought their sweets

Above: Clyde Cottage at Hawkinge, Kent, where Frank settled for some years during the First World War after his travels on the Continent. He made a gift of it to his first housekeeper, Miss Beveridge, when she retired

Below: A garden party at Mandeville (*c.* 1931)

Above: Frank's second housekeeper, Edith Hood, entertaining the president (John Wernham) and the Hamilton librarian (Roger M. Jenkins) of the London Old Boys' Book Club in the garden at Rose Lawn

Left: Rose Lawn at Kingsgate, Kent, which Frank bought in 1926; it was to become his main home until the end of his life

Top left: Frank's niece – and Dolly's daughter – Una Harrison (now Mrs Hamilton Wright), aged eight. At this time Frank read his *Magnet* stories to her before they went to press

Top right: Dolly in the garden at Mandeville (1938)

Above: Frank and Dolly in the garden of her house, Mandeville. Frank is 'playing Bunter games with Easter eggs' (1930)

Top: Frank's study at Rose Lawn, showing some of his books, his two Remington typewriters and (on the left) the small desk at which he wrote most of his stories

Bottom left: The sitting-room at Rose Lawn

Bottom right: Frank in his early sixties in the garden at Mandeville (1939). Frank installed the parallel bars for the use of his small niece Una, but he loved limbering up on them after long spells at the typewriter

Top: Frank enjoying a game of chess and the company of one of his cherished feline companions

Bottom left: Frank with R. J. Macdonald, the most long-standing and popular illustrator of the *Gem*

Bottom right: C. H. Chapman in his eighties in the studio of his house near Reading. He was one of the principal *Magnet* illustrators from 1912 to 1940

Above: Frank is visited by some of his young fans at the end of the 1940s

Below: Frank reading a Greyfriars story

There is no doubt that Frank Richards was to exercise a consider-able influence then and in the future not only on the boys', but on the girls', story. In this context it is interesting to consider how his manly boys complemented and contrasted with the spiffing schoolgirls of Angela Brazil, who was the founding mother of the girls' school genre. Both writers were Victorians (Angela being born in 1869 and Frank in 1876), but, although in many ways the products of their age, they were able to respond to the challenge and 'modernity' of the twentieth century. For example, they wrote about 'pupil power': Angela presents Gipsy Latimer's radically democratic ideals in *The Leader of the Lower School* (1912) and as early as 1907 Frank wrote in *Gem*: ' "We're quite within our rights in forming a Juniors' Union and going on strike," said Tom Merry. "Everybody goes on strike nowadays when he's dissatisfied with anything. It's a regular cus-tom, and we're not going to be behind the times. Down with the tyrants!" '[4] Before they began to write there had been many tales of school life, but in 1906, with *The Fortunes of Philippa* and the St Jim's stories in *Pluck* respectively, Angela and Frank laid the foundations of what was to become a new and exciting genre – the twentieth-century school story. It is interesting that they both turned their talents to producing school sagas in that particular year, as each had an earlier history of a different type of writing. Something liberating must have been in the air, which they were quick to pick up and punch home. Ideas of the 'New Woman' were having some im-pact on Edwardian society, and in general both boys and girls were being better and more humanely educated than in previous decades.

As school-story writers, their success was immediate, considerable and enduring. Apart from their obvious skill as story-spinners, an important reason for their popularity was that they were in sym-pathy with children, having the gift of writing from a young person's viewpoint without obviously imposing adult comment or ethics. (Neither author married nor became a parent, and it seems probable that they were still living out their own childhoods in their fictional creations.) In fact, they did make strong moral points, but without holding up the action of the plot or giving the juvenile reader the feeling that he or she was being indoctrinated. Frank was always very much aware of the necessity of putting over standards and values 'too deftly for the youthful reader to detect the pill in the jam'.[5] Here Angela and Frank differed from previous children's writers, who were more concerned with preaching than with providing entertainment in their stories.

The use – and, indeed, invention – of schoolchildren's slang was an expression of their desire to write about young people as if from the inside. The Greyfriars fellows 'jawed' and 'scrapped' and 'punted' footballs, and Bunter's celebrated 'Yarooh!' has given a new word to the language. Angela's slang was just as colourful: 'It gives me spasms'; 'Well, I call it a grizzly swindle'; 'It's a sneaking rag to prig their bikkies!'

There is a great deal of humour to be found in the fiction of both writers, but whereas much of Angela's is unconscious, Frank was a master in this field. We not only chuckle with the Famous Five at the slapstick antics of Bunter, but also respond to the superb flashes of irony that are to be found in the *Magnet*. This highlights one of the major differences between them; his stories stand up better to adult appraisal because of their ironic insights and social awareness. It is this, together with Frank's capacity for creating characters that appeal both to children and to adults, that makes him unsurpassed as a writer of school stories.

Both went on writing to the very end and, apparently, when Angela's publishers heard the news of her death in 1947, 'someone in the Blackie office suggested it wouldn't be long before they received the manuscript of *The School at the Pearly Gates*'.[6] (Miss Brazil was so astute that this might more probably have been called *First Term at the Pearly Gates*, thus allowing the possibility of a follow-up.)

Angela and Frank had great respect for their juvenile readers, never 'writing down' or being too busy at any time in their lives to deal meticulously with the numerous letters they received from them. They were wholly and appealingly English – adept at expressing the mellow mood, the exhilaration of sporting endeavour and a sense of fair play. They were intensely patriotic, especially in times of war. Sadistic, bull-necked, heel-clicking Huns met their match time and again in terrible tomboys from Angela's St Chad's or plucky Greyfriars fellows. Angela and Frank were inclined to be suspicious of foreigners in peacetime too, their inept mossoos and hysterical mam'zelles throwing British spunk and tolerance into sharp relief, as well as adding colour and humour to the stories. However, they were also constant champions of the underdog or odd man out, and neither had any time for snobbery or bullying. Many of their most satisfying tales are those that deal with the outsider making good,

EVERY MONDAY,   The " Magnet " LIBRARY   ONE PENNY.   9

' The horsemen reined up, and a young officer signed to the juniors to approach. He was a fair-haired German, with a thick, blonde moustache turned up at the ends. The two juniors approached him with thumping hearts. "Ou allez vous?" he asked.

or the loner who cannot quite swallow the dollops of *esprit de corps* so often served up to children of the time both in real life and in fiction.

Angela was personally rather more attracted to the unusual than Frank, and her schools were therefore less rooted in tradition. Her girls flirted with fortune-telling, occultism and Celtic faerie lore, whereas Frank's 'progressive' characters were usually rated as eccentrics – like the 'Faddist Form-master' who forced the reluctant Removites into skipping, the wearing of sandals and the adoption of a food-reform diet. Yet Frank, as we have seen, could also be

extremely challenging about the established structure of society –
especially the activities of lawyers, bureaucrats and politicians:
' "Ought to be boiled in oil!" said Bob Cherry gravely. "In fact,
boiling in oil would be too good! He ought to be shut up in the House
of Commons and made to listen to the speeches for hours on end till
he perished in anguish!" '

The sea fascinated both writers. For Angela it represented adventure and danger, and her girls, with astounding frequency, were cut
off by the tide and hopelessly marooned. Frank's resourceful (male)
juniors were, of course, more likely to find the strength and skill to
master the challenge of the elements, but even heroes like Harry
Wharton & Co. sometimes went adrift when they could no longer
control a small boat in a storm. On various occasions in the
Greyfriars stories the presence of the sea provided Removites who
were under the threat of condign punishment with the chance to save
Mr Quelch from drowning – and thus to have the sentence of
flogging or expulsion rescinded.

Both used sport as a potent symbol of healthy-mindedness.
Charles confined himself mainly to popular games like cricket and
soccer, and could provide lively, suspenseful copy from cliff-hanging
inter-school matches. Angela, however, seemed almost carried away
by the sporting motif; the physical energy of her teenage heroines

As if moved by the same spring, the Remove footballers hurled themselves at Coker, floored him, and rolled over him, while
Vernon-Smith, beating the defence with ease, sped on towards the Upper Fourth goal !

was, to say the least, exhausting. They indulged in orgies of chest-expanding, tree-climbing, long jumps, high jumps, every kind of race from the obstacle to the three-legged, exercises with Indian clubs and dumb-bells and games of lacrosse, hockey and cricket. (They were not too brilliant at cricket, fielding balls 'in their skirts' and bowling 'half over-, and half under-arm'.)

Perhaps their most significant contribution as children's writers was their flair for describing the friendships that played such an important part in the stories. Angela's flaming relationships were possibly more superficial than the understated but none the less deep ones that existed between the chums of Greyfriars, but both authors gave two or three generations of children an ideal of what friendship might be, a standard to which they tried to conform. Crushes and calf-love were there too, and Angela's all-girl affairs were the more excessive: ' "I'm falling in love with her", she admitted to Wendy. "I was taken with her, of course, the moment I saw her, but I believe now I'm going to have it badly. I think she's beautiful. If there were a peach competition she'd win it at a canter." ' Compare this with the stammering, low-key expressions of Bob Cherry's passion for Marjorie, which was sustained from 1908 until 1940, when the *Magnet* ended, and beyond, in the post-war Bunter books.

Boys' and girls' attitudes towards their Heads were very different. In many of Frank's stories, one could truly say that a boy's best friend is his headmaster. Dr Locke, in particular, is just, kindly and always likely in situations of crisis to give an erring pupil the benefit of the doubt and another chance to make good. Angela's headmistresses were, in contrast, formidable, humourless ladies who struck more terror into the hearts of their charges with their tongues than Greyfriars masters could bring about with their birches.

There are suggestions in the stories that both authors had a minor fetish for food of the sweet, sticky and child-appealing variety. (Edith Hood comments that during the time she was housekeeper to Frank Richards he had a fairly small appetite, rarely wanting meat, but always enjoying cakes and jam-tarts.)[7] In Angela's case, the apotheosis of bliss was the dormitory feast, and in her autobiography, *My Own Schooldays* (1925), she reminisces happily about crumbs in her bed from food smuggled into the dorm. In Frank's stories, communal tuck consumption more often took place in study teas, on caravanning holidays or at picnics where there were popping corks and hampers on the banks of always sunny streams. Those hearty fictional adolescents did themselves very well with pies, puddings, cakes, jam-tarts, lemonade and ginger-pop.

Rustic and village scenes could be counted upon to provide vivid atmosphere. Angela's forte was botany rambles: 'Even the mistress herself . . . finally flung prudence to the winds and skirmished through the coppices with enthusiasm equal to that of her pupils.' Not quite so ecstatic in his response to nature, Frank was nevertheless at his best when describing those perpetually sunlit pre-war summers of the 1930s, when the Greyfriars juniors rowed endlessly up and down the serene River Sark. As Frank was fond of saying, 'the world went very well then' – or, at least, so it seemed. Greyfriars and St Chad's began as pioneering establishments, suggesting new responsibilities and new freedoms for children and adolescents. They ended as last bastions of innocence.

Angela's long-reaching influence can be seen in hardback novels for girls by other women writers, who emulated, embellished and improved upon the psychological structures of her microcosmic school communities. With the creation of Cliff House in the *Magnet* and its development in the *School Friend*, Frank also put his stamp on the girls' school story. His influence is most evident on the authors and editors of girls' papers (such as *Schoolgirls' Weekly* and the *Girls' Crystal*), which followed in the wake of the *School Friend*'s success. These were written by men who used wonderfully feminine pen-names for the purpose. Differences between the two branches of the genre (books and papers) were, it seems, sexually determined. Eves, who had become editor in chief of the Amalgamated Press's group of girls' papers, upheld the belief of Harmsworth (by then Lord Northcliffe) that women, with their instinct to protect the girl (and particularly the girl's reputation), could not produce really lively stories for them, while men, who were likely to be less protective, could write exhilarating and uninhibited adventures for girls. Whether or not this assessment was correct, the hardback tales written by women had a slightly moralistic tone, which the masculine writers for girls' papers managed to avoid. One suspects that some of them had a good time creating teenage variants of their fantasy women, for many gym-slipped pulp heroines may be seen in this light. The overriding image presented by this section of the genre, however, is the exuberant and edifying one of girls who had abandoned suffocatingly genteel attitudes and become extremely active in their own interests. And this sprang from Frank Richards.

With all this going for his Cliff House stories, it is a very great pity that Frank (writing as Hilda Richards) was allowed only to write the first few (probably six) tales for the *School Friend*. It was suggested at the time that these lacked the right touch for girls, and, had he continued to chronicle the Cliff House saga without interference, he would almost certainly have decided to soften and round out here and there and to tone down some of his extremes of characterization. (Bessie Bunter, for instance, whom he originated as a clowning fatty, was later, in the hands of other writers, to be mellowed into a 'plump and lovable duffer' in the girls' papers, though she maintained her strident image in Frank's *Magnet* stories.)

There were reasons of expediency behind the decision to take him off the *School Friend*. Down, who was editing the *Magnet* and *Gem* until Hinton's return from war service, became increasingly alarmed at the potential of the new schoolgirl paper. He felt that Eves was in the process of stealing the star writer of the boys' weeklies. Not unnaturally, he was convinced that even the prolific Frank would be unable to maintain his output at high enough levels to keep four weekly papers (*Magnet*, *Gem*, *Boys' Friend* and *School Friend*) flourishing. So Down appealed to Tod Anderson, the Amalgamated Press's director in chief. Frank was then told that in future his priorities should be to provide copy first for the *Magnet*, next for the *Gem* and then for the *Boys' Friend*. It was galling for Frank to lose the girls' paper assignment, but his anger was compounded when he learned that the exploits of the Cliff House girls would continue in the *School Friend* in the hands of other authors, who would use the Hilda Richards byline. Thus he not only saw the school and characters he had carefully set up being taken over by others, but also virtually lost a pen-name particularly associated with Frank Richards. (During the twenties and thirties it became a common belief among *Magnet* and *School Friend* readers that Frank and Hilda Richards were brother and sister.) It is small wonder that even many years later this episode in his relationship with the Amalgamated Press continued to disturb him and to inspire caustic comments in his autobiography and letters to readers. Small wonder too that he kept his version of Cliff House alive in the *Magnet* by frequently including Marjorie, Clara, Bessie and other denizens of the school in his Greyfriars stories. He produced several inspiriting *Magnet* series in which Marjorie, in particular, played a prominent part; the Hazeldene's Uncle and Cliff House Feud series are good examples.[8] Frank also resurrected the

Hilda Richards pseudonym for some of his stories after the Second World War.

Soon after Frank suffered the *School Friend* setback, there was further disruption at the Amalgamated Press. Hinton's return to the fold after distinguished service as a captain in the Coldstream Guards proved to be short-lived. He had once again assumed the boys' paper editorial chair, and, with Down as second in command, it seemed that they would settle in to their successful pre-war collaboration.

At first things went smoothly. Frank may not have realized the extent of Down's intervention in the *School Friend* affair, and blamed this entirely on the directorate; at any rate, he always retained a high regard for Down. This was perhaps not quite so strong as the admiration he felt for Hinton, whose magnetism seemed to have grown as a result of his war service. This rugger-playing editor, the model for Hamilton's St Jim's New House hero, George Figgins, was the stuff of which myths are made. One, for example, is that on seeing a van-driver ill-treat a horse, Hinton jumped up from the pavement, yanked the offender down from his dray and thrashed him soundly. Hinton liked to add fuel to the fire of these stories, and also frequently promoted himself in his editorial chats. During the 1914–18 war he published fictitious letters from readers, which slated him for not joining up. Claiming to have received positive flurries of white feathers, Hinton hoped that this rather bizarre published correspondence would stir readers to his defence and add dramatic interest to the papers. It seems a strange procedure on the part of an editor of boys' weeklies, which at the time were highly charged with patriotism and exhortations for general and wholehearted involvement in the war. And Hinton was certainly no coward. His war service eventually began in 1916, by which time he had surely tired of his white-feather charade.

He was not only plucky but fastidious. He had his share of trench warfare and, when questioned regarding the hazards of this, seemed far more concerned about the ever present vermin than the constant threat from shell-fire. (It is said that his first question when considering the engagement of a new office-boy was never 'Is he capable?' but 'Is he clean?') The ultimate fall from grace of this charismatic and influential editor, who was held in great esteem by Northcliffe himself, was extraordinary. Towards the end of 1920 he very suddenly left the Amalgamated Press.[9] Legend has it that, living beyond his means, he augmented his income by publishing a substitute Grey-friars story, which he claimed to have written. This was a rather silly episode, which he called 'Bunter's Baby'. However, an astute office-boy (who, ironically, had been hired by Hinton because of his excellent memory of the Greyfriars and St Jim's tales) spotted the fact that 'Bunter's Baby' was a scissors-and-paste rehash of 'Harry Wharton's Ward', which had originally appeared in 1909, and of excerpts from other Frank Richards stories. (Unlike Down, Hinton had little story-telling skill of his own.) So Hinton's bright star was totally eclipsed, and his career at the Amalgamated Press ended. Undaunted, he set up a rival boys' paper called *School and Sport* and persuaded Frank, as Clifford Clive, to write its lead stories about Harry Nameless of St Kit's. The paper soon folded, and Frank's contributions were confined to the first few numbers, because Hinton failed to pay him any fees.

In his autobiography Frank speaks with regret of Hinton's departure, but assiduously avoids any reference to what he calls 'the whys and wherefores', commenting instead on his perpetually hearty handshake, cheery grin and boyishness. Although sorry to see him go, he was pleased to find that Down was taking over as editor in chief of the *Magnet*, *Gem* and *Boys' Friend*. Frank claimed to have 'turned out quite a mountain of copy' for Hinton's *School and Sport*, and said that 'little spots of bother had never made any difference' to his liking for his ex-editor. They lost touch in the early twenties, but Frank contacted Herbert again during the Second World War, and 'they had many friendly talks over the telephone'. This overture on Frank's part may have been prompted by expediency as much as friendship; it was made at a time when all his Amalgamated Press publishing outputs had suddenly dried up, and he might have seen Hinton as a possible alternative publisher.

After having survived so many vicissitudes, Hinton, then the editor of *Dalton's Weekly*, died tragically at the age of fifty-seven on New Year's Day 1945. The train on which he was travelling stopped just outside the station he required; in the black-out he stepped from the train to fall to his death down a steep embankment. Frank does not refer to this in his autobiography, his last mention of Hinton being simply: 'Whether he ever knew that he was Figgins of the Fourth I cannot say.'

Soon after the end of the First World War, Frank decided to indulge once again his taste for foreign travel. He gave up Broughton

Farm Cottage in the Chilterns, and in the spring of 1921 visited
Wimereux-sur-Mer, near Boulogne. 'Wandering was in his blood;
the sound of foreign tongues music to his ears. When he stepped
ashore from the Channel boat, years and years seemed to fall from
him.'[10]

    Clyde Cottage at Hawkinge was now his main base, but in 1922 he
bought a chalet at Wimereux. The rate of exchange favoured the
pound at the expense of the franc, and in his autobiography Frank
recalls 'going about Boulogne giving orders for the furnishing of his
chalet'. What he does not mention is that he would travel from
Wimereux to Le Touquet to play *La Boule* at the casino. The war
years had cut him off from the gambling playgrounds of the Continent, and in England casinos were then illegal. He had been obliged
to appease his passion for gambling by flutters on the horses and the
stock exchange, investing in which he saw as just another form of
gambling.

    Whether or not he did well at the gaming tables, he was producing
and being paid for somewhere between 80,000 and 100,000 words a
week at this time, so there was no shortage of money. (He later told
Bagley that his earnings between the wars amounted to just under
£3,000 per annum, but it is probable that occasionally they exceeded
this figure.) The attractions of the French casinos failed to obscure
from him the fact that he was past the first flush of youth and that his
carefree pre-war days could not be repeated. Also Miss Beveridge
disliked gadding off to Boulogne, so he eventually sold the Chalet des
Courlis at Wimereux (and a second French property he had acquired at Menton) and, after 1926, never visited the Continent again.

    For much of Frank's life he had shared a house with Dolly and
Percy, whose daughter Una was born during the 1920s. Frank now
rarely visited the Amalgamated Press offices in London, and, deciding to spend most of his time in Kent, dispatched Miss Beveridge on
a house-hunting expedition in the Thanet area, which, he thought,
would be healthy and bracing for the young Una. Miss Beveridge
found Rose Lawn in Percy Avenue, Kingsgate.

    Frank seems to have divided his time between this new home and
Clyde Cottage for a year or so. He had a bungalow – Appletrees –
built at Hawkinge in 1931, so that he had yet one more house to
juggle with. On Miss Beveridge's retirement in the early 1930s,
however, he made her a present of Clyde Cottage. Edith Hood, who
had been nursemaid to the Harrisons' daughter, then began her long

and felicitous employment as Frank's housekeeper. There is no doubt that he felt at ease with Edith. He called her 'Deedy', from the very young Una's mispronounced attempts at her name. Edith's admiration for Frank had begun when, as a small girl, she had met him at Hawkinge in 1914.

Rose Lawn was an unpretentious, but light and roomy, house; the sea lay at the end of the road, which, of course, was a great attraction for Frank. When he bought it in 1926 there were also cornfields at the bottom of the garden. Having an eye for property, Frank also bought Mandeville, a house opposite Rose Lawn, for Dolly. He maintained Appletrees as a holiday home, and in many ways he preferred the gentler countryside around Hawkinge to the frequently cold and windswept Thanet coast. (He installed Edith's brother there during the Second World War and subsequently sold it to him.)

In the mid-1920s his eyesight suffered some drastic deterioration (another factor in the curtailment of his travels). He spoke subsequently in letters and articles of an 'accident' to his eyes, but no one seems to have had firsthand knowledge of this. Una Hamilton Wright believes that there might be some author's licence in his mention of an accident. She feels that he might – as his autobiography suggests – have suffered acute eye-strain, possibly through over-exposure to extremely strong sunlight or through having lenses that were too powerful. At this time, whatever the cause of his visual problems, Frank blessed the invention of the typewriter with renewed fervour, finding particularly heavily inked ribbons, which 'caused his typescript, like Chapman, to speak out loud and bold . . . He even flattered himself that, like Milton, he found the inner light shone all the more brightly for the outer dimness.'[11] In the same vein, he writes in his autobiography that, although he is 'not a conceited fellow', he thinks some of his writing is 'not too bad' and that the best of it has been done 'since it pleased God that his eyes should be darkened'. It is important to stress that Frank was not, as rumour sometimes has it, blind, but there is no doubt that his sight after this difficult period was always very poor.

It is probably true that the weakening of his vision enabled him to live even more totally in the worlds of his creation. He had only a very brief non-productive time, and was soon once again clicking out his quota of words on the well-worn Remington.

In 1926 when, to use his own words, he 'dotted his eyes', Frank was fifty, with every appearance of being a confirmed bachelor. The domestic arrangements were in his housekeeper's efficient hands, and life at Rose Lawn was smooth, harmonious and conducive to writing. As well as producing school, detective and adventure stories, Frank was now dabbling in a very different genre, at the behest of little Una Harrison. Years later, in a letter to Tom Johnson (a composer who wrote a *Greyfriars Suite* in 1947), Frank mentioned that he was 'very far from feeling lofty about the nursery, for I think that writing for children of eight to ten is both useful and fascinating. To tell you a secret, some years ago, when my niece was a little girl, I used to write nursery rhymes and little plays for her to act with other children, and no end of fairy tales.'[12] He goes on to say that Una and her friends would march into his study and ask for a play, 'and Billy Bunter had to be laid aside on the spot while Uncle wrote this'. The plays and fairy stories were strictly for this private audience and not for publication at that time, but it would be intriguing to see them.

Una remembers her uncle as never appearing to be middle-aged. He had an infectious sense of humour, and seemed, when she was a child, like an elf or gnome – a bridge between children and grown-ups. Very fastidious about his appearance, he wore mildly eccentric outfits. He did not favour the conventionally cut man's jacket, as he felt that this was not appropriate to his proportions. (Photographs suggest that there is nothing abnormal about his figure, but he always thought his head was big.) Earlier, when frock coats were fashionable, he had worn these with less reluctance. Indoors he wore ordinary trousers and waistcoats or V-necked sweaters over impeccable stiff-collared shirts; a dark-blue or purplish dressing-gown went on top of everything. As he was sensitive about the hair loss that began when he was quite a young man, Frank wore a toupee during this period. Suddenly noticing something strange about his hair, Una – then very young – innocently asked her uncle if he was wearing a wig. He was disturbed by the question, which, vanity prevailing, he answered in the negative. Later Edith Hood made him two skull caps so that he could abandon the toupee, and he continued to wear skull caps, when indoors, for the rest of his life.

The quality of his *Magnet* stories reached a high peak during the mid-1920s, and many have dubbed these years, together with the early 1930s, the golden age of Frank Richards's writing. Some of the innocence of the early adventures had disappeared along the way, but so too had the occasionally rag-bag episodic structure, the cartoon-like quality of the characterization and the few quirky inconsistencies.

The power of his writing is evident in his depiction of the masters at his most celebrated schools. Roger M. Jenkins, an authority on the works of Frank Richards and once a schoolmaster himself, wrote that, for the adult reader, masters 'have an especial interest ... [they] were not mere cardboard constructions as a schoolboy might imagine them. The reader was privileged in being able to participate in their private thoughts and conversations, since he was taken behind the scenes, as it were.'[13]

When Bagley asked what advice Frank would give to young writers, part of his reply was: 'Never say caddish things about elderly women – Thackeray and Dickens and Gilbert did, but that does not make it less caddish.' In fact, in his stories Frank's natural sense of chivalry was often at odds with the expression of basic schoolboyish humour. For example, at several of his fictional schools Frank used the theme of pupils embarrassing schoolmistresses, various ladies of uncertain age and, of course, schoolmasters by involving them in anarchic pseudo-matrimonial capers. Trailing clouds of Victorian fustiness, Miss Primrose, the Head of Cliff House School, is fair game – especially in the pages of 'Alonzo's Plot', which is aimed at a preponderantly masculine audience.[14] She and Mr Quelch skirmish in the most unlikely of romantic liaisons. Two members of the Remove, sarcastic Skinner and bullying Bulstrode, persuade Alonzo Todd, the form's prize duffer, that Penelope Primrose and Henry Samuel Quelch are smitten with each other, but too shy to voice their feelings. Alonzo, who will fall for anything, agrees to try to bring the two together and sends each an unsigned telegram. Quelch's simply says that someone who loves him will see him that day; Miss Primrose's tells her that her admirer awaits her in Dr Locke's summer-house (where Quelch goes on fine half holidays to work on his ever un-finished manuscript of the history of Grey-friars): 'She'll come like a shot,' says Bulstrode, with conviction. She does too:

Miss Primrose did not really like receiving telegrams. They threw her

into a flutter . . . The astonishment Mr Quelch had shown on
receipt of his telegram was nothing to that Miss Primrose
displayed. But mingled with astonishment there was another
emotion, absent in Mr Quelch's case.

A simpering smile came over the calm, middle-aged face of
Miss Primrose, and her eyes beamed a little. Her whole attitude
bore a resemblance to that known as 'bridling', as she read the
telegram through for the second time.

'Bless me!' she murmured . . . The good lady, like most of us,
grew older outside than inside. Time had written its wrinkles
upon her, certainly; but her heart was still young, her spirit
cheerful and somewhat romantic . . . It is a thing the young find
difficult to understand . . . Miss Primrose, at twenty, had
known dreams like most of us, and they had not left her yet,
though many and many a year had passed since then.

Despite the assumption of a middle-aged narrative voice, Frank
was only thirty-four when he wrote this episode. Could he, perhaps,
have begun to feel that some aspects of life were already passing him
by? Certainly in his writings there is little suggestion that he had ever
set his sights on marital bliss:

Mrs Mimble [the Greyfriars Tuck Shop proprietress] in the
present state of her nerves and temper, simply had to snap at
somebody. So Mr Mimble was getting the benefit of it. Like a
good husband, he bore it patiently; only looking a little as if he
wondered, rather late in life, whether marriage was, after all, a
mistake.[15]

But back to Mr Quelch and Miss Primrose. We are given a wryly
comic vignette of dear old Penelope (most women in fiction before
the Second World War seemed to age prematurely), garbing herself
in 'her sweetest gown and a wonderful bonnet' and proceeding
twitteringly to the summer-house. The resolute Quelch, who has
long dismissed his enigmatic telegram from his mind, is startled out
of his delvings into Greyfriars's ancient past by the unusual sight of
the Cliff House Head blushing and simpering and burbling about his
sweetness: 'Mr Quelch felt very embarrassed. He had had to deal
with all sorts and conditions of boys in his time, and men too, but a
middle-aged lady with a wandering mind was a new experience to

" You are wasting time, Bunter ! " said Mr. Quelch, in a grinding voice.   " Unless you translate immediately I shall——"
" Oh, yes, sir ! It—it's quite easy to me ! " gasped Bunter.   He glanced at Skinner's book and read out the pencilled
translation thereon :   " ' To the lackadaisical we give vitamins——' "   Mr. Quelch stood transfixed, while the Remove
fairly roared.   " Ha, ha, ha ! "

him.' They engaged in a rambling, stammering dialogue in which –
ultimately – the hoax is revealed. Miss Primrose puts an end to the
discussion (though not to Quelch's embarrassment) by swooning
into his arms just as the Greyfriars Head appears majestically upon
the scene, and rebukes Quelch for his 'unseemly' behaviour: ' "My
wife, sir, or my little daughter might have passed at any moment,"
said Dr Locke, "and to see you embracing this lady . . ." Mr Quelch
turned scarlet. "Doctor!" '

Needless to say, the whole encounter is observed with relish by
Skinner and Bulstrode, who have concealed themselves behind the
bushes, and this dubious lark ends with Quelch determined to seek
out the 'villainous practical joker' and extract vengeance.

It is interesting to compare the Quelch of the early *Magnet*s with
the character he became by the late 1920s and early 1930s. In the
encounter with Miss Primrose, for example, although far from being
a fool, he is still not in control of the situation. His boys could often
make rings round him, even though – in the tradition of the comic
papers – retribution might come in the last frame of the story. Over
the years he sharpens rather than mellows, and truly metamorphoses

into the gimlet-eyed 'just beast' and 'downy old bird' with a voice like the filing of a rusty saw, whom the Removites have learned to treat with respect.

Quelch never let up in his constantly waged wars against Bunter's obtuseness, sloth and flagrant untruthfulness, the Bounder's defiant potential for slipping into shady and smoky activities, and any schoolboyish 'cheek' that went beyond acceptable bounds. As Jenkins writes, 'Pulling the leg of the Remove master was a diversion somewhat similar to twisting the tail of a tiger.'[16]

Christopher Carboy, the joker of the Remove, pushes his luck many times, and Quelch's response in 'The Japer of Greyfriars' is characteristic.[17] He dictates a letter that Carboy has to write to his father: 'Mr Quelch has the choice of believing that I am either an incorrigibly impertinent young rascal, or else a boy whose stupidity amounts to an intellectual defect. He is giving me the benefit of the doubt; but not being trained to take care of the mentally defective, desires my immediate removal from the school.' Carboy realizes at last that he has gone too far and begs his form-master not to make him send that letter. After a few ferociously sarcastic remarks from Quelch, Carboy has to admit that there is nothing wrong with his brain and that he has been 'spoofing' – which, of course, Quelch has known all along:

> 'Insolence is a matter with which I am quite capable of dealing!' said Mr Quelch grimly. 'Stupidity such as you have assumed would be beyond my powers . . . Hand me the cane from the shelf, Carboy . . . I think there are three there – give me the stoutest!' . . . The Remove master rose to his feet . . . 'Bend over that chair, Carboy!'

Once again Mr Quelch has completely routed the enemy.

There are moments when one feels that Frank, despite strong differences between his semi-reclusive life and Quelch's heavily populated one, identified with the master of the Remove. Both were single, scholarly, understanding of – if somewhat remote from – adolescent boys, imbued with a passion for the classics and utterly dedicated to their chosen professions. Mr Quelch's

> life was wrapped up in his work at the school; and like many schoolmasters he had rather a lost feeling outside the school

walls . . . Mr Quelch, seeing a Greyfriars fellow, felt like the war-horse snuffing the battle from afar. It was like the smell of the barracks to an old soldier.[18]

Life is never all beer and skittles for the competent and conscientious Quelch. When he is not keeping his boys in line, he is likely to find himself in conflict with other, more tetchy teachers on the Greyfriars staff. Battles of the beaks were popular themes in the *Magnet* and *Gem*; young readers enjoyed seeing the dignity of Olympian or pompous adults eroded in caustic, facetious, even fearfully belligerent, exchanges. For the adult audience of these papers, there is delight in Frank Richards's trenchant and jocularly expressed insights into the foibles and frailties of human nature. In 'The Form-masters' Feud' Quelch falls foul of Hacker, the 'Acid Drop', who is in charge of the Shell.[19] There is never a great deal of love lost between them. Without actually saying so, Frank Richards manages to imply that Quelch dislikes Hacker for his excessive sternness and because, like Paul Pontifex Prout, the master of the fifth, he is always offering gratuitous advice on how Quelch should handle his supposedly turbulent form.

Tensions between Quelch and Hacker topple into outright antagonism when Bunter – to save his own skin – becomes involved. Hacker pokes his nose into an impromptu rainy-day football match on the Remove's landing, and, accidentally stopping the ball with his chin, falls heavily down several stairs. The footballers disappear like puffs of smoke into their studies – and Bunter emerges, peering over the landing to investigate the gasping and spluttering coming up from below. Hacker rallies: 'He was shaken; he was bumped; he was bruised. He was in a towering rage. He was coming up the stairs three at a time with a vengeance in his wrathful countenance . . . Mr Hacker had been reduced to the primitive state of a man who was hurt, and wanted to hurt somebody else.' Mistaking Bunter for the football-kicking culprit, Hacker is on him like a tiger, boxing his right ear and sending him reeling to port; then his left, to spin him to starboard.

Bunter, for once receiving an unjustified punishment, flees, yarooh-ing in anguish all the way, to the protection of his form-master's study. Quelch is out, so the Fat Owl locks himself in to escape Hacker's demoniac wrath. The Acid Drop knocks on the door, unconscious of the quaking Bunter's presence within, to lay the severest of complaints before Quelch. In a flash of inspiration, Bunter harnesses his unexpectedly brilliant ventriloquial talent, talking through the locked door and pretending to be Quelch. Hacker's complaint is received with contempt, and, in his form-master's 'well-known barking tones', Bunter tells him to shut up, to clear off, to cheese it and to go and eat coke! For good measure he adds, still in quasi-Quelchian voice, that Hacker talks bosh, butts into other people's business and is a bore. Not surprisingly, perhaps, 'Mr Hacker was almost driven to suspect that Quelch had comforted himself with strong liquor during his walk on that rainy day . . . "I – I refuse to keep up a – a degrading altercation with you, Quelch!" he gasped. "I am surprised, shocked, astounded! I could never have believed a member of Dr Locke's staff capable of taking such a line . . ."'

The subsequent frostiness between Hacker and Quelch is the talk of the masters' common-room for days:

Of course, nobody on the staff at Greyfriars wanted to see two members of the staff at loggerheads . . . It was unseemly, subversive – all sorts of things. Nevertheless had Common-room examined deeply into its own feelings on the subject, Common-room would have had to admit that it was deriving a

Long Complete School Story of Harry Wharton & Co., the world-renowned chums of Greyfriars. By FRANK RICHARDS,

little much needed excitement and entertainment from the
episode. It broke the monotony. It gave them something to talk
about . . . It was a new record on the old, old gramophone!

Outwardly, however, the masters are restrained in their comments:
' "Dear me!" said Mr Prout, with glistening eyes . . . "*Quel malheur!*"
murmured Monsieur Charpentier.' The boys do not bother to mince
their words:

'Two old donkeys!' was Skinner's description of the masters
who were no longer on speaking terms.
  'What a game!' said the Bounder . . .
  'I say you fellows, it's a lark, isn't it?' chortled Billy Bunter.
'Fancy those two goats getting by the ears like this! He, he, he!'

There is here a typical example of the parallel and different worlds of
pupils and masters. The adults operate at one level, and the boys at
another. Bunter knows he is the cause of the trouble and does not
hide his light under a bushel in front of the other fellows. He could, of
course, have put matters right by a word to Quelch, had he dared,
but even if such a word could be given without dire punishment
resulting, he still probably would not have bothered. Neither would
any of the more intelligent Removites, such as the Famous Five, have
dreamed of 'sneaking' to a master to end this or any other unfortunate situation in the school. In the school story – just as in any branch
of art – certain conventions have to be accepted. Frank made his own
rules, and these were based partly on ethical codes applicable both to
his characters and to his readers; but they were also designed to give
structure and, where necessary, suspense and challenge to the plot.
Having put up the goal-posts, he was still prepared occasionally to
shift them somewhat – but for the general run of the stories there had
to be at least an appearance of consistency of moral standards.

Quelch over the years battles with a variety of Greyfriars beaks,
from upstart temporary replacements of Dr Locke to long-standing
adversaries like Paul Pontifex Prout, the fifth-form master who is
appropriately dubbed 'Old Pompous' by the boys. Prout is even
more free than Hacker with advice to Quelch on how to handle his
form; he is also the booming bore of the staff common-room and the
bête noire of the members of his form, whom he tries frequently to
nobble and 'jaw' in their sanctum – the games study – which any

right-minded beak would have regarded as sacrosanct and kept firmly away from:

> Prout . . . was a chatty gentleman. Prout would take a colleague by the arm and walk him from the Common-room to his study for a chat; and the expression on the victim's face at such a time might have moved a heart of stone. Prout would drop into the games study to chat with members of his Form. He believed in keeping up a spirit of free and friendly confidence between master and pupil. What the Fifth Form men felt like on these occasions Prout never knew and never suspected. Sometimes, in a chatty mood he had found the games study deserted at an hour when it was usually full of the Fifth; but he never guessed that was because he had been espied from afar, and warning given in time that Prout was coming for one of his talks. He did not know that Fitzgerald of the Fifth had suggested having a fire escape fixed to the window of the games study, so that fellows could escape by the window when Prout got to the door. Prout valued those free and friendly chats with his Form in his leisure hours. He had no doubt that his Form valued them; and he often spoke of them in Common-room.[20]

Prout's most boring subject of conversation is that of his youthful days in the Rockies and the number of grizzly bears he has – or claims to have – killed:

> Those mighty hunting days – if any – were over now, at all events, and Mr Prout was now rather an irritable old gentleman, who had not seen his toes, let alone touched them, for years and years. Years had touched his form to a riper grace, as a poet has expressed it . . . It was considered in the Fifth that it would have been a good exercise to walk round Mr Prout.[21]

One can imagine with what relish schoolboy readers might have absorbed such descriptions of a teacher and power-wielder.

On one memorable occasion when Quelch is absent, Prout takes the Remove so heavy-handedly that the whole form abandons the school and stages a barring-out (always a popular theme in the *Magnet* and *Gem*) on nearby Popper's Island.[22] The rebellion is the result of Prout's mishandling, but Quelch gets the brunt of the

Head's and other masters' critical comments, because it is his form that is involved: ' "Shocking!" said Mr Capper. "Whoever heard of such a thing?" asked Mr Hacker . . . "Quite unheard-of!" said little Mr Wiggins. "Unprecedented!" said Prout, who never used a word of four syllables if he could think of one containing five.' It is in this series, after several astringently polite, but highly charged, verbal exchanges that Quelch, goaded beyond endurance, eventually calls his pompous colleague an ass. Greyfriars rocked on its foundations.

At St Jim's the masters lacked the light and shade of many of those at Greyfriars and tended to be athletic, good-natured (and rather boring) or outright nasties. In the latter group, Mr Ratcliff, the New House master, stands head and shoulders above all comers. Jenkins aptly entitles an essay on him 'A Study in Sadism'.[23] Possessed of no saving graces (except that his very presence gave a cutting edge to many stories) Ratcliff was installed as the St Jim's New House master from the 1906 *Pluck* stories and remained until the *Gem* folded in 1939. He smiles and smiles and administers beatings while he smiles. Manners remarks, 'I know what that smile means . . . some poor rotter is going to have a flogging.' Battles of the beaks at St Jim's lack the quirky charm of those that take place in the hallowed precincts of Greyfriars, largely because with Mr Ratcliff sour notes are always struck. It seems surprising that many years on from Mr Squeers someone of Mr Ratcliff's sadistic nature should be permitted to retain a post as a schoolmaster. Jenkins suggests 'it is perhaps a mistake to review the St Jim's stories as a whole and try to search for consistency over a 32-year run'. This is an important point in any social or literary criticism of Charles Hamilton's works; the papers containing his stories were intended to be ephemeral and entertaining, rather than educative. Neither the author nor any of his editors back in 1906 would have claimed total authenticity of character or atmosphere, because, first of all, the papers had to sell and, secondly, readers wanted something at least slightly more colourful than life on which to spend their halfpennies, pennies and – eventually – twopences. In the closing years of Edward VII's reign, Charles Hamilton, Martin Clifford and Frank Richards would never have dreamed that their stories would still be dissected and discussed eighty years on.

CHAPTER NINE

WIDER STILL AND WIDER

'Bai Jove! I think I should like to wuff it for a couple of days in the siewwah!' said Arthur Augustus.[1]

There has been a great deal of speculation on the part of *Magnet* readers about the exact location of Greyfriars. If it had not come into existence until *after* Frank had settled at Kingsgate, that part of Kent (North Foreland) would almost certainly have seemed to be its setting. However, as we know, the establishment of the fictional school took place many years before Frank went to live in Thanet or, indeed, Hawkinge. Greyfriars enthusiasts have visited Rose Lawn and drawn maps linking the school to local landmarks and places of interest, and certainly the Kingsgate area has been drawn on by Frank for some atmosphere and trappings. Nevertheless there is a lushness about the school's environs that is more characteristic of other parts of Kent or the green fields of Gunnersbury explored during Frank's childhood than the flat, blustery Thanet. Almost certainly Greyfriars was set in the Kent of Frank's imagination, even though he was later to add genuine local colour.

Until the last few years of his life, Frank enjoyed a brisk walk every day, and he had only to take a few hundred paces from his house to reach the sea. At the end of Percy Avenue is a small sandy bay beneath sharp cliffs; there are several huge outcrops of chalky rock, rather like detached cliffs (the Shoulder in the Greyfriars saga?), and round the bay is the cluster of caves known as the Seven Sisters, which were once used by smugglers. It is tempting to say that the cliff path at the end of Percy Avenue might have fused in the writer's mind when he walked along it with the path from Greyfriars to Cliff House, or to Tom Redwing's fisherman-father's cottage; it is tempting too to think that the local beach blended and blurred with the image of Pegg Bay in the stories (the nearby Pegwell Bay bears little resemblance to this, even if it perhaps inspired its name).

Except for during the Second World War, Frank was to remain settled at Kingsgate for the rest of his life and, after the constant travelling of his earlier days, staying for three decades or so at Percy Avenue seems to present a marked contrast. There is no doubt that his reclusive tendencies developed around the early 1930s, and, secure in the support of Miss Hood (who still lives in Thanet, at Broadstairs, and enjoys reminiscing about what seem to have been very happy years as Frank Richards's housekeeper), he was able to live

> almost entirely in the world of the imagination, of Greyfriars and St Jim's. He had no involvement in local life, he didn't even go to church on Sundays, though he always encouraged me to go. He was religious – but he would often work on Sunday morning as well as during the week. He didn't like to go to the shops, and often sent away for things, but he was always interested in little things that might happen to me when I went out . . . if anything funny or unusual happened, I would tell him about it and often find that he had used it, with suitable variations, in one of his stories.[2]

In some ways Frank Richards has always been an enigma. Apart from the phenomenon of the vastness of his literary output, there are the strange opposites in his nature, each of which seemed to find expression without involving him in the kind of conflict that someone of his sensitivity might be expected to feel. He was a long-term compulsive gambler, yet the code of behaviour he advocated for his readers with, apparently, total sincerity and conviction, was one that would have eschewed and, indeed, condemned gambling. Until he reached his early forties, he was addicted to travelling in Europe, but a decade later was extremely reclusive. With his interest in language and passion for the classics, he was the antithesis of his most famous character, Bunter, yet breathed life into him in a way that has made him almost as archetypal as Cinderella. His published writings are more prolific than any other author's in the English language, yet he was unsure of which profession to follow, and, according to his niece, Una Hamilton Wright, he 'always hoped to be able to break away from writing'.

Around 1928 he was asked by a friend why he had not done 'something better' than write for boys, and his reply was: 'You see, there isn't anything better.' At one level there is no doubt that he believed this and that he put his very best into his stories for young people. However, in giving this answer to his friend's question and publishing it in his autobiography, he could have simply been an astute author giving a good quote. In his letters to friends and fans there is plenty of evidence to suggest that his chosen career would have been that of classics scholar rather than boys' writer. There is a touch here of the comedian wanting to play Hamlet. Had any publisher commissioned him to produce a new translation of Horace, it might have been goodbye to Greyfriars.

During the most static phase of his life so far, he roamed further and deeper into the worlds of his imagination. In 1928 two new series were created, which, unusually, did not have school settings and in which the backgrounds were as important as the characters. The first issue of a new Amalgamated Press paper, the *Modern Boy*, appeared on 11 February and carried the opening chapters of a serial by Frank called 'King of the Islands'. The byline of this story, which ran for twenty weeks, suggested that he, as Charles Hamilton, had collaborated with Sir Alan Cobham, the holder of several world speed records, though the latter had no hand in the actual writing of it. Subsequent stories of Ken King were shown as having been written solely by Charles Hamilton, who produced 209 episodes featuring this boy skipper of a trading ketch called 'Dawn'. There is a harking back to Frank's very early sea adventures, but a dip into Ken's colourful South Seas exploits quickly illustrates the maturing of Frank's style and powers of characterization some twenty years on. Details of lush lagoons and vegetation make fitting backdrops for Ken's thrilling encounters with pearlers and savages and the like. The series was very appropriate to the mood of *Modern Boy*, which, as its name suggests, aimed for a vivid, up-to-the-minute flavour, with strong emphasis on careers, adventure and discovery. Frank must have enjoyed creating a boy character somewhat older than the heroes of his best-known schools, and one who was in command of his own destiny, without the ready backing of a group. The island setting gave the Ken King stories a whiff of Stevenson and of Robinson Crusoe, as well as some of the escapist charm of the Hollywood island films, with which many *Modern Boy* readers would be familiar. Most of all, from Frank's point of view, these stories gave

him the chance to do much imaginary sailing, and thus offered a potent satisfaction.

The other memorable character whom Frank created in 1928 was the Rio Kid, who began to ride the range in the *Popular* in January of that year. The *Popular* had been going strong since 1912, and the Rio Kid stories were unique among its contents in that they were brand new adventures: the paper was essentially made up of reprints,

offering repeats of many of Frank's early Greyfriars, St Jim's or
Rookwood tales, often in serialized form. Some other writers were
represented, but the *Popular* was, in the main, another Frank
Richards paper; he chose Ralph Redway as his pen-name for the new
series. Like Ken King, the Rio Kid was considerably older than the
Greyfriars chums and he was a loner. Described as 'the boy outlaw',
he could have been any age from eighteen to twenty-one. There was
an intriguing mystery about his background and early days, for in
the first story we gather that he is on the run, framed for some
unspecified crime he had not committed. His sterling character and
dashingly chivalrous behaviour left his innocence beyond doubt in
readers' minds, but a denouement establishing both the nature of his
supposed crime and his innocence was never to take place. This kind
of carrot was often dangled in front of boys'
paper readers, with heroes like high-
waymen and outlaws who, in spite of
falling foul of the law, were evidently
good men. Of course, had their true
identities and innocence been
sorted out too early in the series,
much suspense and *frisson* would
have been lost.

Frank had experimented earlier
on with Westerns, as we have
seen, but he had never produced a
cowboy hero with the authenticity
of the Kid or a series that so
persuasively conveyed the tang
of horses and cattle, the
clanking of the stirrups,
the alternating
exhilaration and
tedium of the long,
lonely, winding trail. (His
early stories, such as the
1904 serial 'The Adventures
of Dead-shot Dick',[3] though
full of pace and perilous feats,
lack the atmosphere of the
Rio Kid tales.)

For Frank Richards's fans, the series is unique in providing a really sympathetic American character, who is tough without being brash, compassionate when appropriate, and, naturally, quicker on the draw than anyone when it counts. He was the archetypal lone rider, turning up just in time to right some desperate wrong and put baddies (twice his age and three or four times his number) to ignominious flight. His language was colourful, and whether or not it exactly resembled that of real cowpunchers (cleaned up a bit, of course), it worked well enough to seem to readers the 'gen-u-wine' article.

As plucky – and almost as resourceful – as the Kid himself is Sidekicker, his faithful grey mustang, who accompanies him on his wanderings from Texas to Mexico, Arizona, Nevada, Wyoming, then through the foothills of the Rockies to New Mexico. Further travels took him to Hollywood, where he became briefly involved with the film world, and this, in fact, introduced an unreal note. The period in which the Rio Kid's adventures took place had never been specified, but one had imagined it to be sometime just before the turn of the century, when, without the existence of modern communications, it would have been easier for a teenage boy on the run to have kept out of the clutches of the law than in modern times.

The Rio Kid stories ran for nearly three years in the *Popular*, and his further adventures were chronicled in the *Modern Boy* during 1937 and 1938. Many Rio Kid stories from the *Popular* were reprinted in the monthly *Boys' Friend Library*, some even being run twice in this publication, which indicates the character's popularity. There is at times an almost lyrical quality about the series that suggests that it was something special in the eyes of its creator.

He was to produce yet another Western series, the Packsaddle Bunch, in short stories for the *Gem* from January 1935. The Packsaddle saga is close to a slapstick version of Cedar Creek (the Canadian backwoods school he had created almost two decades earlier as the supposed setting for his schooldays). Again we have a Western-cum-school story. Packsaddle is in Santanta County in the Lone Star State of Texas, and it is nothing much more than a straggle of wooden buildings along what is grandly called Main Street. There is the office of the Town Marshal, Ezra Lick; the Red Dog Saloon for the gambling and drinking members of the community; the store, Hanson's, the only building of any size; and not much else. It seems strange that so small a community could support a school, but as

THE SCHOOLMASTER WHO "FANNED" A TWISTER—WITH HIS GUN!—

The PACKSADDLE BUNCH!

Packsaddle offered boarding facilities ('the bunkhouse'), presumably its catchment area included Hard Tack, the nearest substantial township, some twenty miles away, as well as outlying ranches. It is real he-man country; no girl ever puts in an appearance or is mentioned at Packsaddle. The school includes, in log-cabin style buildings, the Headmaster's quarters, the cookhouse, bunkhouse, chuckhouse (dining-room) and the masters' rooms, all enclosed by a wooden fence. No reference is made to playing-fields or to any organized sport or physical recreation. There is a simple playground, but its only attraction is a pump, under which hot-tempered pupils are sometimes held until they cool down.

All this is a far cry from Greyfriars and St Jim's, with their cricket and football pitches, cloisters, ancient elms, ivy-clad buildings, and masters rustling to and fro in gowns and mortar-boards. The Head and founder of Packsaddle is Bill Sampson, ex-cowpuncher of Kicking Mule Ranch, who is completely lacking in academic qualifications, but, seeing a need for a school, just went ahead and started one. Sensibly he installs a trained teacher, Mr 'Small' Brown, a

college graduate in frock-coat and horn-rimmed glasses, who would
have been scragged silly by Packsaddle's boisterous pupils if Bill had
not been around to maintain discipline. He does so by sheer force of
personality and by liberal application of his cowman's quirt. At the
beginning of the first story, the school bell is missing, and Bill,
determined to retrieve it, questions the whole school (there seem to
be no separate classes), and, in particular, the two exuberant chums,
Slick Poindexter and Mike Kavanagh:

> 'I guess,' said Bill, 'that it was one of you two that cinched that
> pesky bell. Ain't you the gol-darndest, all firedest pair of
> scallywags in this here school? I'll tell a man! You ain't letting
> on?'
> 'Not so's you'd notice it!' answered Slick . . .
> Bill glared over the class.
> 'Any other guy got anything to uncork about that pesky bell?'
> he demanded.
> No reply.
> Bill Sampson swished the quirt.
> 'Stand up!' he barked.
> The boys stood up.
> 'Lean over them desks.'
> Thirty boys leaned over their desks.[4]

We can bypass the rest, but it is interesting here to see Bill Sampson
beat his whole school indiscriminately, because he cannot trace the
specific offender. At the Hamilton schools in England there were
sometimes cases of rough justice, but not that rough. When, for
example, Mr Dalton canes the whole of the Rookwood fourth, it is
because they have all been cheating. However, none of the Packsaddle pupils appears to resent Bill's frequent laying-on of his quirt;
indeed, the bunch seems to admire him for it.

The leading character at Packsaddle is Dick Carr, a Britisher
whose father has come to work in Hard Tack. Gamely standing up to
the inevitable ragging imposed upon a tenderfoot, he proves his
pluck and becomes leader of the Poindexter–Kavanagh Co.

The Packsaddle Bunch has to cope with rather more hazards than,
say, the average English schoolboy of the 1930s; the pupils and the
Head are thrown into mud swamps by rustlers; kidnappers lurk just
beyond the school corral; boys fall into torrential mountain streams

or are imprisoned in underground caverns. It is all too zany to be taken seriously, yet not eccentric enough for pure farce. After the peak he reached with the Rio Kid, Packsaddle represented a decline in Frank's tackling of the Western, despite its humour, the competence of the story-telling and its popularity with readers.

In the 1950s, long after the story-papers that featured his works had become defunct, Frank tried his hand with another Western, a full-length pulp novel called *The Lone Texan*. It was never quite clear whether this was intended for a young or for an adult readership; at any rate, it had none of the freshness, charm or authenticity of the Rio Kid tales; neither did it have the sheer gusto of the Packsaddle series. At this time he also produced a few stories with cowboy settings for papers such as *Sharp-shooter Western Album* and *Ace High Western*. The stories were far too short to allow the development of character and atmosphere that was Frank's forte, and, although mildly enjoyable, these are pale shadows of past triumphs.

The local colour in the Cedar Creek adventures, the original series of which ran from 1917 to 1921 in the *Boys' Friend*, seems extremely persuasive. It is possible, however, that in real life the school's young and attractive Head, Miss Ethel Meadows, might not have been considered suitable to run a school so deep in the backwoods that it was vulnerable to attack by rustlers, various baddies on the run and even, on occasion, grizzly bears. There are some most impressive episodes when Miss Meadows endeavours to keep all the pupils inside the school buildings for safety, while she tackles some threatening intruder. Of course, Frank Richards & Co. are not prepared to allow her to meet such challenges without their back-up, but she does remarkably well, equipped with her shotgun and a great deal of girlish determination. (The gun seems more of a symbol than a weapon; Frank Richards almost certainly shared the view of most popular writers of the period that heroines should never actually be allowed to kill.)

Despite her robustness, Miss Meadows is subjected to the same indignity as Miss Primrose, the fusty Cliff House Head, and is the victim of a hoax by one of her pupils in 'A Peculiar Persecution', which puts her, apparently, in the matrimonial market.[5] The matter is taken more seriously by its author than the encounter between Penelope Primrose and Henry Quelch. The nastiest inmate of Cedar Creek, Kern Gunten, a German-speaking Swiss, alters the wording of an advertisement that Miss Meadows has prepared for the local newspaper, so that, instead of inviting potential handymen for the school to apply to her, she seems to be requesting would-be husbands to get in touch. The cruelty of the trick is emphasized, and the story is told in a seriously dramatic vein rather than in the comic one Frank Richards used when teachers from other schools were similarly hoaxed. Miss Meadows's hopeful husbands-to-be are many and varied: the owner of the Chinese laundry, a rather crude gold-miner, a bartender, a cattleman, and a card-sharp are among the applicants. Miss Meadows's assistant, Mr Slimmey, who has admired her for years but been too shy to propose, is prompted by the bogus advertisement to declare himself, and is turned down. It is all very touching. Even the editor of the newspaper emerges as a suitor. The mystery of who caused all this matrimonial mischief by altering the advertisement is finally unravelled by handsome Sergeant Lasalles of the Royal Mounted Police. We know that the Mounties always get their man, and we are led by the author to hope that it is really only a question of time before this particular bronzed and hunky Mountie gets his woman: dear Miss Meadows.

Writing the stories under his Martin Clifford pseudonym, Frank could, without appearing to be immodest, have created a special relationship between Miss Meadows and the young Frank Richards who, judging from the pen-pictures we have of the rest of the Cedar Creek pupils, must have been far and away the star student. However, restraint prevailed, and there is no sign of the young and fictitious Frank being teacher's pet or favourite. (It is possible that Miss Meadows was a projection of the author's anima; the kind of teacher – or romantic partner – whom he would like to have had in real life, and not only in his stories.) As a Cedar Creek schoolboy, Frank was very much the wordsmith of the school. In 'The Cedar Creek Pantomime' he writes a book of the play they put on, *Little Silverhair and the Three Bears*;[6] he also writes regularly for the Thompson Press (the local newspaper publishers) and on one occasion is direly dealt with by a 'substitute' author, which must be seen as an example of Frank giving some of his real-life writing rivals (and his editors) a backhander.

Before moving away from Frank's excursions into imaginary cowboy country, we should look back at some occasions when he sent the boys of St Jim's and Rookwood off to the golden West. The first of these trips began in 'Tom Merry's Voyage', when Tom is invited to travel across America with a party of chums to stay at the Arizona

"Dear me!" said Skimpole. "It is ve y annoying to be captured like this! Yet I um glad it has occurred. This is certainly wild life in the Rockies!"

ranch of his wealthy uncle, who is considering making him his heir.[7] (He does, of course, so the unpretentious, happy-go-lucky leader of the Shell has 30,000 acres and five million dollars to look forward to whenever – or if ever – his long, long schooldays end and he is allowed to grow up.) The party of juniors is strangely assorted. It includes the intellectual Skimpole, who sees the whole trip as a process of gathering material for a learned tome on American society and culture, and Gussy, who remains sartorially impeccable throughout every hazard, including encounters with (spoof) scalping redskins. There are plenty of high spots: a railway bridge is swept away in a torrential flood, and the juniors have several days of hard tramping and camping-out in the Sierras ('I wegard this as a gwand opportunity of showin' how Bwitish boys can wuff it . . . It's wathah cold to have a dip in the cweek . . . but anythin' is bettah than uncleanliness'); Tom Merry lassoes a savage mustang, and Gussy nonchalantly breaks it in when hardened cowhands have failed.

After Cedar Creek and the Rio Kid, Frank's most memorable adventures with a Western setting were those that beset the juniors of Rookwood School, when in 1923 Jimmy Silver & Co. spent thirty-five weeks in Canada. It seems likely that Frank and the Amalgamated Press editors were considering a permanent transfer of the Rookwood chums to north-west Alberta, where this Windy River Ranch series took place. However, the pull of the old country eventually prevailed, and the ancient precincts of Hampshire's Rookwood School were eventually once again to become the Co.'s stamping-ground. There is no doubt that these Canadian stories were popular with readers, otherwise Jimmy Silver & Co. would have been catapulted back across the Atlantic much sooner.

W. H. Gander, the editor of the *Story Paper Collector*, which was published in Canada, wrote in 1950 about the appeal of these Windy River Ranch adventures:

> While reading once again the stories that I have in this Canadian series I naturally (being resident in Western Canada for many years) kept a lookout for little errors in description, customs, and so on, but they are amazingly few, in fact almost non-existent. This is quite remarkable, when one considers that the author, Owen Conquest, was never in Canada.[8]

He goes on to say that he wondered if the dialogue really caught the way in which Alberta cowboys would speak, but, on checking with someone who had 'conversed with Alberta ranch folk', felt that this was authentic. Despite what must have been his meticulous research, Frank did make mistakes about the level of water in the creeks during the different seasons, a matter of some importance when drowning, or saving someone from drowning, was central to the plot. On this point Frank's keen, but long-distance, research seems to have been uncommonly inadequate. It is unlikely, however, that many members of his schoolboy audience were disturbed by the discrepancies.

Another series of significance that Frank created during the 1930s featured High Coombe, the 'School for Slackers'. This began in the *Modern Boy* soon after his King of the Islands series had ended in 1935. Untypically for Frank, the main schoolboy characters are to be found in the fifth, and not in the fourth, form. They are Aubrey Compton, the snazzy dresser, Bob Darrell, one of the very few High Coombe inmates who is keen on sport, and Teddy Seymour, a rather bland boy who generally agrees with whatever the last speaker in a dialogue or conversation has said and so is without the discipline of decision-making.

The series is unusual because the hero is really the Headmaster, James McCann, a young and energetic teacher who takes over High Coombe when it has already established a reputation for itself as the School for Slackers. Each episode deals with a struggle between McCann and Compton & Co.; there is an uneasy imbalance of power as McCann wins more of the battles than the boys. Nevertheless, as no boys' paper series could be successful if it did not at least appear to be on the side of the pupils, Compton and his chums have to seem occasionally to get the upper hand, so McCann is sometimes shoved into the river or simply barged into and buffeted by the more obstreperous boys. It is difficult to imagine how determinedly lazy teenagers can be made to appear sympathetic over a series of stories, but Frank Richards manages on the whole to be convincing by giving the High Coombe fifth-formers a precocious elegance. The chink in their armour is that at least one or two of them, and Bob Darrell in particular, have a taste for sport, which – after various vicissitudes – McCann succeeds in harnessing, and the slackers play at least one cricket match with a will to win. Reform cannot be stable, however, because if it were, there would no longer be a School for Slackers. Inevitably, therefore, the series proceeded by fits and starts, and had about it a patchy, curate's egg quality.

Rather surprisingly, Frank Richards was to write some new High Coombe adventures in the 1950s for *Billy Bunter's Own Annual* and *Tom Merry's Own Annual*. Although the anarchy embodied in the School for Slackers might have been more in keeping with the mood after the Second World War than during the 1930s, there seems no evidence that these fictional accounts of battles between boys and their beak had much appeal for the young readers of the period. (Even adults with a nostalgic appreciation of Frank Richards's stories probably found the School for Slackers tame stuff during the 1950s.)

He was writing regularly throughout the 1930s for the *Magnet*, and frequently for the *Boys' Friend* and *Modern Boy*, but for part of that decade the St Jim's stories had been reprints of his own early stories.

(Eric Fayne, headmaster of a private school in Surbiton, had suggested to the Amalgamated Press that Frank's own early St Jim's stories should be repeated in the *Gem*, which had been publishing a number of sub-stories before this plan was instigated. There is no doubt that the decision to reprint Frank's tales represented sound editorial policy.) Frank began to write new stories again for the *Gem* towards the end of the 1930s.

He was becoming more reclusive and less inclined to visit his editors or to wander from home. However, he remained close to Dolly, who came frequently with her family to stay at Mandeville, her house opposite Rose Lawn. Apparently he spent many of his Christmases and Easters at the Harrisons' home in Hampstead, and Una Hamilton Wright describes one such visit in an article entitled 'Christmas with Frank Richards'.[9] The Harrisons looked upon his visits as homecomings, and, it seems, they were quite a marvel of organization on Frank's part. Everywhere he travelled, the Remington had to go too; to transport himself, the typewriter and a large variety of personal props, he would hire a large car and fill it 'unceremoniously' with whatever he might need for his visit, plus a large number of presents for his sister and her family. Frank would often spend several weeks with the Harrisons, but during this period of his life he rarely visited other places. At this Hampstead home from home he could enjoy the family festivities, and also keep the Greyfriars saga, and any other stories that he was currently producing, ticking over on his typewriter. One of his foibles, apparently, was that 'he would not work by artificial heat': his niece states in her article that 'under his influence we had no fewer than five coal fires burning daily throughout the Christmas holidays!'

At Rose Lawn Frank's first-floor study was light, airy – and sacrosanct. He really did not like to allow anyone access to it, and even Miss Hood was admitted only grudgingly in order to do the necessary cleaning and dusting. His struggles to keep this, and earlier, sanctums undisturbed – particularly by the tidying, female touch – were probably the happy inspiration of the story 'Miss Priscilla's Peril'.[10] Tom Merry's former nurse seems, on the surface, to be a mild and harmless old darling, but there is a certain stubbornness about her, a rigidity of attitude and conduct, that she will in no circumstances alter. In this story she is allowed by the Head to take refuge at St Jim's after receiving an anonymous threatening letter, which has thrown her into more than her usual

There was a sudden cry from the elms. "Tommy! my darling, stop!"

flutter. Sanctuary, however, is not enough. She has to interfere drastically with the school's domestic arrangements. Within twenty-four hours of her arrival at the school, no fewer than ten members of staff have handed in their notice, and Dr Holmes ignobly acknowledges his longing for her to leave on the next train. Frank comments drily that 'Any woman with a duster is a terror to a literary man', and describes Miss Priscilla's insistence on 'tidying' the Head's study while he is engaged in giving Greek instruction to the sixth. She throws away his old, but favourite, pen and firmly screws up all his handwritten notes (three years' preparation for a book on Aeschylus) and dumps these in the waste-bin; then she flattens the corners of eleven books that he has turned down for reference during many hours of work and puts them back in the wrong places on his shelves.

Her study-tidying mania drives not only the Head, but several pupils, to despair. Manners finds that she has unrolled several of his unused camera films and wound them all into one (light-damaged) roll in order to save space: 'As the unfortunate photographer had paid three shillings a roll, his feelings may be imagined.' Brandishing her duster aggressively, she whisks Blake and D'Arcy out of their study, with the humiliating suggestion that 'You dear children had better retire while I dust the study. You may run away and play marbles.' Even the school captain's sanctum receives her resolute and irritating attentions, but Kildare accepts the situation without rancour, because 'he was an Irishman, and willing to take anything from the gentle sex'.

Naturally, Frank's study was the room at Rose Lawn that most fully reflected his personal tastes. (I visited the house during the 1970s. Although this was some years after Frank Richards had died, Miss Hood had kept his 'den' just as it was in his lifetime.) Presumably because of his poor eyesight, Frank was extremely particular about having the light on the left-hand side when he was working, so his writing-table and stool were positioned in his study with great care. These were so low and small that it is difficult to imagine how he could have sat and typed with comfort, especially when his leg became weak and had to be propped up straight out in front of him, but obviously he did so. He was, in most things, neat, compact and self-contained, preferring, for instance, to have a small bedroom with the minimum of furniture and trappings. As well as his Remington and writing-table, the study contained a cabinet gramophone and a small armchair. A second typewriter of ancient vintage stood on a proper-sized desk in front of a wall lined with bookshelves, which, like the bookcase along another wall, was crammed with the author's large and varied book collection.

In spite of delving deeply and widely into his imagination for the creation of new plots, schools and settings, Frank always found time each day for several hours' reading from the classics or from the writings of some of his favourite English-language authors. It is doubtful whether he made a comprehensive study of other school stories of the period, for, as he frequently said, his precious time for reading could be far better spent on Horace or Dante or Milton. In his autobiography he states that '*Alice in Wonderland* delights a child of seven: and is good reading for a man of seventy'. He also comments that if he lives to be a hundred, he will still find entertainment in Edward Lear's work, and claims, disingenuously perhaps, that he still finds pleasure in the school chapters of *Tom Brown's Schooldays*. However, writing to Bagley in 1944 he says that he 'never could stand *Tom Brown's Schooldays* – a rotten book for boys, in my opinion. Parts of it, of course, are good . . . But the author does not seem to understand that cruelty to animals is a crime, and there is hardly a page of it not disfigured by the killing or tormenting of some wretched animal, bird, or fish.'

As books were so important to him from early childhood, the contents of his library at Rose Lawn are particularly interesting. Jenkins has written about these in two articles in the *Collectors' Digest*: 'Return to Rose Lawn', and 'The Library at Rose Lawn'.[11] He comments on the inclusion of school stories by other authors:

> Here can be seen Alec Waugh, P. G. Wodehouse, Desmond Coke, Rudyard Kipling, H. A. Vachell, Hugh Walpole, Talbot Baines Reed and G. F. Bradley, to name a few. All had been read, and parts which particularly interested Charles Hamilton were marked in pencil. It is clear that his stories owe nothing to these authors . . . but it is also interesting to note that he was not unaware of what his rivals had to offer.[12]

In the second of these pieces Jenkins shows particular interest in Frank's numerous travel books:

> The really great [*Magnet*] series were all set in countries that [he] had never visited, and I had always felt convinced that he had carefully studied the backgrounds. He used to read with a pencil in his hand, and he made liberal use of it, underlining, encircling, and using other markings where items really interested him. It was comparatively easy to follow the trail that he had blazed.

Drawing on these markings, Jenkins suggests how Frank extracted backdrop detail for his celebrated 1930 China series from Buxton's *China – The Land and People* (1920) – 'the absence of horses, the use of donkeys and wheelbarrows, the abundance of pigs, but the absence of sties' – and for the 1936 Brazil series from Haggard's *Red Macaw*

(1934), Fleming's 1935 edition of *Brazilian Adventure*, and the celebrated *River Amazon from its Source to the Sea* by Franklin (1914), which is well marked for its references to pumas, anacondas and peccaries: 'also used was the description of how macaws get their beaks trapped in nuts'. Apparently a Blue Star Line brochure for South American tours fell out of one book, and there were annotations 'against the times taken by the various steamers and their ports of call, Lisbon, Madeira and Tenerife – all duly visited by the Greyfriars juniors in *Magnet* 1,462'.

Frank was a dab hand at digging out facts and figures for his overseas stories, and at breathing life into these so that he appeared really to have travelled in the five continents. However, Jenkins goes on to point out that there were occasional limitations in the Rose Lawn armchair-travel researches:

> The real find . . . was *Pacific Tales* by Berke (1925 edition) which substantiated my theory that the Ken King stories were years out of date. This book was originally published in 1897 and its references to beachcombers and blackbirders were . . . ancient history when it was first published, but it nevertheless was made extensive use of by Charles Hamilton.

Frank's book collection has been preserved intact on its original shelves and is now housed at the Kingsgate Castle Charles Hamilton Museum. (Many other Frank Richards artefacts, manuscripts, letters, etc., can be seen here, and also at the Hamilton Museum at Maidstone.) The books make fascinating browsing, ranging as they do from Agatha Christie in Esperanto through *The Garden of Allah* by Robert Hichens to the Bible in Latin and the Old Testament in Greek. They are much thumbed and, as Jenkins remarked, many are liberally annotated with pencil markings; several have been given new and detailed indexes by Frank. There is no way of being absolutely certain which books he consulted for reference and which purely for pleasure, but there is no doubt that almost all his books were frequently used. Of course, the classics are well represented: Horace's *Odes and Epodes* seems to have been one of the most read in this section, and it contains a new pasted-in index, made on the Remington in the purply-blue type that Frank favoured. As well as Horace, we find Cicero, Virgil, Livy, Tacitus, Seneca, Homer, Aristotle, Aeschylus and Euripides.

The travel section is extremely comprehensive. There are Baed-
ekers of France, Italy, the Rhine, Southern Germany, the Eastern
Alps, the Mediterranean, Belgium and Holland, Spain, Portugal,
Ireland and Egypt, several of which, judging from the pencilled
notes they contain, were almost certainly used on Frank's own trips
abroad. In addition to the titles mentioned by Roger Jenkins, Frank
collected many other travel books, of both the reference and the
'romance' variety. English poets occupy a fair chunk of shelf space,
as do novels by Dickens, Hardy, H. G. Wells, Jack London, Sapper
and Stevenson.

It is interesting that, although the stories of Greyfriars and St
Jim's seem to have been virtually self-propagating, Frank had
several volumes about real-life schools, which at one time or another
he used for reference. There are, for example, the enormous *Patons
List of Schools and Tutors*, *A Schoolmaster's Diary* by Patrick Traherne,
Fifty Years of Eton (in Prose and Verse) selected by Hugh Mac-
naghten and *Public School Life* (Boys, Parents, Masters) by Alec
Waugh. Shakespeare, Dante, Darwin (with whose evolutionary
theories Frank vehemently disagreed) and Carlyle rub shoulders
with the 1946 hardback of George Orwell's *Critical Essays*, which
includes his 'Boys' Weeklies' piece. There are various dictionaries
and lexicons, many examples from Marlborough's *Self-Taught* language series (Greek, Arabic, Sinhalese, Dutch, Norwegian, Spanish,
Latin, Flemish, French, Finnish, Hindustani, Japanese and others),
and several Western pulps. This is by no means a full list of his books,
but it gives an indication of the range.

During his settled period at Kingsgate before the Second World
War, Frank would suddenly decide to go to Appletrees at Hawkinge
for a rest or, at any rate, a change of air. For this purpose he would
order a chauffeur-driven car, as he did not drive himself. He was an
enthusiastic cyclist, but his bicycling days came to an end in the
1940s, when the density of London traffic, and possibly his de-
teriorating eyesight, made it very hazardous for him.

Miss Hood has described a typical working day at Rose Lawn.
Frank never took early-morning tea in his room, but would always
come down punctually for breakfast soon after eight o'clock, fully
dressed, in his neat, but unusual, garb. Often he would already have
taken a walk to the shore. He liked to work in his study from 9.00 am
to 1.00 pm and Miss Hood would hear the constant tip-tapping of
the typewriter during this part of the day. After lunch he would rest,

then often return to his study to work from 3.00 pm to 6.00 pm. (After the war, when the *Magnet* and *Gem* had folded, Frank, though busy with the Bunter books, had a less arduous word-count to sustain. Then, apart from reading chunks from his morning's output to Miss Hood, an ever willing audience, he would not do any further work after lunch. He liked, however, in the evenings to think about his next day's work.)

Even though Frank might have preferred to spend his time reading and translating the classics, he never lost his freshness in writing about his most celebrated schools. As we have seen, he approached them not only as a professional writer, but with affection and empathy. When W. Bagley asked him in 1944 if, starting afresh, he would still write school stories, Frank replied, 'Certainly. I love the subject, and would rather write school stories for a small income, than anything else for a large one.' (As we have seen, his income during the 1920s and 1930s was actually far from small.)

Frank enjoyed pottering in his garden (the heavy work was left to a paid gardener), but his main hobbies were the indoor ones of reading, listening to operatic records and playing chess (either actual or postal games or mental reruns of great games previously played). Miss Hood remembers that he liked to try to compose at the piano, and 'had a very pleasant voice, and would sing his own songs, Gilbert and Sullivan, or arias from *Il Trovatore*. He loved opera – and hated jazz!'[13] Apart from the Harrisons, he welcomed few regular visitors. He enjoyed his young niece's visits, and liked children generally, but did not have a sustained relationship with any of them, except Dolly's daughter.

Frank's reclusive tendencies led to some strange contrivances. When he required cash he wrote himself a cheque and sent it to the bank, and then money arrived by registered post. It was lucky for him that he lived at a time when such services were readily available. In his younger days he enjoyed browsing in bookshops but later on he ordered books and all his clothes by post or telephone. This practice might have inspired some *Magnet* episodes in which Quelch, or Bunter, illicitly using his form-master's telephone, had to endure a great deal of aggravation before making the desired contacts. In 'Bunter's Brainstorm' Bunter has the brilliant idea of pretending to be his form-master during Mr Quelch's absence one afternoon, and telephoning the local department store to order an enormous feed for immediate delivery, charged to Quelch, of course:

'Chunkley's Stores!'

That answer came through when Bunter rang up. Chunkley's Stores in Courtfield was run on the lines of the big stores in London. They had innumerable departments, innumerable telephone lines, and innumerable difficulties in the way of getting at the right person in the right department. They did not say 'Hallo!' or 'Who's there?' like common mortals, when the bell rang. They said 'Chunkley's Stores', and then took a rest . . .

Bunter was imitating the voice of the Remove master, and in that line, at least, Bunter had some gifts. He made his voice quite like enough to Mr Quelch's to pass on the telephone . . .

'Mr Quelch speaking.'

'Mr Squelch?'

'Quelch!'

'Oh, Welch! Yes, sir. What can we do for you, Mr Welch?'

'Quelch!' shrieked Bunter.

'Quite so, sir . . .'

'I require some things in rather a hurry,' said Bunter. 'I am standing a spread –'

'Eh?'

'I mean, I am – am asking some juniors to tea, and I require a large quantity of things to be delivered immediately.'

'I am afraid the afternoon vans have left, sir.'

Bunter was afraid of that too . . . 'It's very important. I simply must have the things this afternoon. Expense is no object!'

That was quite a true statement – expense was no object to Bunter. Possibly Mr Quelch might have taken a different view [Bunter then has to wait while he is transferred to the confectionery department] . . .

'Chunkley's Stores' came through on the wires, apparently from the confectionery department.

'Mr Quelch speaking from Greyfriars. I require goods by special delivery this afternoon. A large cake –'

'That will be the ironmongery department, sir.'

'What – what?'

'Rakes are in the ironmongery department, sir. Hold the line, and I will put you through.'

'Not rakes – cakes!' shrieked Bunter.

" Were you responsible for these—these foodstuffs being placed in my study ? " demanded Mr. Quelch. " I—I brought the man 'ere, suttingly, sir," gasped Trotter. " He said they was for you, sir—special delivery from Chunkley's Stores, sir ! " " Nonsense ! " snorted the Remove master.

But it was too late, the prompt and efficient man at Chunkley's Stores was already putting him through to the ironmongery department. They never wasted a second at Chunkley's.

'Chunkley's Stores!' came through again.

'I want to order cakes and –'

'I am sorry, this is not the department, sir . . .'

'Blow you . . . A silly idiot thought I said rakes when I said cakes!' shrieked Bunter. 'I want cakes – cakes – cakes!'

Bunter intended to make it quite clear this time.

'Please hold the line, sir,' came the courteous reply.

'I will put you through to the confectionery department.'

Bunter waited again. He was getting a little excited now. He was in his Form-master's study, using his Form-master's telephone and his Form-master's name, and the possibility of

being caught there made him turn cold when he thought of it.
In these circumstances, the up-to-date and efficient system at
Chunkley's Stores was a little exasperating.[14]

In fact, Bunter is then interrupted by the operator, tenderly inquir-
ing if he has finished his call; then he gets through to the general
inquiry office, next to confectionery – when he is informed that, after
all, he needs the special delivery department. At last, scarcely
believing his good luck and almost moaning with apprehension and
irritation, Bunter begins to give his order: 'Three dozen tarts, one
large cake – with marzipan on top, three dozen meringues . . . box of
preserved fruits, a jar of ginger, one dozen cream puffs, six bottles of
ginger-beer –' And the recklessly extravagant order continues. This
is for a feed for one, for Bunter on his own. A little later on in the story
Quelch – who returns and finds the extraordinary collection of
comestibles piled in his study before the hapless Bunter has had time
to appropriate them – also goes through a few frustrating telephonic
minutes with Chunkley's, demanding them to take back these
unsolicited goods. He is reduced almost to biting the telephone in
fury as he is transferred from one department to another.

One feels that here is fiction imitating fact and that Frank
Richards must sometimes have paid a very high psychological price
for indulging his reclusive tendencies.

CHAPTER TEN

LOST WORLDS AND NEW HORIZONS

The fact is that a man who cannot see across a room, and
has a game leg to nurse cannot take very active measures.
If the publishers want my work, they know where to find
it: if they don't, there is still balm in Gilead: as a matter of
taste, I would rather read Horace than write Bunter.[1]

At the end of the 1930s, Frank was in his early sixties, but without
any thought of retiring. The flow of stories from his typewriter and
the even tenor of his life at Rose Lawn seemed set to continue. Far
from cutting down his work, in 1939 he began to produce new stories
of St Jim's every week for the *Gem*, as the run of reprints of his early
tales had come to an end. Greyfriars still seemed to be going great
guns in the *Magnet*.

There were some changes, however, in his domestic routines.
After Miss Hood's mother died in 1938, Frank, who was always a
generous employer, agreed that her father could come and live at
Rose Lawn, where Edith could look after him. The house was modest
in size, but Frank, who had never really liked the dining-room,
allowed it to be converted into a bedroom for Mr Hood. Apparently
the two men got along very well together, and Frank was most
concerned for Hood's welfare. When war was declared on 3 September 1939, Edith and Frank kept the news from her father, as his
health was beginning sharply to decline; in fact, he died before
bombing or evacuation could bother him.

Like every other dwelling in Britain, Rose Lawn had to be blacked
out. The garden also took on a wartime aspect. Frank's chief interest
in it had been for the cultivation of flowers, but he decided to make it
over to vegetables (the 'Dig For Victory' theme was echoed satiri-
cally in a 1939 Bunter villa episode, 'The Phantom of the Moat

House').[2] In the early 'phoney war' period there was no imminent threat of invasion, so Thanet was not considered a danger area. Indeed, some families sent their children out of London to the south coast for safety. By the end of June 1940, however, when the German armies had overrun almost the whole of the Continent, things were vastly different, and the south coast was designated a defence area.

They therefore had to leave Rose Lawn, and Frank rented a house in Hampstead Garden Suburb for Miss Hood and himself. (His sister Dolly was then living temporarily at Cheltenham.) Naturally, he regretted having to leave the newly created vegetable garden, but the uprooting from Rose Lawn was less traumatic than the other events that had overtaken him a few months previously. In December 1939 the *Gem* had closed down, and the *Magnet* astoundingly followed suit in May 1940. Frank's income had thus in effect been reduced from several thousand pounds per annum to about £250 – the amount of his fee from the Amalgamated Press for the right to produce the recently started Billy Bunter picture strip in the comic *Knockout*. Frank was stunned and horrified by the *Magnet*'s demise, which circumstances thrust upon him (and his readers) without any notice. Acute wartime paper shortages brought about by Hitler's occupation of the Scandinavian countries were said to be the reason for the ending of the *Magnet* (and several other Amalgamated Press papers), but, in fact, for some years its circulation had been declining. According to Lofts and Adley, weekly sales had slumped from 250,000 during its heyday to 41,660 copies in 1940. (The *Gem*'s circulation had come down to about 15,800 just before its close.) For some time boys' tastes had been moving towards more pacy adventure stories, and the Amalgamated Press's own adventure papers, *Champion* and *Triumph*, had been doing better than the school-story weeklies, so these, not *Magnet* and *Gem*, were kept afloat when the shortage of newsprint made selection inevitable.

It seems that *Hotspur* and other papers from the Scottish-based D. C. Thomson had for some time been making inroads into the circulation of the Hamilton papers. Frank had heard earlier from Down of the increasing popularity of adventure papers, but he had not felt particularly threatened by them. He might, however, have been dealing them a satirical sideswipe in 'The Schemer of the Remove' when Wharton tries to stop Bunter from reading a luridly sensational boys' paper: ' "You jolly well let that alone," exclaimed

THE FIRST DAY OF TERM—AND HARRY WHARTON'S IN HOT WATER
ALREADY!

The SHADOW of the SACK!

By FRANK RICHARDS

Bunter warmly. "I haven't finished reading it yet. I say, you fellows, it's a jolly good story – all about a boarding school for burglars, with the Headmaster a crook, and the assistant masters all convicts. A true-life story you know." '[3]

Ironically, the *Magnet* had been forced to close shortly before the Amalgamated Press could launch a scheme that they had worked out in hopes of revivifying it. This was trailed in the editor's chat of what turned out to be the penultimate *Magnet* (no. 1,682), when readers were told to watch for an important announcement. In the next *Magnet*, however (printed before its editors realized that it would be the very last *Magnet*), it was announced that the mysterious very special scheme must be postponed to some future date because of the paper shortage. The revitalizing editorial wheeze, apparently, was for the establishment of a Bunter Club with branches throughout the world, and all the appropriate paraphernalia of Bunter badges, certificates of membership and so on.

In a sense the *Magnet* went out with a bang and not a whimper for the last story, 'The Shadow of the Sack',[4] was a dramatic one with the promise of interesting confrontations to come, as it was obviously the first in a Wharton the Rebel series. This time there was to have been a difference. In a previous rebel series Harry falls foul of his form-master very early on, and Quelch quickly loses faith in him. Indeed, he seems over-willing to believe the worst, and, after giving Harry a bad name, to try to hound him out of Greyfriars. Quelch fell so far short of being the 'just beast' whom readers had come to respect that some memorable stories were slightly marred. Happily, in the last *Magnet* story, having known Harry Wharton for over thirty years, he finds he can no longer doubt his integrity: ' "There was an occasion, once [actually, several], when I lost my trust in you, partly owing to an unfortunate misunderstanding, partly to your own stubborn temper. That misunderstanding was cleared up and I resolved at that time never to be misled in the same way again." '

It is exasperating not to know the end of the story, and even more infuriating to know that Frank Richards had finished it but that it is lost to us. Manuscripts for four more *Magnet* stories in this series had been received by the Amalgamated Press. These were 'The Battle of the Beaks', 'Bandy Bunter' (first titled 'The Meddler'), 'What Happened to Hacker?' and 'The Hidden Hand'. Legend has it that the *Magnet*'s last editor, Down, when he knew that the paper had finished, put these four unpublished stories into a box, with other office records; he handed the box to Harold J. Garrish, then an Amalgamated Press director. Garrish died some years afterwards, but there was no trace of the missing stories in his effects. Neither, apparently, did Frank keep copies of them. (However, one un-finished *Magnet* story exists. This was collected from Rose Lawn with other papers after Frank's death by his agent, Hope Leresche. Entitled 'Exit Bunter', it was passed to Una Hamilton Wright, his literary executor, and was eventually published in Gyles Brandreth's compilation *Yarooh! A Feast of Frank Richards*.) So, just before Dunkirk, in 1940, the *Magnet* went into apparent oblivion with these last words:

> 'Come on!' roared Bob, and he grabbed Johnny and rushed him off. The other three followed, laughing.
>
> It was a cheery party that went up to Study No. 1 in the Remove to tea. That spot of trouble had blown over and all was calm and bright – for the present, at least; though, had the chums of the Remove only known it, they were at the beginning of what was to be a rather exciting term.

Frank, apparently, had put little aside for a rainy day, because in the literary context there had seemed no likelihood of his ever having to suffer inclement weather. The large sums that he had earned for so long had been whittled away by his considerable generosity towards his family and many other people; also he had gambled away a great deal of his money over the years. He was the owner of several properties on the south coast, but was unable to find buyers for them when he most needed the money they might raise, because, with Thanet declared a danger zone, they were hardly highly desirable residences. His investments, 'once almost gilt-edged', had in the main taken an enormous tumble because of the war. Fortunately, however, a few Gainsborough Pictures shares he had bought some time earlier went up in value, so Frank was able to realize sufficiently on these to keep afloat until such time as things improved.

To make matters worse, just after being informed that his regular Amalgamated Press cheque would no longer appear, Frank found that there was what he called 'a tax hangover', and he received demands for both income tax and surtax. According to Lofts and Adley, Frank, having virtually no income then, sent his surtax demand to the Amalgamated Press, suggesting that they might pay it, as they were responsible for his present predicament. The reply was uncompromisingly in the negative.

During the long runs of the *Magnet* and *Gem*, Frank had often sent up the (as he saw it) iniquitous system of taxation and many other government policies, believing they were Draconian or stupid or impinged unnecessarily on the freedom of the individual. A memorable instance occurs in 'The Mystery of Mark Linley', when Harry Wharton & Co. and Mark Linley, the Lancashire scholarship boy, walk into the village of Friardale to have tea at Uncle Clegg's grocery shop and tea-room.[5] They find the elderly proprietor down in the dumps, endeavouring in vain to make sense out of 'a paper' that some villainous 'covey' has sent him. Mark Linley offers to help with its elucidation:

Harry Wharton & Co. grinned. They really could not help it. Personally, of course, the chums of Greyfriars had little knowledge of such matters, being as yet of that happy age when the Inland Revenue Department does not trouble the mind and disturb the serenity. But they had seen and heard of such troublesome documents at home. Indeed, Bob had heard his father, Major Cherry, make remarks on the subject that were reminiscent of the Army in Flanders . . . The document that had plunged Mr Clegg into the lowest of spirits, and dismayed him more than the revolver of a hold-up man, was simply a paper requesting information as to his income from all sources, couched in language which was probably clear to the brilliant intellect of a revenue official but which might as well have been Greek or Sanskrit so far as Mr Clegg was concerned.

'My belief is,' said Mr Clegg, 'that it means something. Would the Government go to the expense of printing them papers and sending them to folks if they didn't mean anything? 'Course they wouldn't! But what do it mean? That's what gets me!'

'It's not really very complicated, Mr Clegg,' said Mark.

'It looks worse than it really is.'

'The barkfulness is worse than the esteemed bitefulness,' remarked Hurree Jamset Ram Singh . . .

'Far as I make out they give you something for every child, and you puts in the number of children. Makes a man think he

"Well, 'ere's the paper," said Mr. Clegg. "You young gents look at it, and see if you can make 'ead or tail of it." The document was shown to the Removites and they looked at it with interest, wondering what on earth it could be.

might have done better to get spliced after all . . .' said Mr Clegg.

'They don't give you anything,' said Mark hastily. 'They make an allowance off the tax.'

'Oh!' said Mr Clegg, disappointed, but apparently consoled for not having become 'spliced' in his far-off youth. 'That's it, is it? I thought there was a catch somewhere.'

'You can always depend on one thing, old bean,' said Bob – 'they don't give anybody anything. They take! They think it is more blessed to receive than to give!'

'I wish I'd never 'eard of the thing,' said Mr Clegg, unconsciously voicing the sentiments of some millions of taxpayers. 'I was a fool to go in for it – that I know . . . If I'd 'ad any sense I'd have let it alone.'

'But you can't do that,' said Wharton . . . 'The income tax is like the rain and the thunder and the hail – it happens whether you like it or not.'

'Well, they never worritted me before,' said Mr Clegg, shaking his head. 'I fair asked for this, I did. You see, this is 'ow it come about: when the War was on I put my savings in War Loan. Put up your money for your country, they says. Then I found they was sneaking some of it.'

'Wha-aaa-a-t?'

The juniors jumped. They had not, perhaps, a very high opinion of the gentlemen who manage, or mismanage, the affairs of the Empire on which the sun never sets. But really they could not imagine even a professional politician 'sneaking' any of Mr Clegg's little savings.

It turns out that from his interest of four and a half per cent, tax has been deducted at source, and that claims for refunds have to be made on the official form. Mark Linley helps him to fill in the form, and he realizes that Mr Clegg has never kept proper account books. The patient junior slogs diligently for a week or two through a several-year-old accumulation of accounts scribbled on grocery bags and odd scraps of paper to collect the documentation that will prove to the Inland Revenue that Mr Clegg is not liable to pay tax (his earnings being less than £135 per annum). The happy outcome is recorded in the next number of the *Magnet*. With surprising and highly commendable speed, the Inspector of Taxes has considered

Mr Clegg's case and sent him a cheque for the sixty-pound rebate that is due to him. (Evidently the Inland Revenue worked rather more quickly in the twenties than it does in the computerized eighties!)

Hitler's war continued to present Frank with plenty of challenges. He learned that the Amalgamated Press had not only dropped his school stories, but, because of an agreement signed with them several years previously, claimed to hold the copyright on his Greyfriars characters, including, of course, the money-spinning immortal, William George Bunter. This meant that even if he could find new publishers in those days of wartime paper shortages, he was not allowed to write for them about his most charismatic creations.

He had one piece of good luck, however. He had tried to rent the house in Hampstead Garden Suburb that he and the Harrisons had once occupied, but as this was not available had settled on another nearby. The one he had originally favoured was soon to be wrecked by a bomb, while the one in which he and Edith had installed themselves 'never had anything worse than a chunk of metal through the roof . . . So there was Frank, settled for the duration, with the nightly Hun roaring over his roof: and the typewriter once more going strong. For Frank just had to write.'[6] He wrote many stories of Carcroft, a new school he evolved as a Greyfriars replacement. It had all the ingredients: good story-lines; the heightened intensity of the boarding-school microcosm; the comic fat boy, 'Turkey' Tuck; a likeable junior captain, Harry Compton; and a bounder-ish character called Dudley Vane-Carter, who harked back to Herbert Vernon-Smith. But, although Carcroft appeared regularly in *Pie* magazine from 1944 and later on in various boys' papers and annuals, it never had the addictiveness of Greyfriars and St Jim's.

During the war years Frank also planned and wrote books and stories about a new character, Jack of All Trades, who can be seen as a nostalgic embodiment of the youthful Frank and his wanderlust, despite the fact that their physical circumstances are very different. Jack Free (who also called himself Jack Nobody) is in his teens, but rather older than the heroes of the Greyfriars Remove or the St Jim's fourth form. Apparently an orphan, Jack has had a tough childhood, and much of his teenage life seems to be spent on the tramp, looking for work. Four short stories and three hardback novels featuring Jack were published after the war (from 1949) but, because these appeared with a disregard of chronology, their impact was considerably lessened. Readers were left in the air with many loose ends untied and the frustrating knowledge (if they had read Frank's autobiography) that only a handful of his many stories about Jack had been published and that the keys to some of the riddles concerning his multi-faceted life probably lay deep in the stack of still unpublished tales. Frank's resilience as a story-teller is aptly demonstrated in the books and stories about Jack, with their narrative shift from the viewpoint of boys in privileged, protected positions (at public school) to that of an older youth of striking independence, who has to make his way without the support of a home, family and stable education.

As well as Jack and Carcroft, during these wartime wilderness years Frank produced a great deal of poetry (some of which was later published), a comedy novel called *Hiker's Luck* (which does not seem to have been printed), the memoirs that were to form the basis of his autobiography, some songs and music and a book of crossword puzzles in five languages. In his own words, 'times were tough', but even with no potential publishers in sight, he settled into a routine of word production more or less similar to that which had previously been necessary to meet the relentless demands of the Amalgamated Press papers.

Possibly there were reasons other than a compulsion to communicate for his tying himself to this treadmill at a time of life when he might have been expected to disengage himself from heavy work commitments. In 1940, in addition to battling with wartime conditions, the Amalgamated Press and income tax, Frank had been forced to face yet another challenge, from which he smarted for some time. The March issue of *Horizon* magazine had published George Orwell's essay 'Boys' Weeklies', two-thirds of which was taken up with the Hamilton papers; they were described, among other things, as being out

FRANK RICHARDS

writes his second

SCHOOL STORY

for PIE

DOES the old magic remain?' That was the question we asked in our last issue when we printed the first of a series of tales of Carcroft School by Frank Richards, the man who invented Billy Bunter. Our postbag gives the answer. It is yes, yes—a thousand times yes.

of date: 'A good many boys now regard them as old-fashioned and "slow".' Two months after the essay was published, publication of the *Magnet* ceased; perhaps for the first time in his long and successful writing career, Frank must have considered the possibility that his stories were indeed out of date. (After all, the Amalgamated Press had kept *Champion* and *Triumph* going in preference to Frank's papers.) Certainly, from this time onwards his letters to correspondents and his articles for the collecting magazines that were to spring up in the mid-1940s are frequently at pains to point out that Orwell was talking 'rot' when he suggested that Greyfriars and St Jim's were out of date. So when Frank continued to churn out copy after the *Magnet* had ended, 'all ready for the brave new world, and for a publisher who may desire to make half a million pounds, as I have been told one of my former publishers did',[7] he was not only stashing away the wherewithal for a future income, but justifying himself professionally and exorcizing the sting of Orwell's comments.

Frank was given the opportunity to reply in detail to Orwell's criticism in the May issue of *Horizon*, and this duel between two such strangely assorted sparring partners is an intriguing literary curiosity. The language and thrust of both Orwell's trenchant attack and Frank's spirited defence are persuasive. Orwell finds it difficult to believe that 'a series running for thirty years' in the *Magnet* and *Gem* could actually be written by the same author every week and concludes that a team was responsible. Frank, the arch juggler of his real self and his other personae, drily comments in his reply, 'In the presence of such authority, I speak with diffidence: and can only say that, to the best of my knowledge and belief, I am only one person, and have never been two or three.' He also takes Orwell to task for suggesting that the stories were written deliberately in a style 'quite different from anything now existing in English literature', which could be easily imitated (so that the sagas might be maintained by many different authors):

> The style, whatever its merits or demerits, is my own, and – if I may say it with due modesty – inimitable. Nobody has ever written like it before, and nobody will ever write like it again. Many have tried; but as Dryden . . . has remarked:
>
> > The builders were with want of genius curst,
> > The second building [*sic*] was not like the first.

Here Frank is once again fighting with relish his campaign against substitute writers.

Orwell notes that sex is 'completely taboo, especially in the form in which it arises at public schools' (Frank does not specifically take up this point), but 'very rarely there is something approaching a mild flirtation', which is conducted always in the spirit of good clean fun.

Frank's defence of his stance on sex – or the lack of it – is that the *Magnet* is intended chiefly for readers of up to sixteen years of age and is read by both boys and girls. (What he did not make clear was that many of these readers were in fact between the ages of eight and ten, and in the 1920s and 1930s even the most precocious of these was unlikely to want sex as a major motif of the stories.) Frank suggests that people who try to condition children to be prematurely concerned with sex 'generally suffer from disordered digestions . . . They go grubbing in the sewers for their realism, and refuse to believe in the grass and flowers above ground – which, nevertheless, are equally real!' So far, so refreshing – but Frank pushes innocence over the top when he goes on to remark, 'If Mr Orwell supposes that the average sixth-form boy cuddles a parlour-maid as often as he handles a cricket-bat, Mr Orwell is in error.'

Orwell suggests plagiarism of some earlier school-story writers and particularly of slang from *Stalky & Co.* In his best Quelchian manner, Frank replies that he never read Desmond Coke's books till the 1920s, that he had not even heard of the author Gunby Hadath and that it was not *Stalky & Co.* that provided the 'slang' mentioned by Orwell, but Chaucer ('to jape') and Lewis Carroll ('frabjous', 'chortle', 'burble'): 'such expressions, once in existence, become part of the language, and are common property'.

Orwell makes many telling points concerning Frank's attitudes towards the aristocracy and the working classes, the absence of emphasis on social issues in the stories (he must have missed Skimpole, Alonzo Todd and Gussy in campaigning mood), but Frank neatly parries these comments. Their dialogue on foreigners and patriotism has already been considered, as have their conflicting views on fantasy worlds. Frank tackles every criticism in a patient manner more in sorrow than in anger, with plenty of literary and classical allusions thrown in for good measure. However, one senses the intense irritation that prompts him to write: 'what I dislike most is Mr Orwell telling me I am out of date'. He points out that if, as Orwell says, a boy in 1940 can identify himself with a boy in the *Magnet*, then that *Magnet* character must be 'a boy of 1940'.

On the positive side, Orwell concedes that Billy Bunter is 'a really first-rate character' who must be 'one of the best known' in English fiction. This must, of course, have been gratifying to Frank, but he was to be moved to anger by a footnote to the Orwell–Richards exchange in the form of a letter by Harold A. Albert, which appeared in the June issue of *Horizon*. In this Albert remarks that the reason ('current in Fleet Street') why the *Magnet* and *Gem* stories give such 'scant reflection of the modern world' is because they regularly revolve in an eight-year cycle, when 'the old stories are touched up and painted over' by Frank Richards to entertain a new generation of boys. Albert also suggested that this procedure cleared up the mystery of Frank's 'otherwise inexplicable literary output'.

Horizon published Frank's scathing reply in the same issue. He accused Albert of talking nonsense and cast doubts on his claim to be 'a professional writer' or to be on gossipy terms with editors: 'Mr Harold A. Albert must have provided himself with an Ear of

Frank Richards and Martin Clifford were now together, and batted very steadily until Frank Richards was smartly run out !

Dionysus seventy-seven times amplified, to hear even a whisper of such gossip in Fleet Street.' He comments sarcastically that, although Albert's time no doubt is extremely valuable, a few precious moments of it should have been sacrificed to proper research in the Amalgamated Press files, which would establish the fact that the *Magnet* stories all had new and original plots. He also writes:

> the *Magnet* author knows his business so well, that every number is right up to date . . . The Human Boy is Frank Richards's subject, and except for light externals the Human Boy has not changed since Tom Brown went to school. Frank Richards keeps a careful eye on those light externals; for the rest he is content with human nature, as it was in the beginning, is now, and ever shall be, world without end.

Mr Harold A. Albert might well have been subdued by this onslaught.

In his article 'Boys' Writer' in *The Saturday Book* Frank mentions George Orwell's 'diatribe', but comments that 'he is one of the few present-day writers who can write' and that he is readable even when he writes nonsense: 'In *Horizon* his article stood out from the dull mass like a jewel in a toad's head . . . But on the subject of Boys' Books he has yet to learn his ABC.'

Orwell reviewed this edition of *The Saturday Book* for the *Manchester Evening News* in a two-column piece; some two-thirds of this was concerned with his remarks on Frank Richards's contribution. He referred to the occasion when he and the Greyfriars author had crossed swords, and made this *amende honorable*:

> In reprinting the essay I have corrected the original error (the statement that the *Magnet* and *Gem* stories were written by relays of hack writers) but in case this reaches Frank Richards's eyes I should like to explain how I came to make it. The fact is that it just did not strike me as possible that any human being could write a long complete story every week for thirty years. In that time Mr Richards produced something like 45,000,000 words . . . it is quite true as I now know from several sources.
>
> Mr Richards adds that one of his ambitions is to write a book on religion. I look forward to that work. Meanwhile, good luck to him and soon may the *Gem* and *Magnet* reappear.[8]

Sadly, neither has Frank's book on religion been published, nor were the *Gem* and *Magnet* relaunched (though the Howard Baker Press started producing excellent facsimiles at the beginning of the 1970s).

Apocryphal stories about Frank Richards's 'poverty' during the war years occasionally circulated, one being that he could not afford tobacco and had to fill his pipe with dried rose leaves. What seems to have been a true story concerning the pipe, which visitors say he was always relighting and tamping, is that when there was a scarcity of matches, some of his copies of the *Magnet* and *Gem* were torn up and used as pipe-lighters. Jack Corbett, an enthusiastic reader of Frank's stories, said in a letter to him that 'collectors could weep over such a crime', but Frank simply replied, 'Have you ever been minus a match?'[9]

The *Horizon* exchange drew public attention to Frank's composite identity, possibly for the first time. In October 1943 the London *Evening Standard*, which was much more widely distributed than *Horizon*, published an interview with him; it made the point that Frank Richards, Martin Clifford, Owen Conquest *et al.* were the same man. As a result hundreds of letters from former readers immediately flowed in, to be followed later by letters from all over the world, including many from servicemen. Frank tried punctiliously to answer them all, and from that time onwards was to receive a consistently large amount of post and to maintain a correspondence with many of his readers. (During one Christmas season he received over five hundred greetings from his fans.)

Less than a year after the *Magnet* closed, it had become apparent that it was a case of 'The *Magnet* is dead. Long live the *Magnet*.' Gander, who was living in Manitoba, Canada, published the first issue of the *Story Paper Collector* in January 1941. Although not concerned solely with the Hamilton papers, it used them as one of its main pillars; it also discussed the Sexton Blake and Nelson Lee sagas and a wide range of boys' papers. The *Story Paper Collector* was published periodically until 1966, when it was incorporated with the British-based *Collectors' Digest*, which had been founded in 1946 by Herbert Leckenby, a Yorkshireman, and was carried on after his death in 1959 by Eric Fayne. These papers both stimulated interest in and focused attention on Frank Richards's stories; former *Magnet* and *Gem* readers from around the world began to correspond with each other (as well as with Frank), and they sometimes got together to discuss their favourite boys' papers. Old Boys' Book Clubs were formed, starting in London and branching out into a network covering many regions of Britain and parts of the Commonwealth. These book clubs were publicized on radio and television programmes and in various newspapers; the media placed its main emphasis on the character of Billy Bunter and the high prices for which second-hand copies of tattered *Magnet*s and *Gem*s were often to change hands.

Frank relished the publicity and the fact that he and his works were by no means forgotten by readers. He was particularly touched to receive letters from young men who told him that certain *Magnet*s had travelled with them to keep up their spirits throughout the western-desert campaigns, the second front or whatever. (Orwell had noted, with less enthusiasm, that adults as well as children responded to Frank's stories: 'Recently I offered a batch of English papers to some British legionaries of the French Foreign Legion in North Africa; they picked out the *Gem* and *Magnet* first.')[10]

Despite the building up of pressure for more Greyfriars and St Jim's stories, there was still no sign of the Amalgamated Press weakening and allowing Frank to write about Harry Wharton, Tom Merry and their respective schoolmates. Frank slogged on with Carcroft, Jack of All Trades and other projects. He was also stimulated by points raised in his readers' letters to talk more about his approach to his work than he had ever done before.

In September 1944 he was approached by Bagley, who struck a sympathetic note with his lengthy questionnaires ('general knowledge' papers, as Frank called them), and Frank's answers lift at least the edges of the curtains that cover the baffling business of just how he managed to be so prolific over so many years. Frank was almost seventy when this correspondence began, and he comments that although 'the Blitz and the fly-bombs have passed me by unharmed . . . my old enemy Father Time has hit rather hard'. He had for some time been suffering from a bad leg, which he had to keep propped up for long periods; this must have added to his difficulties when typing for hours at a time. His eyes, as always, were not strong, but this did not prevent him from writing as much as he wanted or from reading for as long as five hours a day, which he tried to do whenever possible. (We do not know just how much of his extensive library he managed to move with him from Kingsgate to Hampstead Garden Suburb, but certainly his most loved classics had travelled with him.)

In answer to Bagley's suggestion that producing a million and a half words a year must have been 'a strain', Frank replied, 'Not in the least. Frank Richards always had an easy day's work. He could easily have passed the 2,000,000 mark if he had chosen to give up other things . . . The secret of doing one's job without getting tired is to keep fit.' In this respect he mentions the undermining effect of keeping late hours and 'pushing back' too many whiskies and sodas, and the positive consequences of the tennis, boating and mountain-climbing in which he had indulged in the past. (Though far from being a fitness freak in the jogging, dieting and working-out sense of the 1980s, Frank made a point of taking regular exercise throughout his life. For example, he installed parallel bars at Mandeville in Kingsgate, ostensibly for the benefit of his niece Una, but he loved to use them himself. In his early sixties he was, in Una's words, 'very strong and very good at gymnastics'.)

Frank was intrigued by a series of articles by Bagley in the *Writer* on plotting technique;[11] this, he said, was of particular interest as he had never had any method of his own:

I have lived for fifty years by writing stories: but I still have not the remotest idea of how a story comes into existence. Sometimes I have written a synopsis, to please an editor who did not know any better, but it always seemed to me that a story written to a set pattern lacked life: there was little or no spontaneity in it: it was in fact a mere 'catalogue of ships'. My own system – so far as it can be called one – was to sit at the typewriter, think on the subject I wanted to write about, and smoke a pipe till the idea germinated. Then I began to write: and somehow or other – I have not the least idea how – the story took shape and form. I never knew what any character was going to say, till he said it: and seldom what he was going to do, till he did it. I suppose this must have been because the characters, to me, seemed to live: and being, for the moment, living people they had wills of their own and did what they liked. It is difficult for me to imagine an author writing in any way other than this: but no doubt different writers have different methods.[12]

Asked by Bagley whether he ever used a secretary or a dictating-machine, Frank replied that he never did dictate. Although a sociable sort of old bean other-wise, it cramped my style to have anyone in the same room while I was at work. Even my dog was excluded, when he would consent to remain outside. But I never had Carlyle's nervy necessity for silence: I could work quite as easily with piano practice going on in the next room, and often did so. Neither do I think that I could have talked so fast as I could type: fifty words a minute would be rather a strain on the vocal organs. And an author must work fast if his work is going to be any good: slow writing makes heavy reading. James Joyce told a man once that he had made 'good progress' one afternoon: he had written one sentence! After that, it hardly needs a glance at his work to see that it is worthless.[13]

And now perhaps we come to the nub of the matter:

A whole story was always floating in my mind when I began to write. It really is an odd process, which I do not quite under-stand myself: once you get going, the characters seem to walk and talk of their own accord, as if the breath of life had been breathed into their nostrils: the author has little more to do than to record their sayings and doings. *Sometimes it almost seems like writing to dictation* [my italic].[14]

Frank Richards was a phenomenon, and by their very nature phenomena can never be fully understood. The hint to Bagley of automatic writing, however, suggests that, like acknowledged artists in more respected fields of creation than boys' papers, he might be dipping into some common pool of knowledge and experience and fishing up Bunter and the Famous Five without any conscious direction of will. It may seem strange and pretentious to accept the heroes of the Greyfriars Remove as archetypes (one shudders to consider Jung's response to this), but nevertheless for countless readers they project just as surely as Robin Hood or King Arthur that quality of being more real than real which widely influences, inspires and satisfies.

It must therefore have been with a feeling of despair that Frank was cut off from writing about his most celebrated characters. In articles and countless letters to readers he tried to put a good face on it – but no one, including himself, was convinced or happy when in the *Story Paper Collector* he said:

> Billy Bunter, alas, is dead and buried. Never again will his fat voice be heard to ejaculate 'I say, you fellows!' Never again will Bob Cherry's cheery 'Hallo, hallo, hallo!' wake the echoes of Greyfriars. That schoolboy world is gone, 'like an unsubstantial pageant faded'. But Frank Richards, like Milton's shepherd, folds his mantle blue, tomorrow to fresh woods and pastures new!
>
> Frank Richards believes that his new characters are better than the old bunch. He hopes that his readers will agree with him. 'Carcroft School' will soon be before the public . . . a sample of the good things to come! . . . And if all goes well – as why should it not? – Carcroft School, after the war is over, will appear regularly, as Greyfriars used to do. Though perhaps Frank Richards, at his present time of life, cannot quite hope for another run of thirty-three years![15]

This sense of the ending of much-loved old things and the coming of the new was in keeping with the overall mood of 1945 when at last the Allies could feel sure that victory, the liberation of the occupied countries and the expansive world of peace were not far away. As Frank put it in the same article: 'the war is not quite over, but the pernicious paper-hanger [Hitler] is on his last legs, and will soon, I hope, go the way of the paper he used to hang. Like a ship-wrecked mariner, Frank Richards sees land at last.'

Nevertheless it was with mixed feelings that Frank and Edith Hood packed up and prepared to leave London to return to Rose Lawn. Frank was happy to contemplate being by the sea again, but, despite his natural optimism, he must have wondered what his future writing career might hold in store. Good things, however, were waiting in the wings, in the shape of enlightened publishers and a new generation of readers yet to be awakened.

CHAPTER ELEVEN

STILL BUNTERING LIKE BILLY-O!

> I am writing Greyfriars again – with my feet in a sheepskin bag and mittens on my hands! But what does the cold matter, or the snow and the ice, now that Billy Bunter is rolling off the typewriter once more? As Shakespeare so nearly said: Now is the winter of our discontent, made glorious summer by this son of Greyfriars![1]

When Frank returned to Rose Lawn after the war, the first challenge he had to face was restoring the damage done by several years of neglect. He found everything 'in a shocking state ... fences were down – chimney pots fallen – the garden a jungle'.[2] But Frank counted himself lucky that his house was still standing, when so many people's homes had been destroyed in air raids. Once some sort of order was established, he went back to his typewriter, and, although he found the paper shortage 'a trial and a tribulation', he hoped that soon many more stories from his stockpile would be published. Tales of Carcroft School had already been printed in *Pie* magazine during the previous year, and soon various small publishing firms were to produce mini-paperbacks of stories of some of his other newly created schools, such as Topham, Lynwood, Headland House, Felgate and Sparshott. Many of these announced on the covers that the stories were by 'Frank Richards, Author of Billy Bunter', but the sales were not as high as Frank had hoped they might be, and none of his new schools showed promise of settling into a long-running series. The W. C. Merrett Sparshott School publications, however, opened an important door for him.

To mark the launching of this new Frank Richards school, Hulton's popular and widely distributed fourpenny weekly, *Picture Post*, ran a three-page illustrated article on Frank called 'Do You

Remember Billy Bunter?' Greyfriars and St Jim's fans from all over the world were glad to see, often for the very first time, photographs of the author (in dressing-gown and skull cap) who had given them so many hours of youthful pleasure. Charles Skilton, a young publisher, picked up a copy of this edition of *Picture Post* in a hotel lounge while on honeymoon in Oban. He conceived the idea of publishing Greyfriars stories in bound form, contacted Frank Richards with little hope that such an established author would agree to write for him and quickly received a positive response. The Amalgamated Press had to be approached, as they had claimed the rights to the Greyfriars characters, and Monty Haydon, one of their senior editors, confirmed to Frank towards the end of 1946 that they had no objection to his writing Greyfriars stories, so long as these were to be published in hardback by Charles Skilton. (Obviously, what the Amalgamated Press feared was that stories of Greyfriars might be printed as regular attractions in children's periodicals, as these might compete with their own current weeklies.)

At last Frank was really in business again. He informed Charles Skilton that his fee would be thirty shillings per thousand words (which is what he had been receiving for his stories just before the war). Skilton, whose honesty and helpfulness were to touch Frank deeply, pointed out that the author would do better to accept payment on a royalty basis, and when Frank agreed to this he earned approximately £1000 on *Billy Bunter of Greyfriars School* instead of the £150 pounds or so he had expected. The books were well printed and bound, and generally attractive in presentation. The first seventeen books in the series were illustrated by R. J. Macdonald, who had been the longest-running artist of the *Gem*. His pictures were always first-rate, and were in a style long associated with Frank's work, but they naturally evoked St Jim's rather than Greyfriars. Macdonald died in his early sixties and C. H. Chapman, to the great delight of *Magnet* nostalgists, as he had drawn Bunter, Wharton & Co., Quelch and Coker for so long, took over. (Leonard Shields, who had shared the illustration of the *Magnet* with Chapman for many years, had died in 1949.) The first ten Bunter books were published by Skilton, and he delighted in the fact that Frank was 'always cheerful and uncomplicated, ever reliable in delivery'.[3] Also 'his copy was perfectly prepared, typed by himself in purple ink on foolscap sheets, needing no alterations before sending to the printer, and with no author's corrections in proof'.

After the first ten books, all of which sold extremely well, Skilton found that the project had become too big for his firm's resources, and the series was sold to Cassell in 1952. Frank's new and larger publishers maintained the same format for the books, with the attractively coloured Chapman dust-jackets and his black-and-white line drawings inside. Frank continued to produce two or three of the books each year until he died at the end of 1961, and the series ran to thirty-eight titles.

The Bunter books appealed not only to former readers of *Magnet* and *Gem*, but also to a new generation of children. They were stylishly written and substantial in plot, though shorter than the *Magnet* stories and slightly less demanding in terms of vocabulary and intricacies of construction. They struck the right note with the children of the television age, who had moved away from story-papers towards comics and picture-strip publications. The Bunter books were a 'jolly good read' and, although they were set in text rather than in pictures, the spirit of the post-war period was subtly and appropriately harnessed in these lively, inventive stories. They had the advantage over the *Magnet* of being acceptable to public libraries, thus pulling in an even wider range of readers than just those who could afford to buy copies of the books. (The first book in the series retailed at five shillings and the last, in 1965, at eleven shillings and sixpence.) In 1949 the series was augmented by *Bessie Bunter of Cliff House School*; disappointingly, no further titles about the Cliff House girls were to follow. Frank must have hoped that this book would represent a relaunch for Cliff House and lead to a subsequent series in which, thirty years on, he could have exorcized the ghost of the lost *School Friend* opportunities of 1919. *Bessie Bunter of Cliff House School* provides the deepest exploration of friendship between girls (Marjorie and Clara) that Frank has ever produced; had this Cliff House story been followed by others, these two chums might have developed a friendship as classic as that of Wharton and Nugent, or Vernon-Smith and Redwing in the *Magnet*. (In the Amalgamated Press's *Schoolgirl* of the 1930s, Marjorie and Clara were bosom chums, but their relationship was not then chronicled by Frank.)

After the success of the Bunter books (which by no means concentrated only on the Fat Owl, though his name was used to popularize the series), Frank's post-war writing opened out in other directions. In 1950 the first *Tom Merry's Own Annual* was published by

Mandeville; in 1953 they launched *Billy Bunter's Own Annual*. Other
St Jim's and Rookwood books were to follow, but no series lasted the
course like the Bunter books.

Frank still longed to see his most famous schools appear once
again in weekly papers; Greyfriars and St Jim's stories were adapted
(or newly written by Frank) for various newspapers and periodicals,
but sufficient space for character and plot development was not
allowed, and these series never seemed to catch the imagination of
either the new generation of child readers or of those adults who
retained fond memories of the *Magnet* and *Gem*.

All the same, Frank was steaming ahead once again with his
stories, and he was perpetually busy with correspondence from his
fans, which he gave a great deal of time to answering. In January
1946 (before he was producing the Bunter books) Frank wrote to
Jenkins (with whom he had been corresponding since the publication of the *Evening Standard* article on him in 1943): 'Such letters as
yours are very pleasant to read, and very encouraging. You see,
laddie, it is not the easiest thing in the world to begin life again at
seventy: and every time I get a kind friendly letter from an old reader
it helps.' Asked by Jenkins which of his characters he liked best,
Frank replied that he thought Bob Cherry came first, and then Mark
Linley (the latter is a surprising choice, as he was given little
prominence in most of the stories); he always had 'a sneaking
affection' for the Bounder; he liked Lord Mauleverer and Frank
Nugent; also D'Arcy in the *Gem*.

In 1946 Frank was rather shocked to hear that the price of an old
Gem or *Magnet* ranged from ninepence to one shilling:

> really I don't see why anyone should pay that price for an old
> paper, when new Sparshott numbers can be bought at the same
> figure. Here I must tell you something that gave me a good
> laugh sometime ago. A young man was telling me about high
> prices paid for my old numbers . . . and told me quite seriously
> that he was going to store away Carcrofts, Sparshotts, and the
> rest, as an investment!!![4]

This seems like a little salesmanship for his new series on Frank's
part.

By the late 1940s it was evident that Frank very much appreciated
the collecting circles that were springing up, such as the Old Boys'

Bob Cherry *of Greyfriars*

ONE OF THE FAMOUS FIVE.
THE GENIAL BOB
IS ONE OF THE BEST ALL—
ROUND SCHOOLBOY SPORTSMEN.

Book Clubs around the country and the two boys' paper collecting magazines (*Story Paper Collector* and *Collectors' Digest*). He read, with great interest, the articles they published on his work, and frequently wrote letters to the editors for publication. He might sometimes be slightly waspish if he felt that a contributor had got any facts wrong and, whenever the opportunity arose, would have further digs at the sub-writers ('deleterious bargees') and the editorial policies of the Amalgamated Press, which encouraged them. Serious assessments of his work by Fayne (later to become the editor of *Collectors' Digest*) and Jenkins intrigued him, and he wrote gracious letters of appreciation to them both, as well as to many other contributors to these journals.

In 1951 he said in a letter to Jenkins that in his view 'the schoolboy period is the most interesting part of life, and very much more worth chronicling than the later periods'. (This is an interesting opinion, but one that is very much at odds with his own autobiography; when it appeared during the following year, it began with Frank at the age of seventeen, by which time he had left school.) He added:

> The truth is, of course, that if a book is good reading, it does not matter a hoot whether it is about a boy of fifteen or a man of fifty: the only question really is, is it true to human nature? And in these latter days, people seem to be realizing this, and for lighter reading prefer a real schoolboy to an impossible detective surrounded by corpses, or a neurotic hero falling in and out of lurve!

Frank then, without any suggestion of irony, produced another of his telling statements: 'I have never yet come across a love-novel as interesting as a game of cricket.' In this connection it is worth mentioning that in a postscript to the questionnaire he had completed for Bagley in 1944 Frank had written: 'You will note that I have deleted all sex allusions. Probably you will agree with me that there is too much sex talk at the present day. Frank Richards, at least, would rather subtract from it than add to it.' At the time, and with hindsight, 1944 hardly seems to have been a year when sex ran riot; indeed, it seems a period of innocence – but innocence, one supposes, is purely relative, and he was of a generation for which sex was a taboo subject in polite society.

Although Frank enjoyed corresponding with his readers, he saw very few of them, managing with 'tact and judgement' worthy of

Arthur Augustus D'Arcy to deter them from calling at Rose Lawn. Two of the readers whom he did invite to his home were Roger Jenkins and Eric Fayne. Their separate comments on Frank Richards's poor eyesight are interesting, particularly in view of the rumours that he was blind in the last years of his life. (It is possible that he lost his sight during his very last days. Charles Skilton recalls that when he sounded Frank out about revising his autobiography towards the end of 1961, Frank explained how at that moment he could not work because of his blindness, which he hoped was only temporary. The autobiography was thus never brought up to date.) Frank was in his seventies when Fayne met him. The author's opening remark to his visitor was 'You look a lot younger than I expected', which suggests that his sight might have been better than he normally conveyed to people.

Jenkins writes: 'I have a vivid memory of his short-sightedness because he came right up to me and peered in my face and then sat down again, saying that that would provide him with a visual memory of me while we were sitting talking.' Apparently Frank began to suffer from a cataract in 1951, ten years before he died. He refused to have an operation and, with the aid of spectacles and a magnifying glass, could still see, though his reading had to be cut down. When he met Jenkins, he said, 'There is an advantage in having poor eyesight. When I type my stories I am not distracted by anything else and I can imagine the expressions on my characters' faces as they speak.'

After Jenkins had visited Frank, there is about their correspondence an engaging similarity to the exchanges of Dr Locke and Mr Quelch on aspects of the classics. Frank wrote in October 1952:

> By the bye, I have looked out that verse in Virgil to which you alluded when you were down here: the galloping one. Here it is ... Line 596 in Book VIII of the *Aeneid*: *quadripedante putrem sonitu quatit ungula campum*. The long run of dactyls coming to rest on the final spondee really does produce a fine onomatopoeic effect. One can almost hear the earth shake under the galloping hoofs.

Obviously Jenkins held the same interest in Latin as Frank, and the latter seems to have had a touching faith that his passion for the classics was also shared by many more members of the British public than was actually the case. In October 1952 he wrote to Leonard

Packman (the co-founder, with Robert Blythe, of the London Old Boys' Book Club), asking for his opinion 'as a normal intelligent citizen' about the publication of a new translation by Frank of Horace's *Odes*: 'My idea is to publish a small volume at about 1/6d containing only the alcaics . . . leaving the sapphics, asclepiads, etc., for a later date.' Frank adds that he thinks a new interest in the classics is growing up in the present generation and that 'quite an extensive public' would like a readable Horace. He mentions that the publishers to whom he has suggested this project are not exactly over the moon about it, but as 'the chief characteristic of publishers generally is that they never know what the public want', he is undeterred by this. Frank asks eagerly if the idea appeals or not. Len Packman's reply is not recorded. However, Frank's next letter to him thanks him for replying so honestly and owns that among the people he has consulted, Packman's view is with the majority. He acknowledges that the 'average man' has far more urgent things to think of than Latin, but feels that for this reason he should be the more keen to read the classics in English.

Another of Frank's projects that came to nothing was the book *Faith and Hope*, which he had written during the Second World War. He approached one or two publishers about it, without success, and in the late 1940s he published some sections of it in the Christ Church (Ramsgate) Parish Magazine, presumably feeling that at least the work would in this way get an airing. The extracts are well written, but there is nothing in them that stands out particularly from the rest of this typical parish magazine, except perhaps the suggestion that 'the man who should pray to be permitted to break the bank at Monte Carlo could hardly look for an answer'. (Apparently Frank was considered an agnostic by some of his family until the Second World War, when he seems to have undergone a change of spiritual approach. He often said that only his faith kept him going at this time, for his work and his income were virtually cut off overnight.)

Frank was puzzled by another editorial rejection that he had to suffer in the mid-1940s. He confided to Gander: 'I have made a really good set of cross-word puzzles in five languages, but the editorial fraternity seem not to rise to them.' He adds that every publisher 'seems to guard with his left, if any new idea comes along'.

At the end of the 1940s and the beginning of the 1950s it was a matter of concern to Frank that Miss Hood was very ill. In 1950 he wrote to Joe Wark, a Scottish reader, that 'the poor dear has had

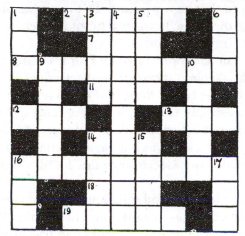

Something NEW in Crosswords!

HERE is something you have never before seen in any boy's paper—a crossword puzzle in simple Latin. See how quickly you can solve it. A minute or two's thought will show you that you know MUCH more Latin than you gave yourself credit for. If you get stuck—get your master to help. He'll be interested, too! The solution (for which no prize is offered) will be published in MODERN BOY next Saturday.

CLUES

ACROSS

2. *I teach.*
7. *A thing.*
8. *Famous Greek city.*
11. *Stand.*
12. *Twice.*
13. *Where.*
14. *Altar.*
16. *Nearer.*
18. *"That," fem. pl.*
19. *To mow.*

DOWN

1. *This.*
3. *Shore, abl. pl.*
4. *Hundreds.*
5. *Be!*
6. *A rodent.*
9. *Appear.*
10. *To shade.*
14. *An axle, acc.*
15. *To love, 3rd subj.*
16. *Through.*
17. *A monarch.*

The Modern Boy 28

more illness in twelve months than I have had in over three-quarters of a century, which is very rough luck and doesn't seem quite fair. But I am glad to say that she is pulling round, slowly but surely.' A year later Edith was still unwell and required a nurse: Frank felt almost ashamed of his own surprisingly good health and commented to Joe Wark: 'I think perhaps we were made of very tough material in the eighteen-seventies! Or perhaps I owe it to remote ancestors who built up strong constitutions on the good old Scottish oatmeal before they crossed the Tweed!' At the end of the war Frank had sold Appletrees, with some regret, as he missed not having a base in the gentle Hawkinge countryside he liked so much. He was at an age when he could no longer cope with any property other than that in which he lived; furthermore, his lack of income during the war years had left him financially straitened. At this time Dolly also sold Mandeville. Her daughter was away at university, and Dolly could stay at Rose Lawn when she wished to be with her brother.

During the 1940s Frank's letters to friends and readers contain much speculation about the publication of his autobiography. He worked on this during the early 1940s and, it seems, rewrote it several times before it was published by Skilton in 1952. The original draft was too long and also somewhat vitriolic about his differences with the Amalgamated Press (over the sub-writers, the *School Friend* affair and the instant cut-off of his stories and income in 1940, one gathers). It is good to record that he was eventually to write again for the Amalgamated Press in the *Comet*, from 1950 to 1951, when he was asked to contribute short Greyfriars stories.

The autobiography was much appreciated by Frank's many fans, even though it was on the whole impersonal and selective. Bagley had suggested that it should be called *Runaway Pen*, an appropriate title, but in the end it was simply called *The Autobiography of Frank Richards*. By the time it was published, Frank does not seem to have had a great deal of interest in it, as he was once again in the full flood of creating fiction, especially the Greyfriars tales for the Bunter books.

Something else happened in 1952, and it had more impact on the public at large than the appearance of Frank's autobiography: Billy Bunter became a BBC TV star. The Bunter books had triggered off a great deal of Greyfriars nostalgia and created a new young audience. With much amusing newspaper publicity, thirty-eight potential Bunters were auditioned for the part of Britain's most famous fictional schoolboy. The role was given to the 29-year-old professional actor Gerald Campion, whose portrayal of Bunter was

GERALD CAMPION IN

'Billy Bunter of Greyfriars School'

Based on the stories by
FRANK RICHARDS

NO. 1. 'THE SIEGE'

Mr. Quelch, Form Master of the Remove................Kynaston Reeves
The Famous Five:
  Harry Wharton..John Charlesworth
  Bob Cherry.............Keith Faulkner
  Johnny Bull..........Barry Macgregor
  Hurree Jamset Ram Singh
                          David Spenser
Frank Nugent
          Michael Danvers-Walker
Billy Bunter..............Gerald Campion
Vernon Smith, the bounder
                    John Rutherford
Peter Todd.....................John Quayle
Lord Mauleverer..........Cavan Malone
Skinner, a cad...............Philip Guard
Wingate, a prefect........John Osborne
Mr. Prout.....................Edward Lexy
Gosling, the school porter
                  Christopher Hodge
Dr. Locke, the Headmaster
                      John Stuart

One of C. H. Chapman's original drawings

Settings designed by Stephen Taylor

Produced by Joy Harington
AT 5.40 and 8.0

excellent. The series was immensely popular, despite some critical condemnation. Frank was commissioned to write the scripts and Joy Harington produced the programmes; each one was transmitted twice – in the afternoon for young viewers and during the evening for adults.

On the strength of his fees for the first series, Frank bought himself a television set. He confided to Joe Wark in 1952: 'It is a wonderful thing – really wonderful – to have football

matches brought into one's own home: I am going to enjoy that thoroughly: and the cricket is coming. To whisper a secret, I am looking forward to this more than to Bunter.'

Despite all the publicity and the fact that the programmes ran to several series, Greyfriars on television was in many ways disappointing. Campion was convincing as Bunter, but the young actors playing the Famous Five were rather inexperienced and not then in the same class as he. Wharton gave no sign of leadership, Hurree Jamset Ram Singh reeled off his mind-boggling metaphors without any expression and Bob Cherry had none of the exuberance and personal charm of the character in the *Magnet*. As Robert Robinson, then comparatively unknown, wrote in the *Yorkshire Evening Press*, 'Concrete realization of character is never as satisfactory as one's own imagined conception.' A major problem with the series was its low-budget flavour: there were just not enough pupils around to suggest the boyish microcosm of Greyfriars, and what was seen of the school buildings seemed flimsy and unreal. In spite of their limitations, the programmes created innumerable new fans for Bunter and

the Famous Five; they ran for five years, and Frank provided new episodes for every series. (Full and intriguing details are given by Brian Doyle in 'Bunter on Television' in *Collectors' Digest Annual 1976*.)

In the event Frank never became a television fan, possibly because his eyes tired of the flickering image. He spoke positively about the Bunter programmes, though he admitted that they were 'not quite perfect, but is anything in this imperfect world?'

Bunter graduated from television to the live theatre towards the end of the 1950s, when the Bunter Christmas shows began. There were six of these in all: *Billy Bunter's Mystery Christmas*, *Billy Bunter Flies East*, *Billy Bunter's Swiss Roll*, *Billy Bunter Shipwrecked*, *Billy Bunter's Christmas Circus* and *Billy Bunter Meets Magic*. (The last two were produced after Frank Richards's death.) Frank did not write the plays; Maurice McLoughlin, a former *Magnet* reader, was the author and producer. Gerald Campion played Bunter in the first few plays, then Peter Bridgmont took over. Frank enjoyed the idea of Bunter treading the boards, but felt unable to travel to London to see any of the productions.

During the 1950s Frank corresponded with Revd Philip Hobson, who was headmaster of Reigate St Mary's Preparatory School. Frank was particularly interested to receive copies of the *Gateway*, the school's magazine, and he wrote two original Carcroft stories for it: 'No Tuck for Turkey' and 'Turkey's Misfortune'. Revd Hobson was extremely interested in Frank's *Faith and Hope*, and tried to help him to get this published. (Stories of Carcroft School were also appearing at this time in the *Silver Jacket*, an attractively presented Australian monthly boys' paper.)

In 1960 Frank responded to a request to write something for the *Bedian Chronicle*, which was the magazine of the Old Bedford Road Secondary Boys' School in Luton. His contribution took the form of a letter from Billy Bunter, in characteristic spelling, and containing some of the Fat Owl's vintage howlers:

From Billy Bunter,
Greyfriars Skool.

I am verry much phlattered by your wish to publish a letter from me in the pages of the Bedian Kronicle. You seem to have a hire opinion of my abbilities than my own form-master, Quelch, who is rather a beest, and always down on a fellow, espechully in matters of speling at wich I am reelly very good. But as Tenneyson says, a profit is not without honner except in his own country. If it wasn't Tenneyson it was Browning. I have grate plezure in sending greetings to the boys of Bedford, and also to the beeks, though as a rule I don't think much of beeks.

Over fifty years after he had bounced into the first *Magnet*, Billy Bunter was as comically inflated as ever.

CHAPTER TWELVE

GRAND OLD MAN

What shall I be at ninety,
    As I do my daily chore,
If I find the world so jolly,
    When I'm barely eighty-four?[1]

(From a Frank Richards parody of Tennyson)

Towards the end of the 1940s, E. S. Turner sent Frank a copy of his *Boys Will Be Boys*, inscribed 'To the Grand Old Man of Boys' Stories'. Frank was delighted, both with the book and with the inscription, remarking in a *Radio Times* article that he did not want 'any higher title than that'.[2] In the last years of his life he was a father-figure to many thousands of readers far and wide. He went on writing the Bunter books to the end, as well as letters to young, middle-aged and elderly admirers, all of whom became 'my dear boys'. (In the 1970s Eric Fayne assembled and published a selection of Frank's letters, mostly written in the decade and a half following the Second World War.[3] As Fayne points out in his introduction to the book, Frank's outlook becomes noticeably more mellow as the years go by.) Old age brought a few problems, but on the whole it treated Frank kindly.

Miss Hood recovered from her three-year illness, and life at Rose Lawn continued to run smoothly. He remained close to his sister Dolly and his niece Una, who, after attending Cheltenham Ladies' College, had read English at London University. It was a source of satisfaction to him that she shared his love of poetry and became a freelance journalist and feature-writer. Dolly's husband Percy Harrison died in the late 1950s, and Frank seriously considered uprooting himself from Kingsgate to be near her, if she wished. He wrote suggesting that perhaps they ought to live nearer together, and saying that if she would like to live at Rose Lawn for part of the year, she would always be welcomed. Or he could come to live with her in London. 'I will do whatever you want me to do if you will only put it plainly. All my affection is centred on you, as it has always been.'[4] In the event he was not called upon to move to London, but brother and sister continued to spend time together, with Dolly visiting him at Rose Lawn. They went on exchanging letters twice a week, as they had always done when apart.

Another visitor at Rose Lawn was Chapman, the *Magnet* artist whose admiration for Frank's stories never diminished with the years. In the 1950s he and Frank seemed to be all that was left of the old guard of Amalgamated Press writers, artists and editors from the palmy *Magnet* and *Gem* days. Chapman, like Frank, retained his talents throughout his long life (he lived to be a nonagenarian); spry and wiry, he also remained an energetic and enthusiastic cyclist and liked to take cold baths every day. Apart from their continuing association on the Bunter books, Frank and Chapman co-operated

on several other commissions during the fifties and sixties. The last of these was an article for *Punch*, in which Frank was invited to write about the reforms he would introduce if he were made minister of education.[5] Chapman illustrated the piece with a typical Greyfriars scene, and Frank at eighty-four was writing as stylishly as ever: 'A boy is like a deponent verb. He may be passive in form – under his form-master's eye – but he is always active in meaning.' (It is interesting that many of his funny and facetiously expressed reforms have now become part of our educational system.)

One of Frank's last letters to Chapman was written on 26 February 1960, when both seemed full of the joys of promised spring, despite their advanced years and the intensity of the winter weather:

Very glad to see your fist again on a letter, and to hear that you have been keeping so active: in spite of Arctic weather, east winds, and all the ills that flesh is heir to as we get on in years. I keep as well as usual: and must conclude that Father Time has left his scythe somewhere and forgotten where he left it. What a day we are having today! As Shelley remarked, recklessly disregarding his subjunctives, 'If winter comes, can spring be far behind?' . . . But really and truly, a spring day like this does make one feel that life is worth living . . . and if one happens to be on the shady side of eighty, who cares? . . . Yes, you are right about the one and only Billy: what should we do without him? The johnny in the opera asked '*Che farò senza Eurydice?*' – but a more pertinent question would be '*Che faremo senza Bunter?*' May he live for ever, as his author appears to be going to do! . . . It must be just lovely up the river on a day like this. O for the day when one used to mess about on boats! But if we count our blessings, we find that we still have quite a lot left.

A year later he struck more sombre notes in a letter to Joe Wark, asking about his proximity to the new Polaris base:

'Holy Loch' certainly is a misnomer, in the circumstances, for a more unholy beast of a thing it would be hard to imagine. It does seem strange that nearly two thousand years of Christianity have produced no better result than this: but the news from all quarters seems to indicate that Satan is still walking to and fro in the earth. I wonder sometimes if we should not be better off if all the scientific johnnies could be packed into a large sack and dropped into the middle of the Atlantic!

Frank had strong feelings about atomic and, indeed, conventional weapons, which had been the subject of a caustic letter from him to *Time and Tide*, published on 9 August 1947. He ends his letter to Joe Wark on a protective note:

If I might add a word of counsel to that of your doctor, I would say, never let anything induce you to put a strain on your eyes. My own have been giving me trouble, and I have to ration my reading very severely: it comes hard, but the sight is the most precious of God's gifts, and worth more to us than all that has been printed since the days of Caxton – even including the works of Frank Richards!

Frank continued to type his letters with the purple ribbon, and his signature in black ink remained bold and firm. He still enjoyed translating favourite items into Latin. In 1958 the Latin newspaper *Acta Diurna* published his sparkling translation of Sir Joseph Porter's song in HMS *Pinafore*. (The editor, Max Lyne, commented on the difficulty of putting Gilbert's lyrics into Latin, and the expertise with which Frank did this.) Other popular songs that Frank transposed into Latin were 'Waltzing Matilda', 'Won't You Come Home, Bill Bailey?' and, perhaps rather wistfully, 'The Man Who Broke the Bank at Monte Carlo'. He began a Latin Bunter story – '*Bunteri Stultitia*', the first instalment of which appeared in *Acta Diurna* (it seems that he died before finishing this tale), and, to his great satisfaction, *The Times Educational Supplement* published a complete Latin story by him, '*Ultio Bunteri*', on 30 June 1961. This occupied a whole page of the paper and was illustrated with photographs from the BBC TV Bunter productions. It must have been popular with readers, because it was also issued in the form of a separate leaflet.

In 1958 *Collectors' Digest* celebrated the golden anniversary of the *Magnet*. Frank was asked to write about his feelings, fifty years on. He starts by quoting from his own favourite writer: ' "*Eheu fugaces!*" Swiftly glide the years, says old Horace. Swiftly indeed.'[6] Frank points out that much has happened in those fifty years:

> a couple of World Wars were among other things. Poles north and south have been explored. Flying men have girdled the earth: and Russian sputniks the heavens. And all the while Billy Bunter has been rolling on his plump way unperturbed . . . I have often been asked whether I like Bunter. Of course I do. How could one help liking the companion of half-a-century! We are told that Conan Doyle became so tired of Sherlock Holmes that he had to kill him off. I never had that experience with Bunter or with any other character of whom I have written. In fact, I don't understand how any author can tire of his creations. They are the children of his imagination and become like real children to him: more so if possible . . . Looking back over half-a-century it seems very pleasant. The Greyfriars Saga has gone on and on and on: written in all sorts and conditions of places – on Swiss mountains, by Venetian lagoons, amid Roman and Pompeian ruins, French vineyards, Dutch canals, and German beer-gardens – and now? Now Father Time has fixed

its author in a sunny spot by the sea in a pleasant county, and his wanderings are over: but his fingers are still active on the keys. Greyfriars celebrates its Golden Jubilee: and Frank Richards, who has quite decided to make his century, looks forward to its Diamond Jubilee!

Sadly, he was not to see this. Three years later, after he had recovered from two strokes, he admitted to being 'a very old man' who could not 'last much longer: it's absurd to worry about death. When death comes, why, I feel it will be like changing trains on a long train journey. That's all there is to it.' He was ill for a few days shortly before Christmas in 1961, and had some difficulty in breathing properly. Frank had a cerebral haemorrhage and died in his sleep on Christmas Eve. Miss Hood found him dead the next morning and telephoned Dolly and Una with the sad news.

His passing was announced in the early hours of Boxing Day: tributes poured in from all over the world and thousands mourned, their grief being the more poignant because Frank had died at

The Famous Five were busy with Christmas decorations when a plump figure appeared suddenly at the open door of Wharton Lodge. "I—I say, you fellows," said Bunter hastily, "I've looked in to say something rather important to Wharton!"

Christmastime – the season that he had always conveyed with a special brilliance in his *Magnet* and *Gem* stories. Seasonable episodes exhilaratingly paraded all the trappings of rollicking, good-time, old-world festivities. As Harry Wharton & Co. began to make their way to one of the chums' homes for the holidays, several feet of snow would obligingly hurtle from the skies to smother the countryside, while the lakes would unfailingly freeze solid. Christmas at Wharton Lodge without snowballing and skating would be unthinkable. Frank Richards knew what his readers wanted, and always managed to provide it. He was the equal of Dickens in conveying the traditional spirit of joy, excitement and goodwill.

Charles Hamilton was cremated at Charing in Kent soon afterwards, and Eric Fayne describes his attendance at the funeral in the *Collectors' Digest* of February 1962, an issue that was almost entirely devoted to the Greyfriars author:

> the weather was hard, bitter – with stinging white roads – snow and ice everywhere . . . Frost and snow hung on the gaunt branches of the trees, the footpaths were slippery, and the roads were like an ice-rink. Friends told me that I was mad to set out – that I should never get there . . . but somehow I knew that I must get there – to be with him at the finish.[7]

Dolly, Una and Edith, of course, were at the crematorium, still stunned from the shock of Frank's death. Fayne suddenly felt that he was there to represent the hundreds of thousands of readers who had loved Frank's stories down the years. He admits that as the group of mourners knelt to pray, he did not hear what the clergyman was saying: 'I was thinking of Tom Merry, dear old Arthur Augustus, Harry Wharton, Henry Samuel Quelch, the Rio Kid . . . When I raised my head the coffin had sunk out of sight. Silently the mortal remains of this great man had left us while our heads were bowed. But his spirit lives on – his influence for all that is good.'

His books live on too, despite the disapproval of a librarian, as reported by Peter Grosvenor in the *Daily Express* under the heading 'Watch Out Rupert Bear, It Could Be You Next . . .'[8] Because Ipswich's chief librarian thought the Billy Bunter books were 'unfair to fatties and a bad influence', she 'had the Fat Owl of the Remove whisked off the public shelves and placed in a reserve category along with sex books'. This prompted a spate of letters to the *Daily Express*

"Yaroo! Back come all the Fanny Hills and Lady Chatterleys—out go all the Billy Bunters."

and other papers, defending Frank's stories and commenting on
their positive influence. It also stimulated a joyous Giles cartoon on
the idiocies of such library censorship, which appeared in the *Sunday
Express*.

In 1969 the publisher Howard Baker, a *Magnet* reader from his
boyhood, decided to republish the *Magnet* in facsimile. No one knew
if this would be a short-lived venture, appreciated only by a handful
of nostalgic Greyfriars fans. In fact, almost twenty years after the
publication of the first facsimile series, the Howard Baker Press has
issued some 250 volumes of *Magnet*, *Gem* and other Frank Richards
magazines. Each volume contains between seven and ten individual
papers, and new volumes are coming off the press at the rate of six or
seven a year. A little while ago the publishers conducted a poll to try
to find out if there was a typical *Magnet* reader, and discovered that
those who regularly buy the facsimiles include schoolchildren, doc-
tors, chartered accountants, lawyers, airline pilots, factory workers,
postmen, miners, Members of Parliament, university professors,
schoolteachers, members of the army, navy and air force, artists,
ministers of many religious denominations, civil servants, bank

managers, police officers, engineers, housewives, interior decorators, photographers, company directors, authors, journalists, musicians, actors, architects, television personalities, librarians, publishers, stockbrokers and magicians. This bears out Frank Richards's frequently stated belief that 'a good story is a good story, whether the reader [or the hero] be fifteen or fifty'.

AFTERWORD

GREYFRIARS GROWS UP!

Bunter and Greyfriars are alive and kicking in other books, as well as the *Magnet* facsimiles. During the 1980s three novels about Bunter as an adult have been published. These are *But for Bunter* by David Hughes and *Bunter Sahib* and *Bunter by Appointment*, both by Daniel Green.[1] Further evidence of the resilience of Greyfriars and its unique place in the public imagination arises in connection with Peter Wright's *Spycatcher*, which, by saying that Harry Wharton had become a member of MI5, stimulated a cartoon of Wright, Wharton and a Wilsonian Bunter by Gale in the *Daily Telegraph* (29 April 1987).

BUNTER CLUNG TO THE TOP OF THE WALL. HARRY WHARTON HAD POSSESSION OF ONE FOOT. THE OTHER, LUCKILY FOR BUNTER, WAS FREE. BUNTER KICKED OUT WITH IT. "WHOOO-HOOP!" ROARED THE CAPTAIN OF THE REMOVE, AS A BOOT CLUMPED ON HIS CHIN.

APPENDIX ONE

REPRINTED FROM THE TIMES EDUCATIONAL SUPPLEMENT FRIDAY JUNE 30 1961

ULTIO BUNTERI

By Frank Richards

Quelchius.

I

Quelchius magister supercilium intrahebat,

Ei displicebat aliquid.
Oculi ejus ad Bunterum nitebant. Discipuli Quelchii in classe sedeb-... Whartonus, Nugentius, Cerasus, ceteri, praecepta magistri attende-nt,—sed non Bunterus. Tempestas ... ada erat, et Bunterus primo ananante, tum dormiebat. Caput ... ss inclinabat, murmure ex naribus nanante. Bunterus in classe non ... tum dormiebat, sed etiam rtebat !

Nil mirum Quelchium supercilium intrahere ! Nunquam erat Bunterus ... iscipulus sedulus, sed adhuc etiam ... unterus non solebat in classe ... rmire. Nimis erat !

" Buntere ! "

Vox Quelchii non clara sed ... ofunda est.

Nil responsum ! Bunterus ... mniens nihil audit. Oculis clausis, ... e aperto, dormire continuat, ... rdus ad magistri vocem.

Pueri in classe ocu'os conjectant, ... entio profundo. Solus Nugentius ... Whartonum susurrat :

" Miserum Bunterum ! Quelchius ... i corium detrahet ! "

" Silete ! " exclamat Quelchius, ... " Silete ! pueri ! " Et repetit, voce ... ariore atque aoriore, " Buntere ! ... untere ! Num dormis in classe, ... untere ? "

Etiam nunc respondet Bunterus ... hil.

Contractio supercilii Quelchii ... grior fit. Ferula ex scrinio sumpta, ... unterum appropinquat.

Omnino ignorat Bunterus, placide ... omniens. Sed repente suscitabitur, ... bi ferula in articulos digitorum ... criter descendit. Tum Bunterus ... altat !

" Yarooh ! " clamat. " Quid est ? ... estia ! " Et Bunterus stupens ... rticulos digitorum vehementer ... ricat.

" Ha, ha, ha ! " rident omnes ... ueri.

" Ow ! ow ! wow ! " anhelat ... unterus.

Copies of this story, in leaflet form, may be obtained from The Circulation Manager, The Times Educational Supplement, Printing House Square, London, E.C.4, price 3s. 9d. for 25, ... s. 4d. for 50 or 14s. for 100. The price includes postage.

" Silentium ! " tonat Quelchius, et statim silentium subsequitur. Nemo oculos Quelchii attrahere vult.

" Buntere ! Dormis in classe ! Hic dormis ! " tonat Quelchius.
Bunterus oculos fricans anhelat.
" O ! Non ! Minime vero ! " balbutit.

" Oculi tui clausi erant, Buntere ! "
" Ita est, sed non dormiebam—."
" Quid est ? "
" Audio melius oculis clausis magister," balbutit Bunterus.
" Verum loquor — verum est, domine."

" Praecepta mea audivisti—? "
" Certe ! Certe ! Audiebam totum quod dixisti—omne verbum —."

" Verum est ? " dicit Quelchius torvus, " Si verum est, Buntere, statim dic quid dixerim."
" O ! " anhelat Bunterus, perturbatus.
" Statim ! " tonat Quelchius.
" O ! " balbutit Bunterus, " Ob—ob—oblivisor—."

" Intelligo ! " interpellat Quelchius, " Dormiebas, nec quidquam audivisti. Poenam capies, Buntere."
" Eheu ! " suspirat Bunterus.
" Versus quinquaginta Virgilii scribes ! Ad conclave meum eos post classem apportabis."
" Sed . . . sed . . . sed . . . magister . . . !"

" Satis est ! " dicit Quelchius acriter : et Bunterus tacitus manet.

Sed quamquam Bunterus silebat, vultu eloquens erat. Versus scribere labor erat : nec unquam laborem amabat ! Dicere quod sentiebat non audebat, sed iracundia suppressa fortior fortiorque fiebat !

II

" AGEDUM, amici mei ! "
Post classem Whartonus, Nugentius, Cerasus, in loco ludendi erant. Ad eos se volvebat Bunterus, loquens.
" Hallo, hallo, hallo ! exclamat Cerasus, ridens. " Etiam vigilans es, Buntere."
" Ha, ha, ha ! " rident Whartonus Nugentiusque.

Bunterus grundit.
" Non dormiebam in classe," asse-verat. " Non dormiebam, sed modo dormitabam brevissime. Sed Quel-chius elegit oredere me dormire ! Quelchius bestia est "
" Asine ! " dicit Whartonus, " Et dormiebas et stertebas ! Nos omnes te auscultabamus."
" Nil moror ! Quelchius bestia est ! " fremit Bunterus. " Sed scio quid facturus sim ! Scio quomodo eum puniam ! "
" Quelchium punire ! " exclamat Whartonus.
" Id obliviscere ! " inquit Cerasus.
" Videbitis ! " fremit Whartonus, " Et Quelchius videbit ! Quinquaginta versus Vergilii scribere mihi opus est ! Ultionem capiam ! Nolit aliquid ponderosi super caput ejus cadere . . . ."
" Quid ! " exclamat Nugentius.
" In caput Quelchii ! " anhelat Whartonus.
" Asine pinguis ! " dicit Cerasus.
" Videbitis ! Scitis-ne ubi Quelch-ius nunc sit ? " rogat Whartonus.
" Foris est ! " respondet Whartonus.
" Bene ! " dicit Bunterus. " Si foris est, omnia tuta sunt ! Scio quid faciam dum abest ! "
Et Bunterus se revolvit.

Poenam capies, Buntere.

" Quid nunc ? Siste, asine ! " tres pueri conclamant.
Sed Bunterus surdus domum se vovit. Oculi trium puerorum eum subsequebantur.
" Quid ille asinus pinguis faciet ? " rogat Nugentius.
" Aliquid stulti ! " dicit Whar-tonus.
" Buntere ! " clamat Cerasus, " Buntere ! Siste ! Huc veni, stulte ! "
Sed Bunterus in aedes evanuit.

III

" WHARTONE ! "
Vox Quelchii erat.
Post classem Quelchius ambulare foris solebat, librum sub lacerto por-tans, saepe legens dum ambulat. Sed hodie tempestas calidissima erat, et Quelchius paulum fatigatus brevi tempore reversus in scholam est. Portas intrat atque Whartonum appellat. Statim ille festinat.
" Quid vis, magister ? " rogat.
" Calidum est, et volo quiescere dum librum lego ", exponit Quelchius. " I in aedes, quaeso, et sellam huc apporta."
" Statim, domine ! " respondet Whartonus : et statim aedes init, et breviter cum sella revertitur.
" Benigne ! " dicit Quelchius, " Sel-lam prope murum in umbra pone. Sol in loco aperto calidissimus est. Sellam hic sub fenestra mea pone."
Manu locum indicat.
Sub fenestra conclavis Quelchii murus in umbra erat. Whartonus sellam prope murum sub fenestra ponit, et abit.
Quelchius sedet in sella, libro aperto, et legere procedit. Super caput ejus fenestra conclavis aperta est. Sed oculi magistri in librum figuntur, et nunquam ad fenestram super caput aspicit, in lectione occupatissimus.

IV

" BESTIA ! "
Bunterus quieta voce illud verbum susurrat.
Est triste narrare, eum magistrum Quelchium ita designare.

Cerasum, Nugentium, longo spatio videt, ceterum alios nullos. Si illi eum videant non curet. Nullum magistrum videt. Deorsum spectare non cogitat. Si spectavisset deorsum, caput magistri vidisset. Sed non ! Totum tutum videbatur. Ex fenestra saltat Bunterus !

V

" O ! " Quelchius c'amabat.
Attonitus erat, atque laesus.
In sella sedens sub fenestra, oculis in librum fixis, totus occupatus legendo, certe non exspectabat aliquid super caput repente descendere. Sed aliquid repente et graviter descendit. Erat Bunterus !—Bunterus ex fenestra saltans !
Fragor !
Nesciebat Quelchius quae res caderet. Nesciebat Bunterus in quam rem descenderet. Stupefacti ambo erant.
Sella eversa, Quelchius humi colla-bitur exan:matus. Super Quelchio collabitur Bunterus clamans.
" Yaroooh ! "
" O ! " exclamant Whartonus, Nugentius, Cerasus, unanimi, ubi casum viderent. Et ad locum con-currunt.
" Quid est ! " anhelat Quelchius. Surgit, et humi sedet, " Ali-qu.d in caput meum descendit Quid ? O ! Buntere ! Bunterus est ! "
" O ! O ! Non ! Ego non ! " balbutit Bunterus.
Quelchius surgens erectus stat, oculis ad Bunterum nitentibus, dum anhelat, paene exanimatus. Oculi Bunteri fere exiliunt ad magistrum.
" O ! O ! O ! " repetit.
" Buntere ! Ex fenestra conclavis mei tu saltavisti ! ! " tonat Quelchius, " In conclavi meo fuisti ! Quid ibi faciebas ? "
" Nihil ! Nihil, magister mi ! " balbutit Bunterus, perterritus, " Lib-rum super ostium nunquam pone-bam. . . ."
" Quid ? "
" Nunquam ! Nunquam ! " an-helat Bunterus, " Nolebam librum super caput tuum cadere. . . . !"
" Hercle ! In conclavi meo librum super ostium ponebas, ut super caput meum caducus esset ! " articulat Quelchius, " Et postea saltabas ex fenestra ! Intelligo ! Me assequere, Buntere ! Statim ! "
Bunterus gemit ! tum, tacitus tristisque magistrum assequebatur, ubi ferula eum expectat.
" Illum asinum ! " dicit Whartno.
Et tres pueri subrident. Sed Bunterus non subridet. Vultus pinguis Bunteri similis est vultui illius regis qui olim nunquam subridere poterat.

FINIS

Fragor !

Has dedit imagine: B.b.c.

Printed for THE TIMES PUBLISHING COMPANY, Limited, London, E.C.4, by THE BRADBURY AGNEW PRESS

APPENDIX TWO

CURRENT PUBLICATIONS AND ORGANIZATIONS
FEATURING THE WORK OF CHARLES HAMILTON

In 1969 the Howard Baker Press began a long and comprehensive series of *Magnet, Gem, Greyfriars Holiday Annual* and *Schoolboys' Own Library* facsimile reprints in omnibus volumes. The series started with *The Land of the Pyramids*, which comprised eight *Magnet*s from 1932; over 250 volumes have now been published, and several new volumes are issued each year. The same publishers produce the *Greyfriars Gazette*, a periodical containing news and views about Frank Richards's stories.

Story Paper Collectors' Digest is a monthly publication concerned with old boys' and girls' papers and magazines, with strong emphasis on Charles Hamilton's stories. It was founded in 1946 by Herbert Leckenby, who was succeeded as editor by Eric Fayne in 1959. Fayne remained in office until early 1987 when Mary Cadogan took over. (This publication incorporates *Story Paper Collector*, which was founded in 1941 in Canada by W. H. Gander and ran until 1966.)

Long-standing Old Boys' Book Clubs are run in London, Leeds, the Midlands, Cambridge and the South-west; their activities prominently feature Frank Richards's work.

There are two Charles Hamilton Museums: the one at 30 Tonbridge Road, Maidstone, Kent, is directed by John Wernham, and the other, at Kingsgate Castle, Kingsgate, Kent, by R. F. Acraman. Associated with the former is the Museum Press, which privately publishes studies of Charles Hamilton's stories.

APPENDIX THREE

CHARLES HAMILTON'S PEN-NAMES

Charles Hamilton wrote under many pen-names and, as new ones are still coming to light, the following list of his pseudonyms (with acknowledgements to D. J. Adley and W. O. G. Lofts) may yet be incomplete.

Michael Blake
Winston Cardew
Martin Clifford
Harry Clifton
Clifford Clive
Sir Alan Cobham
Owen Conquest
Gordon Conway
Frank Drake
Freeman Fox
Hamilton Greening
Cecil Herbert
Prosper Howard
Robert Jennings

Gillingham Jones
T. Harcourt Llewelyn
Clifford Owen
Ralph Redway
Ridley Redway
Frank Richards
Hilda Richards
Raleigh Robbins
Robert Rogers
Eric Stanhope
Robert Stanley
Peter Todd
Nigel Wallace
Talbot Wynyard

APPENDIX FOUR

EDITORS AND ILLUSTRATORS OF THE *GEM* AND *MAGNET*

THE EDITORS

Percy Griffith was the founder and editor of the *Gem* in 1907 and of the *Magnet* in 1908. He was succeeded on both papers by Herbert A. Hinton, who, during his army service (1916–19) was replaced by John Nix Pentelow. Hinton again held the editorship from 1919 to 1920. Charles Maurice Down, who had been on the staff of the papers since their inception, then took over, and he remained editor in chief until the *Gem* closed at the end of 1939 and the *Magnet* in 1940. (There were 1,711 numbers of the *Gem* and 1,683 of the *Magnet*.)

THE ARTISTS

Magnet: Hutton Mitchell was the first artist to portray Billy Bunter and the Greyfriars chums, illustrating the paper from no. 1 to no. 39. Arthur E. Clarke then took over, and continued until his death in 1911, when he was succeeded by Charles Henry Chapman. Chapman, whose drawings were bolder and more cartoon-like than Mitchell's and Clarke's, built up what were to become the traditional images of the boys, the school buildings and the Greyfriars environs. It was he who gave Billy Bunter his larger-than-life, owl-like appearance, and he was also the first artist to portray Bessie Bunter. Chapman remained on the paper to the end, and the zest of his pictures was unflagging.

Leonard Shields's first illustration for a Greyfriars story was in the *Greyfriars Holiday Annual 1923*. He worked with Chapman as a regular *Magnet* illustrator from no. 960 in 1926; although Shields skilfully perpetuated Chapman's likenesses, his characters were more handsome and less prone to be caricatured. Shields, like Chapman, continued to illustrate the *Magnet* for the rest of its run.

Gem: there were two series of the *Gem*, the first of which ran to 48 issues, and the second to 1,663. (Charles Hamilton, as Martin Clifford, wrote all the St Jim's stories in the first series, but only 735 original stories in the second series, because this contained many reprints of his tales, as well as stories by substitute authors.)

The first series was illustrated by H. M. Lewis, Arthur E. Clarke and Hutton Mitchell. Mitchell also illustrated the second series (to no. 30) and a few numbers in 1910 and 1911.

Warwick Reynolds (Jr) produced his first St Jim's drawings for the *Gem* in no. 31 (1908) of the new series. He was the regular artist until no. 47 (1909) and thereafter still illustrated the paper occasionally. He again regularly contributed illustrations for some 150 issues from 1916 to 1919, as the artist at that time, R. J. Macdonald, had enlisted.

Macdonald's first picture for the *Gem* appeared in no. 91 in 1909. Apart from during the period of his military service (1916–19), he was the paper's regular illustrator from 1911 until it ended in 1939. His engaging drawings of the St Jim's juniors, and of Tom Merry and Arthur Augustus D'Arcy in particular, seem as quintessential to the St Jim's saga as Chapman's Bunter is to the Greyfriars stories.

APPENDIX FIVE

SELECTED PAPERS AND BOOKS CONTAINING STORIES BY CHARLES HAMILTON

Post-war papers including radically abridged reprints are not given in the following list.

Ace High Western
Best Budget
Billy Bunter's Own Annual
Boys' Friend (2nd series)
Boys' Friend Library (1st series)
Chuckles
Coloured Comic
Detective Series (W. C. Merrett)
Diamond Library (1st series)
Dreadnought
Empire Library (2nd series)
Funny Cuts
Gem
Goldhawk Books
Greyfriars Herald
Greyfriars Holiday Annual
Happy Story Book
Headland House Series
Jack's Paper
Jester
Knockout (comic)
Knockout Fun Book
Larks (Trapps Holmes version)
Magnet

Marvel
Mascot Schoolboy Series
Mascot Schoolgirl Series
Modern Boy
Picture Fun
Pie
Pilot
Pluck
Popular (1st and 2nd series)
Ranger (1st and 2nd series)
Romance Series (W. C. Merrett)
School and Sport
School Friend (1st series)
Schoolboys' Own Library
Silver Jacket
Smiles
Sparshott Series
Tom Browne's Comic Annual
Tom Merry's Own Annual
Triumph
Vanguard Library
Wonder Book of Comics
World's Comic

Novels by Frank Richards: thirty-eight hardback Billy Bunter books were published between 1947 and 1965, the first ten by Charles Skilton and the remainder by Cassell. Several of these and some *Magnet* stories were reprinted in Armada paperbacks from 1965 to 1972, and the Merlin Press reprinted eight Greyfriars tales from the *Schoolboys' Own Library* in 1967 and 1968. *Bessie Bunter of Cliff House School* (Charles Skilton, 1949) may be regarded as part of the same hardback series as the Billy Bunter books. Six of the Bunter books (edited and updated by Kay King) were published in 1982 by the Quiller Press.

Novels by Martin Clifford: from 1949 to 1951 the Mandeville Press and Spring Books published a hardback series of St Jim's stories and one Rookwood novel.

NOTES

INTRODUCTION
THE IMPORTANCE OF BEING FRANK

1. R. Roberts, *The Classic Slum* (Manchester University Press, Manchester, 1971)
2. 'Boys' Writer', *The Saturday Book* (Hutchinson, London, 1945)

CHAPTER ONE
SCHOOLBOY RIDER OF THE EALING RANGE

1. 'Frank Richards Replies to George Orwell', *Horizon* (May 1940)
2. 'Boys' Writer'
3. *The Autobiography of Frank Richards* (Skilton, London, 1952)
4. 'Some Reminiscences by Frank Richards', *Magnet*, no. 1,000 (1927)
5. U. Hamilton Wright, 'Charles Hamilton: A Background Note on His Early Days', *Collectors' Digest*, no. 183 (1962)
6. Letter to W. H. Gander (26 August 1948)
7. 'The Parting of the Ways', *Boys' Friend Library*, no. 473 (n.d.)
8. 'Boys' Writer'
9. U. Hamilton Wright, op cit.
10. P. Alcock, letter to W. O. G. Lofts (24 July 1986)
11. 'The Prefects' Plot', *Magnet*, no. 1,111 (1929)
12. A. D. Newman, 'On Meeting Charles Hamilton', in J. Wernham (ed.), *Centenary Edition*, Charles Hamilton Companion, iii (privately pubd, Maidstone, 1976)
13. ibid.
14. 'Frank Richards Replies to George Orwell'
15. U. Hamilton Wright, op. cit.
16. 'Boys' Writer'
17. 'The Artful Dodger', *Magnet*, no. 582 (1919)
18. *Bessie Bunter of Cliff House School* (Skilton, London, 1949)
19. 'Tom Redwing's Quest', *Magnet*, no. 1,019 (1927)
20. 'The Feud with Cliff House', no. 1,528, 'The Boy Who Wouldn't Split', no. 1,529, 'On the Track of the Trickster', no. 1,530, *Magnet* (1937)

CHAPTER TWO
MANY TRADES, BUT MASTER OF ONE

1. 'Boys' Writer'
2. ibid.

3. *The Autobiography of Frank Richards*
4. Questionnaire for W. Bagley (1944)
5. *The Autobiography of Frank Richards*
6. ibid.
7. 'Darrell's Secret', *Gem*, 2nd series, no. 37 (1908)
8. *The Autobiography of Frank Richards*
9. 'Captain Nemo', *Union Jack*, no. 171 (1897)
10. 'Bold British Boys', *Union Jack*, no. 274 (1899)
11. 'The Rival Treasure Seekers', *Magnet*, no. 1,024 (1927)
12. 'Adrift in the Pacific', *Magnet*, no. 1,594 (1938)
13. 'Chums Afloat', *Magnet*, no. 267 (1913)
14. P. Alcock, letter to W. O. G. Lofts (6 June 1986)
15. 'Boys' Writer'
16. 'The Packsaddle Bunch', *Schoolboys' Own Library*, no. 305 (1937)
17. *The Autobiography of Frank Richards*
18. T. Hopperton, 'The *Vanguard*', *Old Boys' Book Collector*, no. 1 (1952)
19. 'The Rearguard of "The *Vanguard*"', *Old Boys' Book Collector*, no. 2 (1952)

CHAPTER THREE
THE 'SAINTS' (AND 'FRIARS') COME MARCHING IN

1. Questionnaire for W. Bagley
2. *Marvel*, no. 503 (1903)
3. *The Autobiography of Frank Richards*
4. ibid.
5. ibid.
6. ibid.
7. E. Fayne, 'Charles Hamilton', in memorial edition of *The Autobiography of Frank Richards* (Skilton, London, 1962)
8. Questionnaire for W. Bagley
9. *The Autobiography of Frank Richards*
10. W. O. G. Lofts and D. J. Adley, *The World of Frank Richards* (Howard Baker Press, London, 1975)
11. 'Skimpole's Little Scheme', *Gem*, 1st series, no. 41 (1907)
12. T. Hopperton, 'The *Vanguard*'
13. 'The Rearguard of "The *Vanguard*"'
14. 'The Making of Harry Wharton', *Magnet*, no. 1 (1908)
15. G. Orwell, 'Boys' Weeklies', *Horizon* (March 1940)
16. J. C. Iraldi, 'Greyfriars: Scholastic Shangri-La', *Story Paper Collector*, no. 59 (1956)
17. G. Wilde, 'Charles Hamilton: 1876–1961', *Collectors' Digest*, no. 183 (1962)

18. G. Orwell, op. cit.
19. 'Frank Richards Replies to George Orwell'
20. 'Bunter's Brainstorm', *Magnet*, no. 996 (1927)
21. 'Public Benefactor No. 1', *Boys' Friend Library*, no. 1,138 (n.d.)

CHAPTER FOUR
THE FAT OWL, FOREIGNERS AND THOSE FEARFUL OUTSIDERS!

1. 'The Stolen Study', *Magnet*, no. 452 (1916)
2. 'The Making of Harry Wharton', *Magnet*, no. 1 (1908)
3. 'The Schoolboy Forger', *Schoolboys' Own Library*, no. 397 (1940)
4. 'Bunter Comes to Stay', *Magnet*, no. 1,141 (1929)
5. G. Orwell, 'Boys' Weeklies'
6. 'Frank Richards Replies to George Orwell'
7. 'Rallying Round Carboy', *Magnet*, no. 1,081 (1928)
8. 'Tom Merry in Chicago', *Gem*, 2nd series, no. 48 (1909)
9. 'The Black Man at Greyfriars', *Magnet*, no. 774 (1922)
10. 'The Yankee Schoolboy', *Magnet*, no. 150 (1910)
11. 'Rolling in Dollars', *Magnet*, no. 1,161 (1930)
12. 'The Secret of the Old Oak', *Magnet*, no. 1,380 (1934)
13. 'The Jew of St Jim's', *Gem*, no. 394 (1915)
14. 'Aliens at Greyfriars', *Magnet*, no. 6 (1908)
15. *Magnet*, nos. 1,059–67 (1928)
16. 'The Boy from the East', *Magnet*, no. 1,059 (1928)
17. 'Rivals of the Remove', *Magnet*, no. 7 (1908)
18. 'In the Heart of the Himalayas', *Magnet*, no. 967 (1926)
19. 'The Bounder of Greyfriars', *Magnet*, no. 119 (1910)
20. 'Skimpole's Little Scheme', *Gem*, 1st series, no. 41 (1907)

CHAPTER FIVE
'SUBS', SWEET HEROINES AND SHRIEKING SUFFRAGETTES

1. 'Harry Wharton's Campaign', *Magnet*, no. 50 (1909)
2. Letter to J. Wark (29 April 1949)
3. *The Autobiography of Frank Richards*
4. ibid.
5. U. Hamilton Wright, 'Felix Kept On Walking', in J. Wernham (ed.), *Centenary Edition*
6. *The Autobiography of Frank Richards*
7. ibid.
8. 'The D'Arcy Cup', *Gem*, no. 88 (1909)
9. 'Tom Merry – Sub-editor', *Gem*, no. 70 (1909)
10. 'Cousin Ethel's Chum', *Gem*, no. 951 (1926)

11. 'The Boy Scouts' Rivals', *Gem*, no. 78 (1909)
12. 'D'Arcy the Suffragist!', *Gem*, no. 274 (1913)
13. 'Gussy Among the Girls', *Gem*, no. 756 (1922)
14. 'The Remove Master's Substitute', *Magnet*, no. 28 (1908)
15. 'Harry Wharton's Campaign', *Magnet*, no. 50 (1909)
16. 'The Invasion of Greyfriars', *Magnet*, no. 68 (1909)
17. ibid.
18. 'The Bully of Greyfriars', *Magnet*, no. 69 (1909)
19. 'The Cliff House Party', *Magnet*, no. 70 (1909)
20. 'Kidnapped', *Magnet*, no. 5 (1908)
21. 'Harry's Sacrifice', *Magnet*, no. 12 (1908)
22. 'The Bad Hat of the Remove', *Magnet*, no. 1,533 (1937)
23. 'Barring Bob Cherry', *Magnet*, no. 1,535 (1937)
24. 'The Feud with Cliff House', *Magnet*, no. 1,528 (1937)
25. 'The Girls' School Challenge', *Magnet*, no. 151 (1910)
26. 'Figgins' Foe', *Gem*, no. 288 (1913)
27. 'Tom Merry – Sub-editor', *Gem*, no. 70 (1909)
28. 'Figgins' Folly', *Gem*, no. 223 (1912)
29. 'D'Arcy's Romance', *Gem*, 1st series, no. 36 (1907)

CHAPTER SIX
THAT UNBREAKABLE BANK AT MONTE CARLO

1. Letter to W. Bagley (1944)
2. *The Autobiography of Frank Richards*
3. 'The Greyfriars Trippers', *Magnet*, no. 332 (1914)
4. R. M. Jenkins, *'Faites vos jeux!'*, *Collectors' Digest Annual 1984*
5. Questionnaire for W. Bagley
6. 'Tom Merry's Carnival', no. 111, and 'Tom Merry at Monte Carlo', no. 112, *Gem* (1910)
7. 'Study 1 on Tour', no. 123, and 'The Thief', no. 124, *Gem* (1910)
8. 'Bob Cherry's Chase', *Magnet*, no. 270 (1913)
9. 'The Greyfriars Trippers', *Magnet*, no. 332 (1914)
10. 'The Vanished Sovereigns', *Magnet*, no. 1,263 (1932)
11. *Collectors' Digest*, no. 121 (1957)
12. 'The Girl from Monte Carlo', *Romance Series*, no. 4 (n.d.)
13. 'The St Jim's Airmen', *Gem*, no. 349 (1914)

CHAPTER SEVEN
HEROISM, HUMBUG AND SUPERSLEUTHS

1. 'The St Jim's Airmen', *Gem*, no. 349 (1914)
2. 'Tom Merry in Chicago', *Gem*, 2nd series, no. 48 (1909)

3. J. Adrian, 'Behind the Mask', *Collectors' Digest Annual 1982*
4. 'The Amazing Proceedings of Timothy Tupper', *Greyfriars Holiday Annual 1940*
5. 'The Patriot of St Jim's', *Gem*, no. 445 (1916)
6. 'Looking for Alonzo', *Magnet*, no. 352 (1914)
7. R. M. Jenkins, 'The Early Career of Fisher T. Fish: A Study in Psychology', *Story Paper Collector*, no. 73 (1960)
8. 'Bunter's Anti-tuck Campaign', *Magnet*, no. 401 (1915)
9. 'Coker the Joker', *Magnet*, no. 528 (1918)
10. 'The St Jim's Recruit', *Gem*, no. 364 (1915)
11. 'A Very Gallant Gentleman', *Magnet*, no. 520 (1918)
12. *Magnet*, no. 399 (1915)
13. *Magnet*, no. 406 (1915)

CHAPTER EIGHT
SPIFFING SCHOOLGIRLS AND TETCHY TEACHERS

1. Many issues of the *Magnet*
2. 'The Artful Dodger', *Magnet*, no. 582 (1919)
3. 'The Feud with Cliff House', *Magnet*, no. 1,528 (1937)
4. 'Tom Merry's Working Day', *Gem*, 1st series, no. 18 (1907)
5. Letter to E. Fayne (15 December 1952)
6. G. Freeman, *The Schoolgirl Ethic* (Allen Lane, London, 1976)
7. E. Hood, interview with M. Cadogan (1987)
8. Hazeldene's Uncle, *Magnet*, nos. 1,413–17 (1935); Cliff House Feud, *Magnet*, nos. 1,528–30 (1937)
9. E. Fayne, 'The Strange Case of Bunter's Baby', *Story Paper Collectors' Digest*, no. 282 (1970)
10. *The Autobiography of Frank Richards*
11. ibid.
12. E. Fayne (ed.), *The Letters of Frank Richards* (privately pubd, Church Crookham, n.d.)
13. R. M. Jenkins, 'Paul Pontifex Prout', *Collectors' Digest Annual 1981*
14. 'Alonzo's Plot', *Magnet*, no. 132 (1910)
15. 'The Form-master's Foe', *Magnet*, no. 1,041 (1928)
16. R. M. Jenkins, 'The Career of Mr Quelch', *Story Paper Collector*, no. 67 (1958)
17. 'The Japer of Greyfriars', *Magnet*, no. 1,078 (1928)
18. 'The Greyfriars Cracksman', *Magnet*, no. 1,150 (1930)
19. 'The Form-master's Feud', *Magnet*, no. 1,086 (1928)
20. 'Coker Comes a Cropper', *Magnet*, no. 1,129 (1929)
21. 'The Fellow Who Wouldn't be Caned', *Magnet*, no. 1,042 (1928)
22. 'Bunter the Dodger', *Magnet*, no. 1,376 (1934)
23. R. M. Jenkins. 'A Study in Sadism', *Collectors' Digest Annual 1968*

CHAPTER NINE
WIDER STILL AND WIDER

1. 'Tom Merry in the Rockies', *Gem*, no. 49 (1909)
2. E. Hood, interview with M. Cadogan (1987)
3. 'The Adventures of Dead-shot Dick', *World's Comic* (1904)
4. 'The Packsaddle Bunch', *Schoolboys' Own Library*, no. 305 (1937)
5. 'A Peculiar Persecution', *Boys' Friend Library*, no. 864 (n.d.)
6. 'The Cedar Creek Pantomime', *Boys' Friend Weekly*, no. 1,021 (1921)
7. 'Tom Merry's Voyage', *Gem*, 2nd series, no. 46 (1909)
8. W. H. Gander, 'Jimmy Silver in Canada', *Story Paper Collector*, no. 39 (1950)
9. U. Hamilton Wright, 'Christmas with Frank Richards', *Collectors' Digest Annual 1962*
10. 'Miss Priscilla's Peril', *Gem*, no. 86 (1909)
11. R. M. Jenkins, 'Return to Rose Lawn', *Collectors' Digest*, no. 190 (1962), and 'The Library at Rose Lawn', *Story Paper Collectors' Digest*, no. 334 (1974)
12. R. M. Jenkins, 'Return to Rose Lawn'
13. E. Hood, interview with M. Cadogan (1987)
14. 'Bunter's Brainstorm', *Magnet*, no. 996 (1927)

CHAPTER TEN
LOST WORLDS AND NEW HORIZONS

1. Letter to W. Bagley (1944)
2. 'The Phantom of Moat House', *Magnet*, no. 1,661 (1939)
3. 'The Schemer of the Remove', *Magnet*, no. 1,566 (1938)
4. 'The Shadow of the Sack', *Magnet*, no. 1,683 (1940)
5. 'The Mystery of Mark Linley', *Magnet*, no. 1,116 (1929)
6. *The Autobiography of Frank Richards*
7. 'Boys' Writer'
8. *Manchester Evening News* (6 December 1945)
9. J. Corbett, 'Frank Richards, the Founder of Greyfriars', *Story Paper Collector*, no. 16 (1944)
10. G. Orwell, 'Boys' Weeklies'
11. W. Bagley, 'Plotting Technique', *Writer* (1944)
12. Letter to W. Bagley (28 September 1944)
13. Letter to W. Bagley (18 September 1944)
14. Letter to W. Bagley (4 January 1945)
15. 'Frank Richards Redivivus!', *Story Paper Collector*, no. 21 (1945)

CHAPTER ELEVEN
STILL BUNTERING LIKE BILLY-O!

1. Letter to W. H. Gander (10 February 1947)
2. *The Autobiography of Frank Richards*
3. C. Skilton, preface to memorial edition of *The Autobiography of Frank Richards*
4. Letter to R. M. Jenkins (21 May 1946)

CHAPTER TWELVE
GRAND OLD MAN

1. Letter to C. H. Chapman (26 February 1960)
2. *Radio Times* (4 April 1949)
3. E. Fayne (ed.), *The Letters of Frank Richards*
4. U. Hamilton Wright, 'Felix Kept On Walking'
5. 'Shadowed Cabinet: Minister of Education', *Punch* (9 November 1960)
6. 'Fifty Years On', *Collectors' Digest*, no. 134 (1958)
7. E. Fayne, 'The Funeral of Frank Richards', *Collectors' Digest*, no. 182 (1962)
8. P. Grosvenor, 'Watch Out Rupert Bear, It Could Be You Next', *Daily Express* (14 February 1970)

AFTERWORD
GREYFRIARS GROWS UP!

1. D. Hughes, *But for Bunter* (Heinemann, London, 1985); D. Green, *Bunter Sahib* (Hodder & Stoughton, London, 1985) and *Bunter by Appointment* (Heinemann, London, 1987)

BIBLIOGRAPHY

G. Beal (ed.), *The Concise Magnet Companion '86* (Howard Baker Press, London, 1986)

G. Brandreth (ed.), *Yarooh! A Feast of Frank Richards* (Eyre Methuen, London, 1976)

B. Doyle, *Who's Who of Boys' Writers and Illustrators 1964* (privately pubd, London, 1964)

E. Fayne, *The Letters of Frank Richards* (privately pubd, Church Crookham, n.d.)

G. Freeman, *The Schoolgirl Ethic* (Allen Lane, London, 1976)

W. O. G. Lofts and D. J. Adley, *The World of Frank Richards* (Howard Baker Press, London, 1975)

—, *The Gem Index* (privately pubd, London, 1981)

—, *Greyfriars Since the Magnet* (privately pubd, London, 1983)

P. McCall, *McCall's Greyfriars Guide* (Howard Baker Press, London, 1980)

F. Richards, *The Autobiography of Frank Richards* (Skilton, London, 1952; reprinted in memorial edition, including preface by C. Skilton and 'Charles Hamilton' by E. Fayne, 1962)

R. Roberts, *The Classic Slum* (Manchester University Press, Manchester, 1971)

L. Sutton, *Greyfriars for Grown-ups* (Howard Baker Press, London, 1980)

Charles Hamilton Companion, vols. i–vii (privately pubd, Maidstone, 1972–84):

   i. E. Fayne and R. M. Jenkins, *A History of the Gem and Magnet* (1972)

  ii. J. Wernham and M. Cadogan (eds.), *The Greyfriars Characters* (1976)

 iii. J. Wernham (ed.), *Centenary Edition* (1976)

 iv. M. Cadogan and J. Wernham, *Schoolgirls' Album* (1979)

  v. J. Wernham (ed.), *Rookwood* (1980)

 vi. J. Wernham and M. Cadogan, *The Gem Story* (1982)

vii. M. Cadogan and T. Keen, *From Wharton Lodge to Linton Hall: The Christmas Stories* (1984)

INDEX